SHIPS & SHIPBUILDERS

AQUITANIA

SHIPS
&
SHIPBUILDERS

Pioneers of Design and Construction

FRED M WALKER

Foreword by Trevor Blakeley

Title page: The Cunard liner *Aquitania* under construction at the Clydebank yard of John Brown & Co Ltd.
(© *The National Maritime Museum, Greenwich, G10689*)

First published in Great Britain in 2010 by
Seaforth Publishing
An imprint of Pen & Sword Books Ltd
47 Church Street
Barnsley S70 2AS

www.seaforthpublishing.com
Email info@seaforthpublishing.com

Published in association with

British Library Cataloguing in Publication Data
A catalogue record for this book is available from the British Library

ISBN 978 1 84832 072 7

Typeset by Mac Style, Beverley
Printed and bound in Great Britain by the MPG Books Group, UK

Contents

Foreword

THE DESIGN AND CONSTRUCTION of ships has evolved over thousands of years, to produce the largest and most complex moveable structures ever built by mankind. Without them to provide for the safe and efficient transport and recovery of the world's raw materials and products, modern society as we know it could not exist. However, in this evolution, the eighteenth, nineteenth and twentieth centuries saw perhaps the most dramatic and significant changes to the design and construction of ships, when it became more of a science than an art. This came about at a time of great social and political change.

The design and construction of ships is essentially a team activity conducted by professional engineers in their respective fields and disciplines, often in several countries. However, during this period, a number of individuals made a significant contribution and can rightly claim to have been 'pioneers of ship design and construction'. In many cases, whilst their achievements and lasting legacy may be familiar to those involved in the design and construction of ships, the individuals themselves are less well known, if at all.

In his pen portraits of such men and women, Fred Walker not only describes their achievements, but in doing so charts the development of ship design and construction, seen in the context of the social and economic changes which shaped their lives and work. It is most appropriate that this book should be published in the year when the Royal Institution of Naval Architects celebrates the 150th anniversary of its founding in 1860, since many of those whose achievements Fred Walker describes made their contributions to ship design and construction as members of the Institution.

Trevor Blakeley
Chief Executive
The Royal Institution of Naval Architects

Preface

THE ROYAL INSTITUTION OF NAVAL ARCHITECTS (RINA) has given service to the 'Shipwrights' of the world for 150 years. The RINA has contributed significantly to my professional life, and on this special anniversary, I am pleased to have the opportunity of acknowledging the achievements of this illustrious body. From time to time it is useful to stand back and review the lives and works of naval architects, shipbuilders, engineers, scientists, academics and a host of others who have been instrumental in the development of safe ships for the sea.

With a mere 136 formal biographies included in this book, selection has been somewhat arbitrary, but an effort has been made to ensure most shipbuilding countries and areas are represented as are the main branches of naval architecture and allied professions. To avoid later recriminations, it is essential to state that choice of candidates was mine alone, and selected from lists of the great and the good – all deceased prior to AD 2000. Choosing was difficult and avoiding an imbalance in the book with too many people from the same field, the same locality or the same time-frame necessitated the omission of some worthy candidates. Some readers may disagree with the choices, and some even may feel aggrieved, but I hope that a fairly catholic picture will emerge of an industry and profession run by a group of people who were not always saints, but on the whole were decent, honest and dedicated to their calling.

Care has been taken in ensuring accuracy in the text and in checking primary sources where possible. There are considerable discrepancies between the various published accounts of the lives of those of earlier generations, but I hope this book will neither create new errors nor perpetuate too many of the old fallacies. Citizens of the United Kingdom are described throughout as British, except for those extant prior to 1707 who are identified as either English or Scottish. The names are normally listed in order of date of birth, but from time to time people are grouped together for convenience, an example being the mathematicians Euler, Simpson, Tchebycheff and Thomson whose lives spanned 185 years!

Throughout the fairly lengthy gestation of this book, there has been assistance from a multitude of people and institutions. Hopefully none have been overlooked and all are acknowledged opposite.

Fred M Walker
Tenterden
Kent

Acknowledgements

THIS BOOK WOULD NEVER HAVE SEEN the light of day had it not for the help of the Chief Executive and staff of the Royal Institution of Naval Architects; Trevor Blakeley has given friendship, encouragement and support at every stage and for this I thank him sincerely. It is hardly necessary to remind members of the Royal Institution that we have an excellent headquarters team, but it does give pleasure to do so and to thank all who have given help and backing in the preparation of this book.

I am grateful for assistance from old friends at:

Statens Arkiver, Copenhagen
The Institution of Engineers and Shipbuilders in Scotland
The Library of Lloyd's Register
Glasgow Museums
The Scottish Maritime Museum, Irvine
The National Maritime Museum, Greenwich
Handels-og Søfartsmuseet på Kronborg, Denmark

On a more personal basis I must thank the following friends:

Dr Martin Bellamy, Glasgow Museums
Emeritus Professor Harry Benford, Ann Arbor, Michigan (following deep consideration we have decided not to include his helpful suggestions of Noah and Helen of Troy)
Lars-Erik Brenøe, Copenhagen
The late David K Brown RCNC
Douglas Brown, Gourock
Emeritus Professor John Caldwell FREng, Windermere
David Chalmers RCNC, Bradford on Avon
Mat Curtis, Lloyd's Register
Tom Dunn, Greenock
David Fellows RCNC, University College London
Dr Larrie D Ferreiro, Fairfax, Virginia
Dr Denis Griffiths, Liverpool
Bryn Hughes of HMS *Trincomalee* Trust, Hartlepool
David Hutchings of BVT Surface Fleet (Portsmouth) Ltd
Mrs Barbara Jones, Lloyd's Register
Mrs Mary Kohn, Ayrshire
The late Professor Alexander Kholodilin, St Petersburg
Bruce Stannard, Sydney NSW
Henning Morgen, Copenhagen
Dr Horst Nowacki, Berlin
Mrs Amanda Palmer of BMT
Derek Parsons, Gravesend, Kent
Peter Rossiter of Isherwoods Limited
Julian Mannering, Seaforth Publishing
Sandy Stephen, Balfron, Stirlingshire
Jim Tildesley, Scottish Maritime Museum, Irvine

Special thanks go to my wife Joan, for her patience and support in what has been a longer job than expected.

Part 1
Ship Design and Construction to 1800

It has been said that modern history commenced in 1453 (the year of the Fall of Constantinople). As this date is somewhat arbitrary, a more useful benchmark might be 1600 when the medieval way of life gave way to the modern age. All ship science has been developed in the age of modern history, apart from the enabling work and research of the early mathematicians and philosophers, and it can be said with certainty that naval architecture as a profession had its beginning in the seventeenth century. Naval architecture, shipbuilding and the closely-allied engineering disciplines are unique in that they have conventions that are understood in every corner of the world.

Ship size

Until the introduction of iron to shipbuilding in the early nineteenth century, ship size was limited by the size of available timbers, and a major problem facing ship owners was the poor economic return of ships through limited cargo space and the excessive cost of manual labour. From the earliest times, small vessels were created by being hollowed out from tree trunks, and to this day such craft are found in abundance among the fishing canoes of the Indonesian Archipelago and the Guinea Gulf Coast of West Africa. Such small ships are more sophisticated than is usually appreciated and a dug-out canoe represents a considerable investment in finance and effort by the owning and operating family. Length and capacity is limited by two factors; tree size and the mass or weight which a small crew can handle when fishing or when landing on open beaches in heavy surf.

Of the many primitive hull forms, the one which most closely resembles the modern ship is the open boat constructed on a skeletal frame, usually of timber and then covered with animal skins, canvas or other natural materials made watertight by close stitching and the application of pitch, resin or tar. These are seen to this day in various forms including the elegant curragh still used for coastal fishing in south-west Ireland and the kayak and the umiak of the Inuit peoples of Greenland and North America. If manned by a competent crew, such small ships are capable of passages of up to several hundred miles. Unquestionably St Columba

The dugout, made from a single tree, represented a major development in the history of boatbuilding and water transport. With its directional stability and general robustness it offered a simple solution that has been built on and developed for thousands of years. Despite a myriad of developments, many discussed in the following pages, the dugout is still used today. Here is an example from Ghana, photographed in 1966. *(Author)*

used such a craft on his historic voyage from Ireland to Iona in the Inner Hebrides in AD 563. The subjective model of his curragh, seen today in Iona Abbey, indicates again the inability of a ship of this type to be longer than around 15m (50ft).

The first real successes in producing larger ships came with the invention of wooden planked construction, examples of which have been around for the best part of 2,000 years. One of the earliest known and intact planked vessels is the Nydam Ship discovered in 1863 in South Jutland. It is nearly 24m (78ft 9in) long and is constructed of five clinker strakes per side, with each strake being of two planks butt jointed. With sharp vee forms both forward and aft, this ship is a true precursor of the elegant Viking longships which roamed most of Europe 700 years later. The first major Viking ship finds were in the late nineteenth century in southern Norway at Gokstad and Oseberg, and these fine looking vessels can be seen at the Viking Ship Hall at Bygdøy in Oslo. About seventy years later, in 1959 to be precise, a cluster of ships were found embedded in the mud of the Roskilde Fjord in Denmark. Now excavated and restored at the magnificent Viking Ship Museum at Roskilde, some miles west of Copenhagen, they have enabled proper interpretation to be made of early clinker (or overlaid) planking. It is interesting to note that the Viking ships had a steering oar on the starboard quarter – known as the *Styrbord* (pronounced 'stoorbord') from which the current word 'starboard' is derived.

The size of wooden ships increased gradually, and by the nineteenth century well-built hulls reached in excess of 65m (*c* 215ft). In general longer wooden hulls had a tendency to hog, that is the keel arching slightly allowing the bow and stern to sink deeper in the water than the hull at amidships. There were several ways to overcome this; one was using the longest lengths of timber possible, and another was fitting wire or rope trusses which would restrain the hull from drooping. One of the skills of the great American shipbuilders was to build longer wooden ships than in any other part of the world, and one case in particular is the San Francisco Bay steam paddle ferry *Eureka* which came out at a near-record length of 91m (300ft) by the simple innovation of an iron cage structure of four king posts in the middle of the ship from which hogging trusses were fitted both fore and aft. In the mid-nineteenth century, a further development was the introduction of composite construction, where the skeletal or framed construction was of iron with the outer skin of traditional planked timber. This will be described later.

Timber supplies

Throughout history, the problem of obtaining long and fault free timber has beset shipbuilders, and now in the twenty-first century, the problem is worse than at any previous time. The two most important timbers in a ship are the keel and the sternpost. The sternpost, wherever possible, should be a single and trustworthy timber, while it is accepted that the much longer keel has to be fabricated of three, possibly four, timbers which are joined by complex and carefully-shaped scarfed joints.

In reading the diaries of experienced master shipwrights, it is interesting to note that most of them regarded the selection of timber as one of their most responsible tasks. This involved relentless travelling in forests, the measuring of timber girths and the inspection of stands of timber to find the longest lengths with the fewest knots and blemishes.

Shipboard and building conventions

By the end of the medieval age many aspects of seafaring were common through Europe and the Mediterranean, and as a result ships tended to use similar operating procedures, and they adopted similar conventions – such as the positioning of halyards on the pin boards. This was to ensure an unambiguous and clear response to deck orders in an emergency, irrespective of the language or dialect of everyone working on deck. Mixed crews are not new, and on checking crew lists of British sailing ships of the mid-nineteenth century, it is not unusual to find as many as 75 per cent were not native English-speakers.

Early theoreticians

The seventeenth and eighteenth centuries saw the start of a more scientific approach to ship design. In these years, systematic methods for estimating the volume of displacement of ships were being developed, but despite this designers and builders were faced with the almost insoluble problem of predicting the final draft of any new ship. Furthermore, there were no assured means of assessing weight or weight distribution and there was no coherent guidance on ship stability. Obviously, experienced master shipwrights had a 'feel' for stability, and once a new ship was afloat, they could arrange adequate ballasting – a matter that good ship-masters could handle equally well.

Perhaps the most embarrassing foundering of all time was that of the Swedish royal flagship *Vasa* in 1628, when she capsized and sank on her maiden crossing of Stockholm Harbour from the shipyard to the naval base. Clearly there had been carelessness, as the ship was packed with stores and people and the gun ports on the lower deck had been left open. The inability of the shipbuilder to predict displacement (weight or mass of the ship) and stability (the ability of the ship to return to upright when heeled by some external force) became evident when a squall caused the ship to heel. Had the lower gun deck ports been closed the ship might have recovered, but an inrush of water caused the ship to founder with considerable loss of life. In other circumstances the ship might have been ballasted as

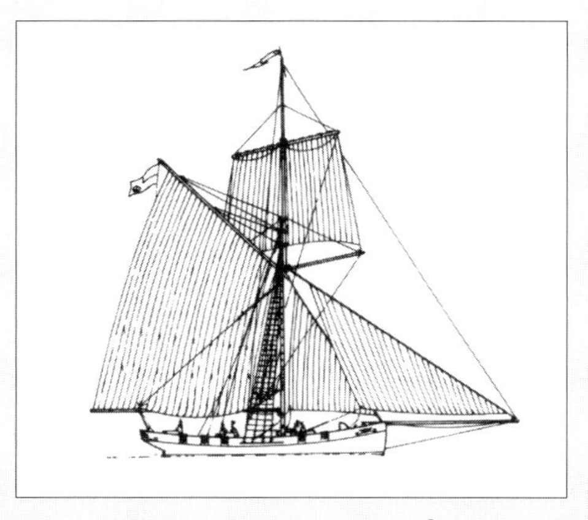

At a time when systematic methods and a more scientific approach to ship design were emerging, it was still the case that the majority of vessels were built by shipwrights who applied hard-won experience and instinct to create fast and weatherly craft, without recourse to any theory, or scientific knowledge of displacement for example. The Revenue cutters, such as *Wolf* (c1805) depicted here, were typical of this sort of empirical development, and constant improvement was demanded in order to contend with the fast cutters and luggers of the smuggling gangs that operated all round the British coast. (*Author*)

was conventional at the time, and then gone on to serve many years in the Baltic. Some good came of the disaster when *Vasa*, which had lain undisturbed for over 300 years, was re-discovered in 1959 and raised from Stockholm Harbour over 90 per cent intact. Now beautifully displayed, she ranks as one of the finest ship restorations in the world. A visit to her comes close to being a spiritual experience, and is enhanced by great displays, including the computer-generated reconstructions of the faces of crew members.

Just six years later in 1634 **Phineas Pett** was presented with the challenge of building King Charles I the first three-decked ship, carrying over 100 guns. He had no academic or certain way of knowing what this new ship would displace, nor what its draft would be, and was naturally concerned about the three towering decks and the high centre of gravity induced by such massive armament. Happily Pett's design was successful, and the *Sovereign of the Seas*, as she was named, truly merited the adjective wonderful and not least because of the magnificent decoration she bore.

Lloyd's Register of Shipping

The number of ships lost at sea in the seventeenth and eighteenth centuries was immense. Seamen had no protection in law and shipowners had little understanding of the vessels which they managed. Marine insurance was a risky matter, especially in the days before limited liability companies. In 1760, an organisation known initially as the Register Society was set up to regulate the quality of materials, the soundness of construction and the fitness of equipment for use aboard ships. As the founders were habitués of Lloyd's Coffee House in Great Tower Street, London, it is perhaps not surprising that the organisation became known as Lloyd's Register of Shipping. Recently the name was simplified to Lloyd's Register, reflecting the ever widening breadth of interest of Classification Societies. Four years after its foundation the Society published their first Register of Ships, an annual which continues to this day. The Register of Ships for 2007–2008 is in four volumes and lists close on 100,000 ships. Lloyd's Register (LR) has distinguished rivals, but all of them were founded in the nineteenth and twentieth centuries, the oldest being Bureau Veritas (BV) which was founded in Antwerp in 1828 and since has moved its headquarters to Paris.

The Industrial Revolution

Two closely-related events took place at the end of the eighteenth century: the Industrial Revolution and the Enlightenment. The Enlightenment in the British Isles is often known as the Scottish Enlightenment as it started in Edinburgh and Glasgow, where also many of the important discoveries of the Industrial Revolution were made. In many respects, Britain was ready for change, and in economic and industrial terms this came about. Most fortuitously James Watt was working at a university with leading academics when he had his inspirational thoughts on steam condensers. Men like Joseph Black were able to help and support him at the start of his quest to devise an efficient steam engine, the machine which was to change the way of the world for ever.

KEY DATES

1514	King Henry VIII of England grants a charter to Trinity House.
1576	First Danish observatory set up at Uraniborg on the island of Hven by King Frederik II.
1588	The Spanish Armada (and a growth of confidence in English ships and seamen).
1600	Founding of the Honourable East India Company.
1603	Union of the Crowns of England and Scotland.
1612	Founding of East India Company Marine – the precursor of the Indian Navy.
1628	Sinking of the Swedish royal ship *Vasa* on her maiden voyage in Stockholm Harbour.
1649	First Anglo-Dutch War.
1675	Setting-up of the Royal Observatory, Greenwich by King Charles II.
1688	The Glorious Revolution: William and Mary come to the throne in Britain.
1696	Battle of the Sea of Azov, regarded as the founding of the Russian fleet.
1697	The Rev Professor Hoste publishes *Théorie de la Construction des Vaisseaux*.
1703	Founding of St Petersburg, Russia.
1707	Union of England and Scotland.
1734	First publication of *Lloyd's List*.
1756–63	The Seven Years War in Europe and North America.
1760	The Register Society, later to be known as Lloyd's Register, founded in London.
1765	James Watt's inspired thoughts on steam condensation augur the Industrial Revolution.
1768	Captain James Cook's first circumnavigation (to observe the Transit of Venus).
1776	United States Declaration of Independence.
1779	Royal Navy authorises sheathing the underwater hulls of all warships with copper.
1783	The *Pyroscaphe* steams on the French River Saône.
1786	Founding of the Northern Lighthouse Board of Scotland and the Isle of Man.
1787	Trimaran *Edinburgh* paddled with manpower on Firth of Forth.
1788	Steamship sails on Dalswinton Loch, Dumfriesshire.
1791	Founding of the Society for the Improvement of Naval Architecture.
1793	French declare war on Britain.

Archimedes of Syracuse

287–212 BC

ARCHIMEDES WAS ONE of the most eminent mathematicians and engineers of antiquity and he is remembered for having laid down the rules of leverage and hydrostatics.

Apart from study at Alexandria, Archimedes spent his life in Syracuse, a Greek city on Sicily. He enabled mathematics, then in its infancy, to become a tool for engineers and scientists, and to be a stimulus for early mechanical inventions. In mathematics he was responsible for many discoveries, the most famous being the definition of pi or π which he calculated as being between three and one-seventh (3.14286) and three and ten seventy-firsts (3.14085) which bears up well to the actual figure which is slightly greater than 3.14159. All this is more remarkable when one remembers that Arabic numerals and modern conventions of mathematics were not in use at that time.

He was a prolific inventor, designing astronomical instruments, cranes, sheer legs, and claw-like defence mechanisms for the protection of Syracuse from Roman triremes and quinqueremes, all of which demonstrated his understanding of leverage. He developed the Archimedian Screw used for a short time as a propulsor on early nineteenth-century steamships, and used to this day for pumping water. He is best remembered for Archimedes' Law and arguably for being the first person to appreciate specific gravity, and thereby developed a system for analysing the purity of precious metals. Archimedes was one of the first people to understand the positioning of objects in three dimensions and could appreciate latitude, longitude and altitude.

Archimedes was killed when Syracuse was invaded by the Romans in 212 BC. It is said that while he was calculating with a stick on the sand, a soldier walked over his work, and on being admonished by Archimedes, drew his sword and killed him.

SOURCES:

Gullberg, Jan
Mathematics from the Birth of Numbers
New York, 1997

John Napier of Merchiston

1550–1617

JOHN NAPIER SERVED the engineering community well, inventing the unique system of calculation now known as logarithms. Born at Merchiston Castle near Edinburgh in 1550, he was the eldest son of wealthy landowners with impeccable connections in the Kingdom of Scotland. At the tender age of thirteen, and only three years after the Scottish Reformation, he matriculated at St Andrews University, staying there for a year or two before, it is believed, travelling in Europe to complete his formal education. Throughout his life he was a convinced Protestant and was deeply embroiled in the politics of Scotland during the reign of James VI. Indeed, he dedicated an academic paper on New Testament theology to the King. In 1608, on the death of his father, he inherited Merchiston and lived there until his death nine years later.

The study – indeed the invention – for which he is remembered is that of logarithms, which he called artificial numbers, but he had other successes as well, including proposing the present notation of decimal fractions, and the construction of an hydraulic screw for emptying coal mines of water. Napier, like most of the landed classes at the time, was interested in astronomy and was dismayed by the massive and tedious calculations which hindered the pleasure of scientific study. As Christian IV of Denmark and James VI of Scotland were brothers-in-law, it was natural that Napier was in touch with the astronomer Tycho Brahe, amongst others, and he absorbed ideas for simplification of multiplication and division. After considerable intellectual effort, Napier put forward the idea of a system known as Logarithms (from the Greek words *logos* [ratio, reckoning] and *arithmos* [number]). The work was published around the time of his death with tables calculated to a natural base. Possibly with the help of the Swiss clockmaker Jost Burgi, he agreed that a base of 10 would be more practical. This breakthrough in calculating work was one of the most important scientific developments of the seventeenth century.

Just before his death John Napier developed a simple calculating aid for multiplication which was used for many years and must qualify as being amongst the earliest of calculating instruments. Known as 'Napier's Bones', they were small square-sectioned rods with accurately measured divisions which when aligned could be used to simplify major multiplications. There were not in any way associated with logarithms, and nowadays are highly sought after collectors' pieces.

SOURCES:
Gullberg, Jan
Mathematics from the Birth of Numbers
New York, 1997

Phineas Pett

1570–1647

THE BUILDER OF THE great warship *Sovereign of the Seas* of 1637, Phineas Pett was fortunate in enjoying the trust of King Charles I, but in his autobiography he records the problems and intrigues encountered by the Master Shipwright of a Royal Dockyard. Sometime in the 1630s Pett had been released from a debtors' prison on the orders of the King, and he decided to show his appreciation in 1634 by presenting the monarch with a beautiful model of a ship of the First Rate. Charles was impressed with the gift and in a short discussion (given verbatim in the autobiography) ordered Phineas Pett to proceed immediately with building the real thing. The ship was to become the renowned *Sovereign of the Seas*, also known as the *Royal Sovereign*, a ship which had a length on keel of 38m (124ft 8in), beam of 14.6m (47ft 11in) and the deep draft of almost 7m (23ft). Three-deckers were not an entirely new concept, but this was a step into the unknown as the *Sovereign's* decks were flush and the number of guns demanded by the King was to exceed 100. Pett tried to persuade the monarch that 90 guns would make for an easier design, but was overruled and then received a further arbitrary command to launch the ship on 25 September 1637. The ship was ready on

The magnificent three-decked *Sovereign of the Seas*, built for King Charles I. Phineas Pett had to resolve the question of stability in such a high-sided ship, which also carried more guns than any earlier vessel. (*© The National Maritime Museum, Greenwich, A6719*)

that date, but despite the wishes of King Charles the height of water did not come up to expectations.

Enemies of Pett included members of that august body Trinity House, who upon hearing of the proposed new building petitioned King Charles to have it stopped. Their grounds included the fact that the depth of water in English harbours was insufficient for the ship to be anchored out of reach of enemies, and that with three decks the new ship would be unstable. (Rather reminiscent of cruise-line passengers who question the high freeboard of modern liners.) In their submission, they reminded the King of the loss of the *Mary Rose* where water had entered the lower gun deck through the gun ports. The King dismissed their views and the *Sovereign of the Seas* was to become the largest warship in the world, painted in black and with a mass of gilded decoration. At the time of the Commonwealth she was laid up 'in ordinary', but re-commissioned at the restoration of Charles II and renamed *Royal Sovereign*.

Phineas Pett was unusual in that he had enjoyed a fine education at Emmanuel College, Cambridge, before commencing an apprenticeship as a shipwright at Deptford Dockyard. His father was the well-known shipwright Peter Pett who had been Master Shipwright at Deptford until his death in 1589. The family tradition continued with two of Phineas's sons – Peter and Christopher – becoming shipwrights in their turn, with Peter (who actually supervised construction of the *Sovereign of the Seas*) becoming a commissioner of the Navy.

Phineas Pett was twice married. He was first Master of the Worshipful Company of Shipwrights when it was founded in 1612, and by carefully siding with Parliament and with the Royalists at the appropriate times remained in remunerative work until his death in 1647.

SOURCES:
Archibald, E H H
The Fighting Ship in the Royal Navy 897-1984
Poole, 1984
Callendar, Geoffrey
The Portrait of Peter Pett and the Sovereign of the Seas
National Maritime Museum, Greenwich, 1930
Perrin, W G (ed)
The Autobiography of Phineas Pett
The Navy Records Society, 1918

David Balfour

1574–1634

THE VERY FIRST SHIP PLANS in the world might have been overlooked in history, had it not been for a fortuitous incident in 1832 at the beautiful Palace of Rosenborg in Copenhagen. During a routine 'spring clean' in the attics of this Renaissance building, several technical drawings were found, all done with pencil and ink on fairly discoloured thin cardboard. They were eventually identified as ship plans drawn for King Christian IV of Denmark by a young Scotsman called David Balfour. They rank amongst the greatest existing technical records of shipbuilding, and being over 400 years old are likely to be the oldest ones that survive.

King Christian IV (1577–1648) came to the throne of the twin Kingdoms of Denmark and Norway in 1588, and was to become one of the most singular rulers of the seventeenth century. His reign was punctuated by wars with the Swedes and the Dutch, while in quieter times he concentrated on strengthening the Danish navy, on the rebuilding of Copenhagen and later on the reconstruction of the Norwegian city of Christiania (later Oslo). His sister Anne had married James VI of Scotland, ensuring that he was aware of the continuous power struggle between the Tudors and the Stuarts, as well as the growth of English sea power. A state visit by James VI of Scotland to Denmark in 1590 cemented the relationship with both kings vying to outshine each other in the realms of science – and here Christian was at a distinct advantage having the observatory of Uraniborg (on the island of Hven, just north-east of Copenhagen) under the direction of the astronomer and mathematician Tycho Brahe. Both kings were intelligent, and both were skilled diplomats and negotiators, and were to keep in close touch throughout their lives. It is more than likely that the name of Balfour, an exceptionally well-educated young shipwright from St Andrews, was mentioned to Christian, as by 1597 he was building two galleys for the Scandinavian king.

Of the early life of Balfour we know little, although it has been suggested that he had education in England. His shipwright training could have

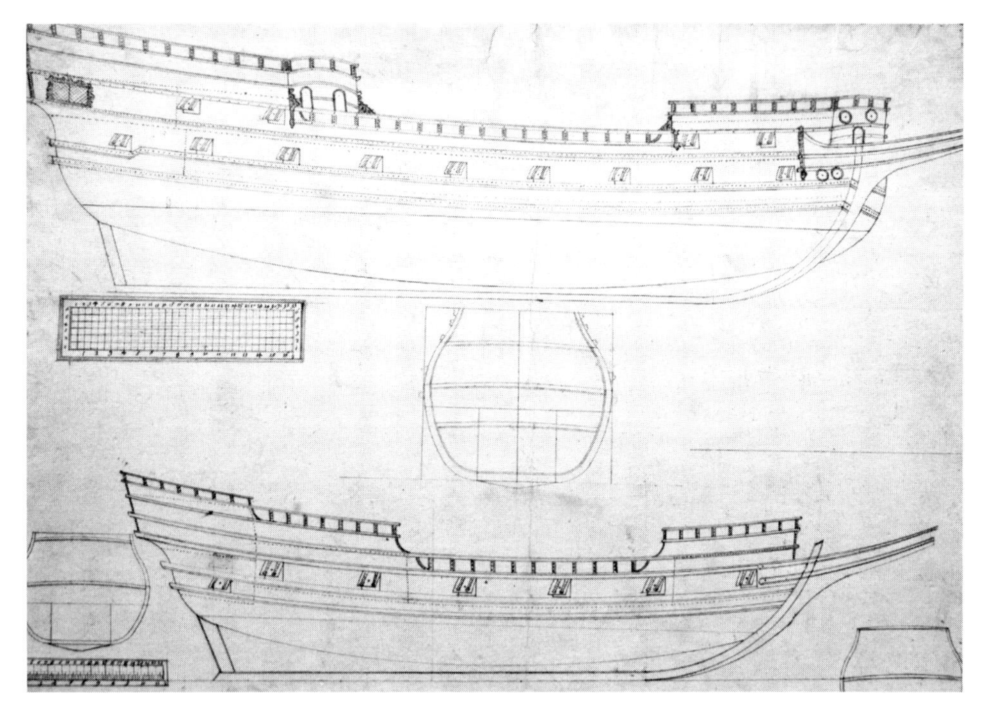

The earliest-known ship plan, a sheer draught produced by David Balfour around 1600 for King Christian IV of Denmark. *(Dansk Statens Arkiver, Copenhagen)*

been in either Scotland or England, as the northern kingdom had started the 'arms race' in the times of Henry VIII, although unable to keep up once the competition became fierce. In 1602, Balfour commenced building larger ships for the Danish Navy, including the 52-gun *Argo* and the 80-gun *Tre Kroner*, both of which were used in the large fleet taken to London for Christian's return state visit to his brother-in-law, now both of them sovereigns of two realms. Balfour continued to do well, but suddenly relations with the King suffered a setback when one of his new ships grounded, clearly being overweight and with too great a draft for the waters round Copenhagen. He was instructed to build to dimensions agreed by the King personally, something which Balfour seems to have found difficult, which is unusual for a man with such an advanced ability on the drawing board. Following a bitter dispute with the captain designate of a ship under construction, the hull was investigated and again Balfour was found to have worked in a manner beyond the agreed specification; retribution was swift, with Balfour languishing for three years in Dragsholm Castle (until he was released following the intervention of King James) and with the captain being relieved of his commission. Balfour then continued to work in Denmark, but other competitive shipwrights were on the scene including a Scot by the name of Daniel Sinclair, and his tasks in the royal dockyards became more mundane.

The importance of Balfour's plans is more than just their age and antiquity: they demonstrate the need for the special consideration which must be given to ships working in the shallow waters of the Baltic, where ships must have seaworthiness and stability whilst operating in shoal conditions. It has been suggested by many commentators that the lower salinity of the Baltic creates a problem, but this does seem unlikely as the difference in density between pure fresh water and that of the most salinated ocean is less than 3 per cent.

As a postscript, the Danish Observatory was moved to the newly-built Round Tower in central Copenhagen between 1637 and 1642. Uraniborg was dismantled and no traces are left on this lovely island on the Øresund. Great Britain had to wait until 1675 for the first national observatory to be completed, now known as the Royal Observatory, Greenwich.

SOURCES:
Balfour Ship Plans Des.E2-9
Rigsarkivet, Copenhagen, Denmark
Bellamy, Dr Martin
'David Balfour and Early Modern Danish Ship Design', *The Mariner's Mirror* Vol 92 (2006)

Sir Anthony Deane

1638–1721

THE SON OF A SHIPMASTER from Harwich and later the author of a superb early book on ship design, Deane was destined to serve an apprenticeship in the Royal Dockyards, and by the time he was twenty-two had become assistant to the redoubtable Christopher Pett at Woolwich. It was during this period – the 1660s – that Deane became acquainted with Samuel Pepys, just five years his senior, and who was to become 'Clerk to the King's Ships'. This friendship was to last many years, and to serve Deane well, particularly as his superior Pett did not enjoy such an easy relationship with Pepys. While at Woolwich, Deane took every opportunity to acquaint Pepys with the method of 'laying out' a ship, of the workings of the Navy and also of the rampant corruption in the Royal Dockyards. The diarist noted: 'I think him (Deane) a very just man, only a little conceited.'

At the age of twenty-six, he was appointed Master Shipwright at the naval base in Harwich, a job that lasted four years, ending with the closure of the dockyard after Britain's victory in the Four Days' Battle of 1666 ended the threat from the Dutch. Deane was moved to Portsmouth becoming Master Shipwright of the Royal Dockyard in 1668, and commenced building larger ships, many of which were stretching the available technology of the seventeenth century. In 1671 he constructed his first 'three-decker' and instituted research into underwater hull sheathing and sundry other matters. It is recorded that one of his early ships at Portsmouth, the 100-gun *Charles Royal*, was narrow and tender, and like many naval architects both before and after, he corrected her insufficient stability by increasing the ship's breadth on the waterline by 'girdling' her with timber.

With his ambition, success in construction and the undoubtedly influence of friends, he was appointed a member of the Navy Board in 1672, a position which led ultimately to his responsibility for all procurement for the Royal Navy. Owing to the political insecurity of the times, he fell out of favour for a while, was stripped of his positions and spent a short time in prison. On his release he set up as a private shipbuilder, but also worked in the King's service until the Glorious Revolution of 1688 when James II was overthrown by William of Orange. Of his subsequent life, only a little is known; he served as Mayor of Harwich and later as a Member of Parliament.

Anthony Deane is remembered mainly for his textbook *Doctrine of Naval Architecture*, published in 1670, which describes the intricate methods of the time for laying out the lines of larger warships. This important book is a milestone in descriptive naval architecture, and bears out the claim that he could estimate the volume and the mass of ships under construction. The acceptance that 35 cubic feet of seawater represents one ton stems from this early period in ship design.

In 1698 **Peter the Great** spent some months at Deptford, near Greenwich, and visited and interviewed the great and the good of England and Scotland while planning for the reforms he was to initiate in Russia. It is believed that Deane, now Sir Anthony Deane, was his tutor in shipbuilding and helped him to nurture and develop his love of ships.

SOURCES:
Deane, Sir Anthony
Doctrine of Naval Architecture
Manuscript of 1670 held in the Pepys Library, Magdalene College, Cambridge
Lavery, Brian (ed)
Deane's Doctrine of Naval Architecture
London, 1981
Pepys, Samuel,
The Diaries
Many editions – originals held in the Pepys Library, Magdalene College, Cambridge

Petr Alexeyevich Romanov

1672–1725

THE TSAR NOW KNOWN as Peter the Great lived a life that is nothing short of remarkable. He unified a country sprawling over eleven time zones, disciplined it and led it through many reforms. One of his greatest achievements was the founding of the Russian Fleet and the setting up of shipbuilding and seafaring in a country which until the eighteenth century was inward looking and almost unwilling to trade outside its borders.

Peter was the first son of the second wife of Tsar Alexei (according to Russian style the second name of a child is the father's) and was brought up in Moscow until his father's early death in 1682. The following fourteen years were complicated, with Peter and his half-brother Ivan acting as joint Tsars, but these years did enable Peter to obtain a broad education, and in turn to develop a love of all matters scientific. In 1688, he found an old English-built sailing boat at his estate in Ismailovo which gave him his first experience of sailing and which led to his abiding love of the sea. Peter never forgot this 6m (20ft) boat, and to this day it is on display in the Naval Museum in St Petersburg, and known as 'The Grandfather of the Russian Navy'.

The Bronze Horseman. The magnificent equestrian statue of Peter the Great, the founder of the Russian Fleet, which was unveiled in the centre St Petersburg in 1782. *(Author)*

In 1696, on the death of Ivan, Peter became outright ruler of the vast Russias and commenced a quarter of a century of territorial expansion and of reform aimed at bringing his country into the European arena and preparing for what became known as the Age of Russian Enlightenment. Peter's methods were questionable, his rule at times sadistic and cruel, but he succeeded as no person had before in making Russia a world power. He modernised the Cyrillic alphabet, was sympathetic to the rights of women and he encouraged education.

One of the Tsar's most unusual decisions was to make a prolonged journey through Europe that became known as the Great Embassy. Peter stopped in what is now known as The Netherlands for nearly five months, first in Zaandam, where there were fifty shipbuilding yards, and later in Amsterdam where he worked as a shipwright himself. He attempted to pass himself off as a simple Russian workman during his stay in Holland, and adopted the name of Petr Mikhailoff, the shipwright, but his great height and the obvious deference of his entourage made remaining incognito nothing short of impossible. At the same time, he remained in full charge of affairs at home and was in receipt of mail on a daily basis. In the early weeks of 1698 he sailed for Britain where he was welcomed by the new King, William of Orange, who presented him with a yacht, *Royal Transport*. Peter was delighted and spent five months in England sightseeing, visiting, interviewing and learning. For a while he was resident in Deptford and was a regular visitor to the Royal Dockyard. On his return to Russia, Peter started the practice of recruiting naval and military officers, shipyard superintendents, academics and other professionals predominantly from Scotland, with others from England, Holland and Denmark. In 1713, of the Baltic fleet's eleven senior officers, only two were Russians.

One lasting aspect of the Great Embassy was the choice of Russian flags; the national flag is a horizontal tricolour of white, blue and red, similar but in a different order to the flag of the Dutch. The naval ensign has always been the Saltire or St Andrew's Cross in reverse colours from Scotland, and the naval jack is a complete reversal of the pre-1801 Union Flag of Britain with the crosses of St Andrew and St George. A true compliment indeed.

The greatest problem which Peter had to deal with was the need for trading outlets to the Black Sea (and hence the Mediterranean), to the Baltic and western Europe, as well as the White Sea and the north and later the Pacific. Turkey's wish to control all operations in the Sea of Azov north of the Black Sea created a severe problem and was faced in a robust manner. Peter instituted shipbuilding in Russia in 1695 with the construction of two 36-gun ships and large numbers of galleys, all completed within one year. This new fleet won its first battle at Azov in 1696, the date now regarded as the founding of the Russian navy. Shipyard complexes opened in Voronezh and continued there till the timber supplies from the surrounding country were exhausted in 1711. By then over 215 ships had been built for the Black Sea/Azov fleet, many with input from the Tsar and one of fifty-eight guns which had been designed by Peter himself with guidance from England.

As there was no outlet to the west, Peter ensured that the east end of the Gulf of Finland was in Russian hands, and on the unpromising marsh lands where the River Neva meets the sea built the city of St Petersburg. Architects and engineers were recruited from all over Europe, and the new capital of Russia was built by countless thousands of workmen aided by even more slaves. Thousands died, but the legacy is a wonderful city, strategically sited for both trade and defence, protected by the fortress and naval base of Kronstadt some miles to the west. This enabled ships a much easier passage to Russia as until then all trade had been through Archangelsk to the north.

Shipbuilding commenced to the east of St Petersburg and ultimately the great Admiralty yards opened in the centre of the city around 1704, making Russia a significant shipbuilding country in its own right. The Admiralty yards continued building the ships for the Baltic Fleet right up till 1844 despite all the logistic difficulties of long ice-bound winters, frozen rivers, immense distances and long annual lay-ups for all ships in the Imperial Navy. Quite apart from obtaining good shipbuilders and naval officers, Peter had to contend with a nation that had no tradition of seafaring. He opened a naval academy and a School of Mathematics and Navigational Sciences, indeed he edited the first edition in 1720 of the Book of Maritime Regulations.

Two years before he died, Tsar Peter held a fleet review in the Baltic. He took the tiller of *The Grandfather of the Russian Navy* and four admirals pulled at the oars. A massive fleet had assembled, made up of twenty-two ships of the line and over 200 galleys, all this achieved in one man's lifetime. He was of immense height and in every sense was 'larger than life'. He liked to adopt a hands-on approach, regularly piloting ships and more than once commanding part of a fleet in battle. It is doubtful if any single person has had such an influence on Russia as Tsar Peter; the soul of Russia is deep and almost unfathomable, but the people are kind and hospitable and their pride in Petr Alexeyevich is genuine and totally justified.

SOURCES:
Massie, Robert K.
Peter the Great: His Life and Work
London, 1981
Mitchell, Mairin
The Maritime History of Russia 848-1948
London, 1949

Pierre Bouguer
1698–1758

AS BRITTANY ALWAYS has been, and still remains, one of the great centres of European shipbuilding, it may come as no surprise that one of its sons, Pierre Bouguer, mathematician and scientist, has been ascribed the title 'Father of Naval Architecture'.

Bouguer was born at the very end of the seventeenth century at Le Croisic about 60km (37 miles) west of Nantes. From an early age Pierre was recognised as a scientific child prodigy, and his father Jean Bouguer (who was Regius Professor of Hydrography at Croisic), personally took control of his education. During his years as a student, Pierre had serious scientific disputes with many of his father's colleagues which may have caused his father some embarrassment, while giving Pierre the reputation for being a precocious young undergraduate. Clearly he had a mercurial personality which became evident in later years when he shared the hard graft of research with others. In a strange turn of events on the death of his father, and at the remarkably young age of fifteen, he was appointed to succeed him in the Chair of Hydrography.

The period of the European Enlightenment, consummately born in Scotland in the late seventeenth century, moved across all Europe within twenty years, encouraging among other things the study of natural philosophy (physics), mathematics, natural sciences and the arts. France embraced the Enlightenment and became one of the world's principal seats of both modern science and engineering science. Pierre Bouguer was to become one of the greatest leaders in the new movement.

In 1727, and while still in his twenties, Pierre was admitted as a member of the French Royal Academy of Sciences; a preferment based on his published research in the quite diverse fields of star observation, compass variation at sea and the analysis of ship rig design. An award of 2,000 livres was made to him for his design of a back-staff in the form of a quadrant where the observer could see both sun and horizon simultaneously.* After this it is believed he was appointed to the Chair of Hydrography at Le Havre, but shortly thereafter moved to Paris.

In 1735, the Academie Royale des Sciences organised an expedition to Peru to carry out work which included the accurate measurement of a length of one degree at the Equator. While there the team, which included Louis Godin and La Condamine, also researched matters as diverse as the density of the earth and the basic theory of photometry. The density problem was attacked by measuring the deflection of a plumb bob within the attraction of a mountain which had been surveyed accurately. During this period, the three scientists fell out over procedural matters. Incidentally, the Rev. Nevil Maskelyne, Astronomer Royal at Greenwich, estimated that the earth's SG was between 4.5 and 5.0.

While in South America, Bouguer studied and wrote on matters as diverse as ship manoeuvres, ship design and ship construction. It was here that he prepared his magnum opus, *Traité du Navire*, in which ship stability was described properly for the first time, and where the concept of metacentric height was proposed.

Bouguer's naval architecture work is in three parts: the first was descriptive, covering ship construction, launching, rigging, equipment and outfitting. It also introduced some basic definitions on ship geometry. The second and most important part described methods of hull measurement, the importance of the position of the centre of gravity and the effects of rolling. In this part the concept of 'metacentric height' was put forward (probably) for the first time. The final section of the volume considered hydrodynamics – then in its infancy.

While Bouguer's work probably had little effect on the shipbuilders of the eighteenth century, it is certain that his thinking was to stimulate theoretical naval architecture. Within six years, Henri-Louis Duhamel du Monceau was to publish *Eléments de l'architecture navale ou traité pratique de la construction des vaisseaux* (The Elements of Naval Architecture). In it Duhamel produced a method for finding the centre of gravity of a ship. Shortly thereafter, the British shipwright Mungo Murray published *A Treatise on Shipbuilding*, a work which was a compilation of all the known technologies of eighteenth-century shipbuilding, and which gave details on the now lost art of 'whole moulding'.

SOURCES:

Bouguer, Pierre
Traité du Navire, de sa construction et de ses mouvements
Paris, 1746

* Howse, Derek
Greenwich Time and the Longitude
Greenwich, 1997

Stoot, W F,
'Naval Architecture in the Eighteenth Century'
and
'Ideas and Personalities in the Development of Naval Architecture'
Transactions of the Institution of Naval Architects Vol 101 (1959)

Blaise Ollivier

1701–1746

ESPIONAGE, BOTH MILITARY and industrial, is as old as mankind, and many naval architects have been involved in it over the centuries. The highest profile case was that of **Peter the Great**'s 'embassies' to The Netherlands and Great Britain, where the Tsar of All the Russias assumed a false name and both the Russians and their hosts pretended the whole matter was an informal trade mission! Many European constructors in training were sent overseas, sometimes openly but often under assumed names. It was expected that Scandinavians would find their way to Britain, examples include the Swede, F H af Chapman, as well as the multitudes of young Danish constructors whose training courses demanded overseas experience. Occasional cases were sinister, like that of Blaise Geslain, a Frenchman who infiltrated the Dutch shipbuilding hierarchy in the early eighteenth century.

Another notable French industrial spy of the eighteenth century was Blaise Ollivier, remembered for his semi-clandestine but assiduous reporting on British and Dutch naval shipbuilding in the 1730s. His recording was first class as can be seen from those parts of his work which have been published in Britain, and from the manuscripts preserved in sundry French archives. At the end of the seventeenth century, Dutch influence in shipbuilding was declining, the Danes and the Swedes were holding their own, and would maintain their position of high technical eminence for some decades, but it was the French and the British who were in the ascendancy and were to become the deadliest of rivals. Clearly the French wished to learn everything possible about their future enemies, and here Ollivier proved himself a most effective agent, displaying a detailed understanding of shipbuilding processes, as well as having the charm and ability that enabled him to see many things forbidden to the citizens of the British Isles. As far back as 1792, periodicals complained that Britons rarely could gain admittance to the British Royal Dockyards, while 'foreigners of any nation if clothed in an officer's uniform find ready admittance'. *Plus ça change!*

Blaise Ollivier's life was short, even by the standards of the eighteenth century, but he did achieve an enormous amount in the forty-six years before his death from tuberculosis. The son of Joseph Ollivier, Master Shipwright at Brest, the highest office for a shipbuilder in France at that time, Blaise Ollivier from his birth in 1701 was destined to follow him. At the age of nineteen he had become a 'sous-maître constructeur', and a mere sixteen years later on the death of his father, was appointed Master Shipwright and given full responsibility for all engineering, building and management of the Naval Base at Brest, and was described as 'Master Shipwright to the King of France'. In those years, shipwrights were assumed to be persons having little formal qualifications and ill-educated by the standards of the aristocracy, but Ollivier (and his British opposite numbers) were to prove the Establishment wrong in this regard.

The sixteen years under the direction of his father were spent well, and included surveys of forests, experimentation on building materials and the submission of reports on shipbuilding timber. He is recorded as having lifted the lines of several ships and prepared sheer draughts for the records of the French Navy. He designed and built smitheries for the Brest Dockyard as well as some building slips in various parts of France, but the most ingenious work was that of improving the efficacy of the dry-docks at Brest which, owing to poor initial design, imprisoned larger ships for lengthy periods around the neap tides. Maurepas, the French Minister of the Navy, invited Ollivier and his father to design and oversee construction of several ships including the well-documented 60-gun ship *Fleuron*, all of which led to some remarkably lucid writings on timber ship construction, such as his *Traité de Construction*. In 1737, under instruction from Maurepas he visited the dockyards of The Netherlands and Britain in great secrecy and produced the report which only recently has been published in English. Starting in the 1740s and for several years before he died, Ollivier taught at the 'petit école de marine' in Paris, one of Europe's first systematic schools for naval constructors.

While Ollivier's high level of training and professional competence coupled with personal tact ensured that his overseas visits were successful from the French point of view, it is pleasing to report that in historical terms his writings have left a real and lasting contribution to naval architecture. His other – and possibly his greatest – contribution to naval architecture was the estimation of ship displacement. Using trapezoids as proposed by **Pierre Bouguer** (1698–1758) he was able to make close estimations on mass and therefore displacement, and while this did not solve stability problems, it did lessen the risk of warships being so deep in the water that their lower gun decks became ineffective. Until metacentric theory was understood, the shipwright's inherent skills at ballasting were needed for many years; when errors did slip through the net, there was always the system of 'girdling' when the breadth of the vessel could be increased by an additional belt of timber around the design waterline. Ollivier was aware of all these techniques but he took the profession one further stage along the line to scientific shipbuilding. His untimely death robbed French and European shipbuilding of an undoubted pre-eminent shipwright. His writings have left a lasting contribution to naval architecture.

SOURCES:
Ferreiro, Larrie
Ships and Science: The Birth of Naval Architecture in the Scientific Revolution 1600–1800
Cambridge, Mass., 2007
Ollivier, Blaise
18th Century Shipbuilding: Remarks on the Navies of the English and the Dutch in 1737
Rotherfield, East Sussex, 1992

Sir Thomas Slade

1703–1771

REGARDED BY SOME AS the most distinguished naval architect of his era, Thomas Slade has left one imperishable eighteenth-century memorial, a wooden ship of the line. Still in commission as one of Her Majesty's Ships, the *Victory* is preserved at the Naval Base of Portsmouth two and a half centuries after her launching at Chatham.

This exquisite model of *Bellona* in the National Maritime Museum, possibly made by George Stockwell the Sheerness craftsman and builder of some of the most beautiful models of the period, may have been used to demonstrate copper sheathing to George III, a development of huge significance to the Royal Navy at a time when the country's global reach was extending fast. *(Author)*

Slade came from a 'dockyard' family; he followed in their footsteps as a shipwright apprentice and then rose slowly but steadily through the ranks, becoming Deputy to the Master Shipwright of Woolwich when he was about forty years old. Six years later, in 1750, his uncle Benjamin Slade, then Master Shipwright at Plymouth, died and Thomas was promoted into his post. During the following five years he moved from Plymouth to Woolwich, then to Chatham with a final move to Deptford then close to the centre of naval administration. At that time Admiral Lord Anson was a positive and successful First Lord of the Admiralty, and he regarded Slade as 'his kind of man'. As a result in 1755 Thomas Slade, later to be Sir Thomas Slade, was appointed Surveyor to the Navy working alongside William Bateley and later John Williams. Despite it being an arrangement in tandem, it is clear that Slade was regarded throughout as the senior. In the eighteenth century the post of Surveyor to the Navy was the highest technical position in the service.*

Until his death sixteen years later, Slade worked on many ships that were to prove their worth in the coming wars with France. He designed and built over forty 74-gun ships, all similar and with generic features, of which the *Bellona* class is possibly the most beautiful. Slade introduced the 64-gun ship to the Royal Navy, but his most important construction was the successful 100-gun *Victory*. The choice of name for *Victory* was surprising, as until then it had not been the name of a happy or a successful ship – all that would change, for despite *Victory*'s fairly short periods in active service, her name became legendary.

Before his death he brought about one long lasting change: the commencement of copper sheathing of the Navy's ships.

SOURCES:
Clowes, William Laird
The Royal Navy, a history from the earliest times to 1900 (7 vols)
London 1897–1903 and a subsequent facsimile edition
Rodger, N A M
The Command of the Ocean, a Naval History of Britain 1649–1815
London, 2004

* The position of Surveyor to the Navy is first recorded in 1546, and was held by a succession of men almost all of whom were shipwrights by profession. The tasks of the incumbent were defined formally in 1588 and at times the post was known as the Surveyor for Shipbuilding and Repairs. In 1860, when Sir Baldwin Wake Walker was Surveyor, his position was elevated to Controller of the Navy, and the new post of Chief Constructor created. In 1875 when Nathaniel Barnaby was Chief Constructor, the new and distinguished title of Director of Naval Construction was promulgated – a title reflecting the vast responsibility of the man charged with designing and supervising construction of Britain's massive navy.

Rene-Nicolas Levasseur
1705–1784

RENE-NICOLAS LEVASSEUR, a ship constructor chosen for his integrity and determination, was sent in 1738 to Quebec charged with setting up the new naval dockyard in Nouvelle-France. Commissioned by King Louis XV for this daunting task, young Levasseur had a more than suitable background; he had been born in Rochefort, then a vibrant French naval base, and had followed in the family profession as a shipbuilder and naval constructor. He commenced his training at Toulon in 1727 and within six years was given the task of supervising a ship under construction; a task known well to many shipbuilders on their path upwards, that of being a 'Ship Manager'.

During the eighteenth century, France was striving to establish Canada as their colony in North America and regular fleets of French ships fitted out at Rochefort and sailed from nearby La Rochelle to the St Lawrence. Bordeaux and other ports also were involved. The authorities in Quebec City had long petitioned the French authorities for the setting-up of a royal dockyard, and to their delight in 1738 learned that Quebec had been selected as a new naval base and that a Constructor was being sent out to take charge. Levasseur must have seen this as a long-term appointment as he travelled with his wife and children, and set up home in the city. He would remain there until 1760 when he returned to France following his country's defeat at the battle of Quebec and the ending of the Seven Years War.

Ship models in churches are a rich resource for technical and historical researchers. This model is of the seventeenth-century French ship *Brézé*, in Notre-Dame des Victoires, Place Royale, Quebec. While not built by Levasseur, she was one of the great French fleet which served between France and Nouvelle-France (Canada) until the end of the Seven Years War. *(Author)*

The twenty years were spent well, and Levasseur allocated his time across a wide spectrum of work. The selection of timber for shipbuilding took him deep into the forests, journeys that had to be taken as often as twice a year. As ship construction barely had started in Canada, this must have been tough, pioneering work, and according to surviving records much of the timber harvested was not of the best quality, and certainly not suitable for the very large ships that France wished to build as they geared up for war. All lumber was floated down the rivers, and for the first few years the pressure of urgent ship construction prevented any lengthy drying-out of timber in the stockyards.

The new shipyard was laid out, men recruited and building started using plans drawn by Levasseur in whatever spare time he could muster. The first building site was on the side of the River St Charles, but within a few years it had been moved to the St Lawrence to obtain better depths of water for launching. This change of position did not prevent a serious launching accident in 1750, when the 62-gun *Original* was seriously damaged on entering the water. All the foremen had come from France and the total workforce is believed to have peaked at around 200 men. In all about eleven ships were built, the largest being the 72-gun *Algonquin*, stated as being of 1,500 tons, which was delivered in 1753.

Difficulties mounted for Levasseur. Timber supplies continued to present problems, the procurement of pitch, tar, spikes and nails became increasingly difficult and the price of everything escalated when the British imposed their blockade. Keeping hold of skilled labour in wartime was one challenge, but trying to please civil servants in France who made ignorant and unreasonable demands was possibly the greatest test of the young constructor's patience and loyalty. Happily he kept the respect of the Quebec administration, and during the bloody battle in 1759 led teams of workers who tackled the fires spreading through the city. In all records he is spoken of as a talented and professional gentleman.

The fall of Quebec ended Levasseur's stay in Canada, and by 1760 he was back in France but almost in penury, a condition no doubt exacerbated by having had to flee his home. Happily the French government recognised his exceptional service, awarding him a pension. He is remembered now as (most probably) the first professional shipbuilder in Canada. Less than one hundred years later, shipbuilding was booming in the Provinces of New Brunswick, Nova Scotia, Prince Edward Island and Quebec.

SOURCES:
Mathieu, Jacques
La construction navale royale à Quebec 1739-1759
Quebec, 1971
Proulx, Gilles
Between France and New France
Toronto, 1984

Leonhard Euler
1707–1783

THE SWISS MATHEMATICIAN whose work enabled engineering design and research to be built on a firm foundation, Leonhard Euler was born in Basel in 1707, the son of a Lutheran minister, but was to spend most of his childhood in the Swiss town of Riehen. In keeping with the times, he became an undergraduate at Basel University while just thirteen years old, and commenced studying divinity with subjects as diverse as Greek, Hebrew and

Biblical studies, all with a view to becoming a pastor. In addition to his work and other student activities, he presented himself once a week for lessons from Johann Bernoulli (1700–82) the notable Dutch/Swiss mathematician. Here Euler's brilliance in mathematics became apparent, and Bernoulli (a friend of Euler's father) persuaded the family that young Leonhard should devote his time at university to this subject. By the age of nineteen he was awarded the equivalent of a PhD.

Euler's first (and possibly only) involvement with ships came in 1727 when he entered the yearly competition run by the Paris Academy on a scientific subject. That year the problem was to find the optimum position for the masts of a ship, a competition in which he took second place with the winner being **Pierre Bouguer**, who became known as the 'Father of Naval Architecture'. Incidentally Euler entered this competition frequently and won it outright twelve times!

Leonhard Euler made great contributions, not only to naval architecture, but to engineering in general with his concept of function f(x), his introduction of *e* for the base of the natural logarithm and the presentation of easily understood notations for trigonometric functions.

In 1727, he became a lecturer in the medical department of the St Petersburg Academy in Russia. He was to marry a Russian lady and remain happily in that city for close on sixteen years, when he moved to Berlin to work at the university. Another twenty-five years of research followed, possibly the most productive part of his life, but Euler's eyesight was becoming seriously impaired and from then he became dependent on first his memory and second his scribes and secretaries. In 1766 he accepted an invitation from Empress Catherine (the Great) to return to Russia and spent the last few years of his life in St Petersburg. His wife died and after three years he married her half sister. He died in 1783 and some time ago was reburied in an Orthodox cemetery near the Alexander Nevsky Cathedral.

SOURCES:
Gullberg, Jan
Mathematics from the Birth of Numbers
New York, 1997

Thomas Simpson

1710–1761

SIMPSON'S RULES ARE amongst the first calculations taught to students of naval architecture, and are essential for the estimation of areas bounded by a base, two ordinates and a 'fair' curve. Using simple extensions to this rule one is able also to calculate volumes bounded on one side by a 'sweet' three-dimensional shape. Their author was Thomas Simpson, the son of a Leicestershire weaver.

As a young man, Simpson was given little encouragement in his pursuit of academic interests. He left home while a fairly young man and lodged with a widow at Nuneaton, whom he married when a mere twenty years of age. His first interest was astrology, but happily he graduated to more respectable subjects and became known as a mathematician and as an astronomer. In 1735 he made his way to London and supported his family and himself by working as a weaver, and teaching mathematics part-time. Despite lack of formal training, by the time he was thirty he had been elected a member of the Royal Academy of Stockholm and three years later was Professor of Mathematics at the Royal Military Academy, Woolwich, distinctions which were crowned in 1745 when he became a Fellow of the Royal Society. Between 1754 and 1760 he edited the *Ladies Diary* and published many papers on mathematics and natural philosophy.

The method of calculating areas was published by Simpson in 1743, and his name has been associated with them ever-since. However the initial methods had been produced by Isaac Newton (1642–1727) and others, and to these persons Simpson gave full acknowledgement in his papers. Owing to domestic problems, his health broke down and he died in 1761 at Market Bosworth leaving his wife and two children. The government awarded a pension to his widow who lived until her 103rd year, dying in 1782. His son, appropriately enough, became an officer in the Royal Artillery.

SOURCES:
Robb, A M
Theory of Naval Architecture
London, 1952

Additional Note

Two methods of calculating areas are ascribed to Thomas Simpson and are known (not unsurprisingly) as Simpson's First Rule and Simpson's Second Rule

Two biographies follow of gentlemen of the following century, but are included here as they had considerable influence in reducing the hard labour and number-crunching in ship design calculations.

Pafnuty Lvovich Tchebycheff

1821–1894

THE INVENTOR OF A simple means of measuring and calculating areas bounded by curved lines, Pafnuty Lvovich Tchebycheff was one of nine children born into a fairly rich and privileged family of the Russian minor aristocracy. His health was less than good, and it was arranged that members of the family along with some private teachers would give him his early education. He was captivated by both music and mathematics, and found in the former a challenge to his analytical thinking. Being unable to play games with other children, he spent considerable amounts of time working on mathematical problems, an occupation that would remain part of his life. In 1837 he entered Moscow University, and would remain there for the best part of ten years, during which time he published papers on many aspects of mathematics including probability. From there he progressed to the University of St Petersburg, rising steadily to the position of Professor of Merit, and retiring in 1882 in order to devote the last twelve years of his life to mathematical research.

Between 1852 and 1858, he had the unusual appointment of teacher of practical mechanics at the Alexander Lyceum at Tsarskoye Selo. This was a school set up in 1811 by Tsar Alexander I with the express task of producing new leaders for Russia. The school remained under the patronage of the sovereign until the revolution; the first intake of students included Alexander Pushkin, the man now regarded as Russia's principal poet, and of such importance that in the late twentieth century the name of Tsarskoye Selo was changed to Pushkin.

While Tchebycheff had little direct connection with ships, his theory has been used in mensuration, enabling areas bounded by curved lines to be calculated with considerable simplicity. The Tchebycheff Rules are probably the most accurate, but requiring careful setting up are the least used in ship design.

The name of Tchebycheff has various other transliterations, including 'Chebyshev'.

SOURCES:

Biles, Professor J Harvard
'On M. Tchebycheff's Formula'
Transactions of the Institution of Shipbuilders and Engineers in Scotland
Vol 42 (1898–9)

Robb, A M
Theory of Naval Architecture
London, 1952
This volume gives clear explanations of the use of Tchebycheff's rule in ship calculation.

James Thomson

1822–1892

THE INVENTOR OF A measuring rule to rival that of **Thomas Simpson**, in 1834 James Thomson had the unusual experience of matriculating at Glasgow University at the very early age of twelve, and even more surprising, he was accompanied by his younger brother William (later to be **Lord Kelvin**, the first scientist or engineer ever ennobled) who was then a mere ten years old. Throughout their long lives, they remained close friends and worked harmoniously, each giving the other all credit as was due.

James had an all-round engineering training which included an apprenticeship with **Sir William Fairbairn** and then more general work in civil and mechanical engineering, before going on to Belfast, which was the city of his birth, to become Engineer to the City Water Commissioners. By the time he was thirty-seven, Queen's College in Belfast (now Queen's University) invited him to become Professor of Civil Engineering, a position he held until March 1873 when invited by Glasgow University to cross the North Channel and take the Regius Chair of Civil Engineering and Mechanics, left vacant on the death of **W J Macquorn Rankine**.

His publications were wide-ranging, with considerable work on hydraulics, tides, strength of materials and railway systems. One particular paper presented to the Royal Society of Edinburgh was entitled 'On the Lowering by Pressure of the Freezing Point of Water' and was regarded as a model of conjoined theoretical and experimental work. His work terminated in 1899 owing to failing eyesight and he died three years later.

He had many involvements with ships and the sea, but in one matter his name is preserved and that is his rule for mensuration of areas under a fair curve. Thomson's Rule is a slight simplification of Simpson's Rules as it allows the use of unity as a multiplier on many ordinates. It has been calculated that both Simpson's Rules and Thomson's Rule give results that are less than 0.1 of 1 per cent different from each other, and well within the levels of accuracy acceptable in hull design.

SOURCES:

Thompson, S P
The Life of Lord Kelvin 2 vols
London, 1910

Fredrik Henrik af Chapman

1721–1808

FROM MEDIEVAL TIMES up to the present day, Sweden has been noted as a country that produces fine ships, designed skilfully and constructed using up-to-date shipbuilding processes. The Swedes, like their Scandinavian cousins in Denmark, Finland and Norway, can take pride in a long and distinguished line of naval architects and innovative shipbuilders amongst whom were four members of the Sheldon family as well as Thomas Day and Robert Turner. Unusually all had some connection to Britain, and all formed a fairly close-knit and conservative group.

Matters were to change as the century progressed as the Swedish constructors were to produce a man with a reforming and scientific mind; he was none other than F H af Chapman, a man to reform ship design from within the Swedish navy and to be remembered as one of the world's greatest naval architects. Chapman was born within the royal dockyard at Gothenburg in Sweden. His parents were British, his father being an officer in the Royal Swedish Navy, and his grandfather before that a farmer in Yorkshire. From the age of ten, Chapman displayed great interest in ship construction as well as aptitude as a draughtsman and soon his avocation became clear. For the following quarter of a century, he was to work and travel in Britain, France, The Netherlands, and Sweden gaining the experience which enabled him in later life to become Head of Construction in Karlskrona, the main Swedish Naval Base. His formal training began at the age of fifteen, when Chapman went to sea, and then was to continue when he worked as a shipwright in London before returning to Gothenburg to become joint proprietor of a shipyard building small vessels.

This period managing a shipyard alerted him to the inability of shipbuilders to predict with any accuracy the displacement, stability and other qualities of ships. He decided on the need for a rigorous approach which involved turning his back on shipbuilding for some years. The atmosphere was right for this move as Sweden was beginning to be swept along in the Great Enlightenment, and men of the stature of Carl Linnaeus and his 'apostles' had a great influence on Swedish society. In 1748 Chapman moved to Stockholm to become a student of the mathematician Frederik Palmquist and a couple of years later returned to London to study under **Thomas Simpson**, then Professor at the Royal Military Academy, Woolwich, but probably best known as the author of Simpson's Rules for the mensuration of irregular areas and volumes bounded by curved lines. He learned the art of engraving and copper etching, a skill that would stand him in good stead in years to come.

After many travels and adventures, including incurring the displeasure of the British and other governments for his obvious thirst for knowledge especially in dockyards and arsenals, the time had come for carving a career in naval construction.

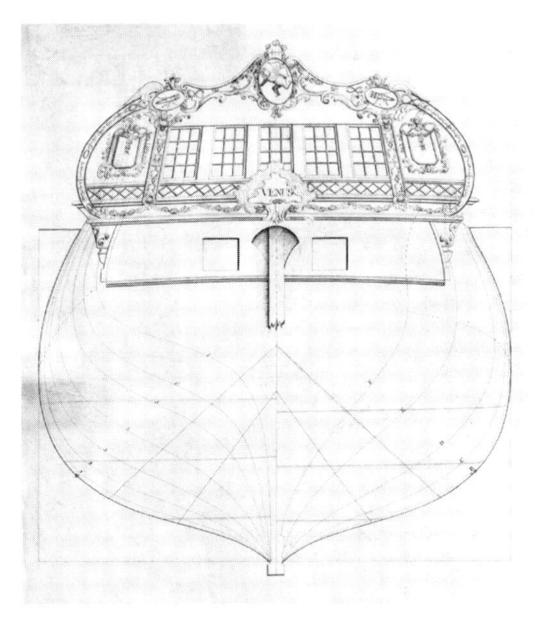

The Swedish frigate *Venus* (1789), designed by Fredrik af Chapman, and taken by the Russians in 1808. This body plan was taken off at Sheerness when she was stationed in the North Sea. Able to carry 24-pounder guns, she could take her place in the line of battle and represented Chapman's solution to the inferior strength of the Swedish navy, always at a disadvantage against the Russians. (© *The National Maritime Museum, Greenwich, J3924*)

Despite an attractive offer from the British First Sea Lord, Chapman returned to his homeland, and joined the Royal Swedish Navy, initially as Assistant Constructor at Karlskrona. Here he would become aware of the suspicions of his more conservative peers, all experienced builders, but none with any pretensions to being advanced designers. After another short spell overseas, in 1760 he was appointed Deputy Master Shipbuilder and posted to Sveaborg under the command of Major General Ehrensvard who was responsible for the defence of what is now the Finnish coast from the Russians at a time when they were increasing their coastal fleet. At this stage he initiated coastal cruises to identify suitable stands of growing timber for the shipyards under his control, and then concentrated on the design of the new coastal fleet.

This inshore fleet was designed to operate and fight in the shallow waters of the Gulf of Finland and to protect the fortress then known as Sveaborg (now Suomenlinna) at the entrance to Helsinki harbour. These long and narrow ships, many propelled by oars, showed marked French and Mediterranean influence and were designed for a multitude of tasks ranging from troop transportation to coastal bombardment. This 'skerry' fleet remains a unique and beautiful Swedish contribution to naval architecture, and ships of this type were used widely by the Danes in their running battle with the British between 1807 and 1814. While not as successful as had been hoped, they were a breakthrough in design and brought Chapman to the attention of not only his immediate superiors, but also the King himself.

In 1764 Chapman was invited to become Chief Constructor, working from both Karlskrona and Stockholm. Few men in the eighteenth century could claim to have risen to the rank of Vice Admiral after having served a shipwright apprenticeship, learned the craft of engraving, and studied under some of the great physicists and mathematicians of western Europe. He gave profound consideration to the most efficient design of ships of the line required for operation in the Baltic, a shallow sea notorious for change of mood. Here he decided on two-deckers, often vessels of sixty guns with gun decks as far above the waterline as was practical, a practice that was to be followed by several other Scandinavian and Baltic countries.

The tasks carried out by Chapman seem unending. On becoming Chief Constructor, he initiated the rebuild of the Karlskrona Naval Base and here his administrative skills became apparent with the introduction of original shipbuilding techniques and the design of some quite innovative machinery. While Chapman did not suffer fools gladly, he was a restrained and genial person, understanding that problems were overcome more easily by diplomacy than by brutality. He did not enjoy as much support as he would have liked from his fellow constructors, largely as they had come from the traditional school and lacked any real scientific knowledge.

Chapman's greatest legacy must be his two volumes on ship design, produced during sabbatical leave. Both must rank as being amongst the greatest shipbuilding books of all time. During the twentieth century, there have been many editions of *Architectura Navalis Mercatoria*, all of which have made Chapman's work better known and which grace the libraries of naval architects throughout the world. Some recent editions include parts of his 'Treatise on Shipbuilding', known originally as *Tractat om Skepps-Byggeriet*, which describes Chapman's thoughts on estimating volume and other matters then regarded as complex. Incidentally, the Swedish navy started to collect all their shipbuilding and associated models in the eighteenth century, and this ongoing collection is available for inspection at the museums at Karlskrona and Stockholm.

While his name is known, his work is as yet not fully appreciated. Chapman displayed the highest qualities of an engineer, an open mind and a questing spirit. He dignified the craft and the profession of shipbuilding by enhancing the work of a tradesman with the scientific knowledge which could be derived from study and experimentation.

SOURCES:
af Chapman, Fredrik Henrik
Architectura Navalis Mercatoria
Stockholm, 1768

———,
Tractat om Skepps-Byggeriet
Stockholm, 1775

Harris, Daniel G
F H Chapman: The First Naval Architect and his Work
London, 1989

John Schanck

1740–1823

A NAVAL OFFICER WHO made a great contribution to ship design at a time of change, John Schanck, a native of the Kingdom of Fife, came from a family with deep roots in Scottish landowning, farming and the Church. From early days he felt a desire to go to sea, and starting at a young age worked on coastal vessels operating in the North Sea, but when seventeen entered the Royal Navy and served for four years as an able seaman on the *Duke* and *Shrewsbury*. Here good fortune came his way in that he was noticed by Captain Hugh Palliser (the same man who befriended his contemporary James Cook) and through this was rated a midshipman and later a master's mate. Again, in a manner similar to James Cook he witnessed the Transit of Venus in 1769, in this case aboard HMS *Emerald* positioned off the North Cape of Norway. This was an important observation, as Venus crossed the face of the sun only twice in the eighteenth century, and by taking close observations in widely spaced parts of the world and at different latitudes (to overcome parallax), the distance between the earth and sun could be estimated with a fair degree of accuracy.

In 1776, Schanck was promoted Lieutenant and placed in command of an armed schooner operating in the St Lawrence River in Canada. Clearly he was stimulated by this independent command, and with twenty years of seagoing experience, his natural mechanical ability came to the fore. In biographies of the man it is reported that his nickname was 'Old Purchase' following on his development of a system of pulleys that allowed someone recumbent in a cot to raise or lower themselves unaided. His former commanding officer, Captain George Vandeput, recommended that he be placed in charge of the fitting-out of the British Great Lakes fleet, and over the coming months, Schanck worked in places as far apart as Detroit in the Great Lakes and Quebec on the St Lawrence. He showed considerable determination, and on one occasion when dissatisfied with the likely finishing time of a 180-ton 18-gun sloop under construction in Quebec, had her dismantled and shipped upstream to another site where she was reassembled and launched as the *Inflexiable* a few weeks later.

In October 1776, Schanck commanded this ship at in action on Lake Champlain and along with colleagues on a handful of other small craft secured victory with commendably small loss of life on either side. During this period, Schanck gave considerable thought to means of traversing guns on deck to enable them to fire to either port or starboard. He continued these studies and experiments for the rest of his life. In 1777, while attached to the army, he designed and built a series of easily-erected temporary floating bridges for General Burgoyne which could be moved speedily from one

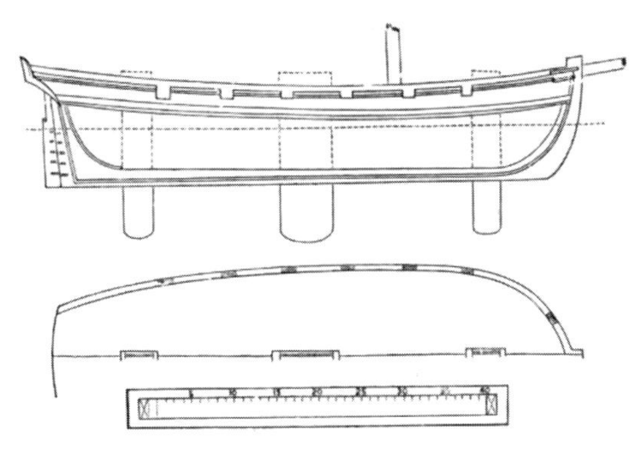

General arrangement plan of HMS *Trial*, a sliding-keel vessel built near London at Deptford Dockyard by John Schanck in 1790. This led to the shallow draft 60-ton brig *Lady Nelson* of 1799 which was part of the later circumnavigation of Australia by the Royal Navy. *(Author)*

place to another. Unfortunately, following a military reverse these fell into the hands of the American revolutionaries.

The contribution to naval architecture for which John Schanck is remembered best is the introduction of centre boards or sliding keels in small vessels. Such appendages have been known for centuries in less-developed local sailing fleets, but were little used in the merchant and naval fleets of the eighteenth-century powers, especially the British and Americans with their (then) lesser experience in close coastal operations. It is said that in 1774 while in Boston, Schanck had discussed the matter with Lord Percy, the heir to the Dukedom of Northumberland and as a private venture a small shallow-draft cutter had been built with a centre plate extending over 80 per cent of the keel. It had performed well, was sent across to Britain and the idea of a new class of inshore vessels was generated. Sixteen years later the Admiralty authorised the building at the Deptford Dockyard of a small boat named *Trial* with three small vertical dagger plates, one forward, one amidships and the other aft. During trials differing configurations of the plates were tried and the experiments pronounced a success. Other craft followed including a five-keeled hull for the Commodore of the Cumberland Sailing Society on the Thames (now the Royal Thames Yacht Club) and a sloop for the Navy named HMS *Cynthia*. The ultimate development was HM Brig *Lady Nelson* of 60 tons also built at Deptford in 1799 with three sliding keels which allowed her to enter shallow harbours. She sailed to Australia, was the first British ship to sail eastwards through the Bass Strait and assisted in the great Australian circumnavigation led by Captain Matthew Flinders.

In the 1790s, Schanck served as transport officer on the British expedition to Martinique, and following this became the equivalent of the logistics agent for transporting men and materiel in the campaigns in the Low Countries. His last major operational task appears to have been the responsibility for coastal defence of a large part of Britain from south-east Scotland to Hampshire. His advice was sought by many organisations in The Netherlands and the UK and in particular by Lord Dundas, the chairman of the extremely profitable Forth and Clyde Canal Company. In later years John Schanck was an active member of the Society for the Improvement of Naval Architecture, and in 1821, at the age of eighty-one and just two years before his death, his promotion was confirmed as Admiral of the Blue.

SOURCES:

*Chapelle, Howard I
The History of the American Sailing Navy – the ships and their development
New York, 1949
This book on American craft gives a good description of Schanck's *Trial*.

Pritchett, R T
Sliding Keels and Centreboards
Vol 1 of the Badminton Library of Yachting, 1894

Henrik Gerner

1742–1787

For a period of nearly 200 years, the Royal Danish Navy was one of Europe's more important and effective fleets. Designed specifically for coastal defence and for operations in the shallow waters and wild conditions of the Baltic, the fleet, ship for ship, was equal to any other of the time. Sadly, the regrettable and questionable British actions off Copenhagen in 1801 and 1807 ended Denmark's command of the northern seas, at least until the

Mærsk Line started expanding in the latter years of the twentieth century.

For 400 years Denmark demanded 'Sound Dues' from all merchantmen sailing through the Øresund, and with Copenhagen's close proximity to the Baltic, there was need first for an effective fleet, and secondly for diplomatically negotiated international treaties with most of Europe. The Øresund is now a narrow strip of water separating Denmark from Sweden, but until 1658 it was within the boundaries of the 'Twin Kingdoms' of Denmark and Norway.* Christian IV (1588–1648), the shipbuilder king, not only made the navy a force to be reckoned with, but he left his mark on the architecture of his capital city with buildings like the beautiful Round Tower, Denmark's Royal Observatory inspired by the work of his Stuart brother-in-law James VI and I at Greenwich. Christian was aware of the intellectual and scientific fervour of seventeenth-century Europe, and he made many changes, and was willing to appoint senior officials from overseas, one of whom, a Scot, **David Balfour**, became master shipwright to the navy, and possibly more important in pioneering terms, around 1600 reputedly produced the first proper ship plan. In 1670, one more change came about when another king, Christian V, arranged what was called the 'nationalisation' of the Danish Navy's construction facilities at Holmen in Copenhagen. This ensured the fleet had a dedicated home base, as well as in-house design and construction teams.

David Balfour was destined to be the first of a great line of Chief Constructors, most of whom were Danish or Norwegian. They included Krags, Benstrup, Stibolt and Hohlenberg, all names well known in Scandinavia at the time, but not commemorated outside their own land nowadays. One of them, however, Henrik Gerner, stood head and shoulders above the rest, despite his life being a mere forty-five years, of which fifteen (1772–87) were as Chief Constructor. Being the son of a constructor must have given him a good start in the navy, but when one assesses the massive workload, the superior design and the introduction of sophisticated management skills to the dockyard in his time, one begins to understand why he is remembered.

As Denmark had no facilities for formal training, aspiring constructors learned on the job in conjunction with study time overseas, with France usually the first choice. Gerner had fairly lengthy spells in both France and England and was impressed by the early attempts to apply mathematics to solving the problems involving displacement and stability. He knew of the mathematical approach of his Swedish counterpart **Fredrik Henrik af Chapman**, who worked mostly at Karlskrona on the south coast of Sweden. Dockyards in the eighteenth century were surprisingly welcoming to overseas students, as it was appreciated that new technologies would take time to be accepted by foreign dockyards and even more time to be built into the fleets of potential enemies. In those days war was much less personal; it was a condition between states and on many occasions did not affect private relationships.

In his fifteen years as Chief Constructor, Gerner oversaw all aspects of the construction of eighteen ships of the line, eleven frigates and many others. At this time, Danish civil servants were often involved in private work, and it is no surprise that the number of commercial jobs he completed far outnumbered the ships built for the navy; they included eleven vessels for the Danish Revenue Service and several for the Royal Greenland Company. Another client was the Danish Asiatic Company, and for them he designed armed merchantmen for the lucrative trade to the East Indies.

One of Gerner's few real disappointments was his failure to establish a proper shipbuilding school; at one stage work was so well progressed that even the name had been selected – 'The Royal School of Shipbuilding of Denmark, Norway and Holstein'. The rules stated that scholars must be able to read and write, and that tuition would be free although the first year would be probationary. Students would meet their own board and lodging costs, but it was hoped these would be met by benevolent shipbuilders, the government and by earnings from commercial work undertaken. The real tragedy of this failure was borne out by a survey, a few years after Gerner's death, which highlighted the fact that of Danish shipyards (outside Copenhagen) only three could work from plans and in Norway only thirteen. Remarkably, something like twenty-two had these new skills in Schleswig-Holstein.

When Gerner was training, he had a slightly older fellow pupil Ernst Stibolt, and there was serious rivalry between them. Relationships were soured when Gerner was appointed Chief and Stibolt had to wait fifteen years for the promotion he had so coveted. This and the problems of the School may have contributed to apoplexy and Gerner's early death. He left behind a good reputation, and while it is difficult to assess the character of a man of over 200 years ago, Gerner does seem to have been well liked, positive and dedicated. No ships constructed by Gerner survive, nor did he leave any important personal manuscripts, but there is a wealth of associated manuscripts and plan material in the Danish Archives, as well as models at the Royal Naval Museum in Copenhagen and the Maritime Museum at Kronborg Castle, Elsinore.

SOURCES:

Bjerg, H C, and Erichsen, John
Danske Orlogsskibe 1690–1860
2 vols (Copenhagen, 1980)
This large two-volume set is one of the finest productions on ship design in the past few years, with large-format plans and drawings. Despite the fairly short English summary, this is a real collector's book and will be of value to any students of the times of the sailing navies.

* Quite unbelievably, despite having lost control of the Øresund in 1658, Denmark continued to exact the Sound Dues until 1857, when by international agreement with all the major shipping countries in the world, the dues were abolished in return for a once and for all payment to Denmark of over 30 million rix dollars, a sum now equivalent to many billion US dollars. It is believed that several of the signatories have not paid up to this day. *Plus ça change!*

George Atwood

1745–1807

A MAN WHO MADE a great contribution to the understanding of ship stability, George Atwood can best be described as a mathematician and natural philosopher. His father was Thomas Atwood, the curate of St Clement Danes Church in London, and he had at least two brothers who followed him to Westminster School and then on to Trinity College, Cambridge. On graduating, the brothers entered the Church, while George opted for academic life but ended up in public service.

After a distinguished school career, Atwood entered Cambridge in 1765 and shortly after was awarded a scholarship. An excellent period as a student brought him to prominence and in 1769 he graduated as Third Wrangler, going on to become a fellow and tutor of his college. Throughout his lifetime he dedicated himself to reviving natural philosophy as an examinable subject at Cambridge, and in doing so built up a network of like-minded mathematicians and scientists including Volta at Pavia University, Nevil Maskelyne, the Astronomer Royal at Greenwich, and Joseph Black, the discoverer of latent heat, at Glasgow University. He gave public lectures at Cambridge which were popular and attracted many prominent people including William Pitt who was to become Prime Minister within a few years. In 1776 Atwood was elected a Fellow of the Royal Society. His experimental work included the manufacture of sundry scientific instruments and by reconciling the results of experimental work with full scale trials enabled empirical results to be stated with confidence. Indirectly this enabled him to develop an understanding of friction.

In 1784, Atwood's former student William Pitt was elected Member of Parliament for Cambridge University, and upon becoming Prime Minister, he awarded Atwood the remarkable salary of £500 per annum provided he resign from Cambridge and take up residence in London. This post was in fact a sinecure organised to ensure that Atwood's talents would be available for the public service and the government in particular. Atwood did not disappoint his patron, and produced outstanding work in many fields, ranging from calculating the British customs revenue to the theory of harmonic motion.

He published papers on a diverse range of subjects in the *Transactions* of the Royal Society, including two (in 1796 and 1798) on the subject of ship stability. These are the first major works in this field produced in Britain. The theory established by Atwood was based on the moment of transferred 'wedges' of displacement when a ship was heeled.

It was correct in all respects, but was difficult and tedious to implement and was little used until interest was rekindled in the mid-nineteenth century by **F K Barnes** who introduced a more practical means of calculation. Atwood described work on a French 74, *Le Scipion*, which had inadequate stability, something which was not cured by doubling the mass of ballast, and was corrected only after the ship had been 'girdled', that is, had a significantly thick belt of doubling fitted in the region of the waterline.

He remained unmarried, and in the last few years of his life was involved in endless work for parliamentary committees and public enquiries; on more than one occasion was beset by controversy and at the receiving end of the hostility of fellow professionals. He died in the summer of 1807 and was buried at St Margaret's Westminster where one of his brothers served as a curate.

SOURCES:

Cotter, Charles H
'George Atwood's contribution to scientific naval architecture'
The Naval Architect
(October 1973)

Stoot, W F
'Some aspects of naval architecture in the eighteenth century'
Transactions of the Institution of Naval Architects
Vol 101 (1959)

———,
'Ideas and personalities in the development of naval architecture'
Transactions of the Institution of Naval Architects
Vol 101 (1959)

Marmaduke Stalkartt

1750–1805

FOR A MAN WHO was a true pioneer in naval architecture, the name of Marmaduke Stalkartt is relatively unknown. This is an injustice to this former Deptford Dockyard apprentice who made significant and long-lasting contributions to ship design in Britain. Stalkartt was born in 1750 near London, and most likely came from North Kent. His service in the Dockyard (then one of the most advanced shipbuilding sites in the country) would stand him well in years to come.

In the late eighteenth century, the area now known as Rotherhithe was developing fast; it was bounded on the north by the Lower Pool of London and on the east by that part of the Thames known as the Limehouse Reach. Deptford Dockyard, dating from the fifteenth century, was one mile to the east and Greenwich just a further mile along the river. In the sweep of land south of the river, Britain's first large wet basin, Howland's Dock, was opened in the eighteenth century and south of that the still existing historic Greenland Dock. In the nineteenth century the whole area would change dramatically with the development of what became known as the Surrey Commercial Docks, a labyrinth of interconnecting small docks and waterways mostly serving the timber, the Baltic and the Russian trades of the capital. It was at Rotherhithe that **Peter the Great** stayed in 1698, where **Sir Anthony Deane** wrote his *Doctrine of Naval Architecture* in 1670 and where, just along the river in 1822, the Navy's first steamship, HMS *Comet*, was built.

Clearly Rotherhithe was an inspiring place in the eighteenth and nineteenth centuries, and it little wonder that Marmaduke Stalkartt settled there for close on twenty-five years. Three significant achievements can be ascribed to him; first building and designing some revolutionary ships, second assisting in the Society for the Improvement of Naval Architecture and thirdly writing one of the great early texts on ship design and construction.

With his boundless energy, he operated a small shipyard for some years around 1790. It was on ground leased near Cuckhold's Point about four miles by river from where Tower Bridge now stands. The fleet list of the yard is uncertain, but it has been established that he built Post Office mail packets, then the thoroughbreds of the continental and the Atlantic shipping trades. One packet the *Westmoreland* made a round trip from Falmouth to the West Indies and back, a distance of over 11,200km (7,000 miles) in seven weeks, achieving 230km (143 miles) per day or a continuous speed over ground of more than six knots – a significant performance for a wooden ship of about 170 tons BOM (Builders Old Measurement).

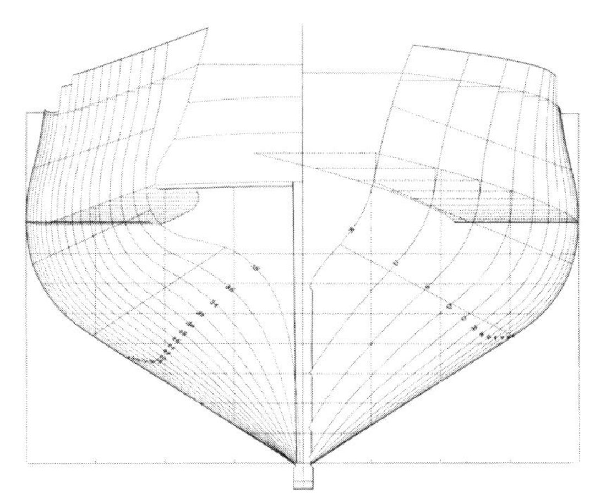

Body plan of a frigate designed by Marmaduke Stalkartt in the 1780s. Note the sharp rise of floor, that is the 'vee shaped' section of the ship, which was favoured at the time. Body plan is the name give to the drawings of the cross sections of a ship; from these an experienced eye can appreciate the full hull shape. *(Author)*

The Society for the Improvement of Naval Architecture carried out a series of open water ship model tests at Greenland Dock, most of which were presided over by **Mark Beaufoy**. Stalkartt was one of the growing group of members and through this was introduced to another member and a consummate enthusiast, the Earl of Stanhope. Stanhope asked Stalkartt to build an experimental steam-powered craft, a 15m (49ft) barge known as an Ambi-Navigator. This small ship, known as the *Kent*, was propelled by vertical oars on either side which drove backwards and then returned to their original position with the oars feathered to create least resistance, a method of propulsion which avoided the need to translate piston strokes into rotary motion. The machinery built by Robert Walker of Rotherhithe must have been well designed as it is reported that in 1793 the *Kent* travelled at 4.8km/h (3mph) in calm water. It is said that Stalkartt had wished **James Watt** to build the machinery, so it is a matter of conjecture that Stalkartt's Ambi-Navigator might just have preceded the real pioneers – the Dalswinton Loch Steamship and the two vessels named *Charlotte Dundas*.

Stalkartt's other great contribution to maritime science was the publication of his *magnum opus*, the great volume *Naval Architecture* first published in 1781, reprinted twice (1787 and 1803) and happily, republished in facsimile in 1991. This volume is made up of seven 'books' and seventeen ship draughts, all of which are amongst the world's most elegant definitions of the art of the wooden shipbuilder.

In 1796, Stalkartt was one of several persons asked to travel to India; the Royal Navy was looking overseas with anxious eyes as stocks of British grown timber were severely depleted, and Indian and South-east Asian hardwoods were regarded as good if not better than home grown oak. His remit was to open commercial avenues for the Navy and other British interests, but little of this part of his life has been researched. It is believed he had shipbuilding interests in India and died there after nine years service.

SOURCES:

Stalkartt, Marmaduke
Naval Architecture or the Rudiments and Rules of Shipbuilding (1787)
Facsimile Edition (Rotherfield, East Sussex, 1991)

Walker, Fred M
Marmaduke Stalkartt, a significant Thames-based 18th Century Naval Architect & Shipbuilder
Shipbuilding on the Thames Symposium, Greenwich, 2003

Jamsetjee Bomanjee Wadia

1754–1821

WHILE MOST PEOPLE know that Mumbai (the old name for Bombay was reinstated in 1995) is a city of great antiquity, few are aware that the maritime tradition of the region is equally auspicious. The shipbuilding connection can be traced as far back as 1661, when a cluster of seven islands near Bombay was presented by the King of Portugal to King Charles II as a dowry following his marriage to the Infanta Catherine of Braganza. Within a few years and in return for a substantial loan, the King handed over the islands to the Honourable East India Company which managed them until 1858 when all the assets of the 'John Company' throughout India were taken under direct British rule. The growth of Bombay, both as a trading port and as a naval base, encouraged the setting-up of what became known as the Bombay Dockyard, which continues to this day. As early as 1695 dry docks were constructed and throughout the eighteenth century the complex became larger with further graving docks of ever improving quality being added. Control throughout was vested in a naval force founded in 1612 and with probably the longest uninterrupted service in the world; it started as the East India Company's Marine, then HM Indian Navy, back to Bombay Marine and later again the Royal Indian Navy which on the inauguration of the Republic of India became known as the Indian Navy.

While not a prolific shipbuilder when compared to commercial organisations in other parts of the world, the Bombay Dockyard is recorded as having constructed several hundred hulls from 1736 onwards. Many ships were built for the Bombay Marine, the East India Company and commercial owners, but at the start of the eighteenth century, a long-awaited breakthrough came with the first order from the Royal Navy. This business developed quickly and was beneficial in many ways; first, Britain, which was at war with France, had a desperate need for more ships, secondly oak (especially English) for hull construction was in short supply, and Continental and Scandinavian timber deliveries to the UK were problematic owing to Napoleon's blockades. Most important, however, was the technical benefit to the Admiralty gained from the quality of Indian shipbuilding and the use of Malabar teak.

Going back to 1736, the upward path of shipbuilding was assured by the commissioning of Lowjee Nusserwanji Wadia as Master Builder for the Hon. East India Company. With this appointment a shipbuilding dynasty was created with a further eight members of the family being either Master Builders or Joint Master Builders and probably a dozen others as Assistants, Inspectors of Machinery and so on. The last Wadia Master Builder remained in office until 1884 and other members of the family held junior appointments until 1913. The family were devout Parsees, members of a monotheistic Zoroastrian faith which had left Persia many centuries before following Islamic persecution. Most moved to Western India, where they led circumspect lives, obeying clear injunctions to offer all others religious tolerance. In the magnificent 1940s ten-volume set known as *The Children's Encyclopaedia* they are described as 'kindly but commercially-minded' people. The family now uses the surname Wadia, but as surnames were introduced only recently in Parsee life, it is probable that the name is a corruption of the word *Vadia* or shipwright.

Jamsetjee Bomanjee Wadia, 1754–1821.
(Courtesy of HMS *Trincomalee Trust, Hartlepool)*

In 1792 on the death of the second Master Builder, the cousins Jamsetjee Bomanjee and Framjee Maneckjee were appointed Joint Masters. They took over a bustling shipyard with excellent guidelines on industrial relations and with clear and well set-out standards of workmanship. An incident a few years earlier, when an officer of the Royal Navy had ordered the flogging of a Parsee workman for an alleged offence, led to serious unrest and then to a formal agreement between the British flag officers and the shipbuilders, that the Master Shipbuilder alone was in charge of all matters concerning the workforce. This was only one of the many duties the Master had to fulfil, arguably the most important role being that of material procurement. With the rise in the number of ships being built for Britain, the demands on local timber suppliers brought about the timely rejoinder that teak supplies were becoming endangered and fear was expressed on the ability of western India to meet the projected requirements. Framjee Maneckjee died in 1804 and his cousin remained in full control until his death in 1821.

During this seventeen-year period, Jamsetjee produced close on sixty ships of which about sixteen were for the Royal Navy. This run of success began with the building of the 54-gun frigate *Cornwallis* for the Hon. East India Company in 1800, a ship that was deemed so good that she was purchased outright by the Admiralty as a Fourth Rate and named *Akbar*. It was clear that teak had many advantages over oak, such as less splintering when hit by roundshot, less corrosion on metal fastenings, shorter seasoning time and an expectation of life several times longer than ships built from European oak. **Sir Robert Seppings** in a report on the quality of teak designated '... prime Malabar Northern Teak as the most valuable timber in the world for shipbuilding'.

One of the most important ships built by Jamsetjee Bomanjee was the *Leda* class frigate *Trincomalee* for the Royal Navy. Ordered from the Bombay yard, the plans were dispatched from Britain aboard HMS *Java*, but with the War of 1812 underway coupled with an unfortunate meeting with USS *Constitution* off Brazil, both the *Java* and the plans were lost. A further set were sent to India on the 74-gun *Stirling Castle*, all went well and the keel-laying went ahead on May 1816, with the Bombay tradition of placing a silver nail in the structure taking place on 29 May. Launching was in October 1817 and in April 1819, this ship arrived at Portsmouth. Having been restored to the very highest international standards, the *Trincomalee* is afloat nearly 190 years after her launch, and is open to the public at Jackson Dock, Hartlepool. In her, now many thousands of miles from her birthplace in Mumbai, the efforts of Jamsetjee Bomanjee are commemorated by this his finest ship.

SOURCES:
Lambert, Andrew
Trincomalee – the Last of Nelson's Frigates
London, 2002
Wadia, Ruttonjee Ardeshir
The Bombay Dockyard and the Wadia Master Builders
Bombay, 1955

Mark Beaufoy
1764–1827

THE SON OF A BREWER, Mark Beaufoy, the chief experimenter of the ill-fated Society for the Improvement of Naval Architecture, had more than a passing interest in matters scientific, and blessed with small but significant financial resources was able to indulge this interest throughout his life. It is said that as a young schoolboy, he had been informed that the easiest way to tow a cone through a fluid was with the base leading, a matter he disputed. This led to his first attempts at what is now called ship model testing, in his father's brewery at Lambeth, then within the County of Surrey. This interest was to remain a life-long interest, and before he had become forty, close on 1,700 ship model experiments had been supervised by him in the open water conditions of London's Greenland Dock.

Naval architects now remember him for his services to our profession, then in embryo, but in the eyes of the public he was a man of some significance, who achieved many of his aims and was undaunted by the opinions of others. His first clash came when aged twenty, he fell in love with his cousin Margaretta Beaufoy, and unable to obtain the blessing of her father for the union (the Beaufoys were Quakers) the young couple eloped and were not the first, nor the last, to be married at Gretna Green. Shortly after, Mark and Margaretta moved to Switzerland and settled in Neuchatel and started to raise a family; clearly they must have been free of financial concerns, as Mark Beaufoy indicated his desire to climb Mont Blanc. While on holiday at Chamonix in France in 1787 he organised a climbing party consisting of experienced guides and set out; with difficulty they reached the summit, and in doing he so achieved the not-inconsiderable distinction of being the first British person to conquer Western Europe's highest mountain.

Shortly afterwards, the family returned to Britain and resided first at Westminster until they set up home at Hackney. Here Mark became an officer in the Tower Hamlets Militia, a forerunner of the Volunteers and of today's Territorial Army. He was gazetted Colonel and was known by this rank for many years, although he and a fellow officer left the militia under a cloud following a series of disputes and then a court martial. As his brother and two of his sons were regular serving officers, this must have been a time of some embarrassment for the family. The period for which Mark Beaufoy is remembered quite justifiably is the last decade of the eighteenth century. For reasons not clear, he had been elected to the Royal Society of London in 1790 and for the following ten years gave mighty service to scientific research.

At this stage we must mention a bookseller named Mr Sewell, who had a deep interest in maritime matters, and was outspoken in his belief that the quality of British ships was inferior to that of those designed and built in France and Spain. The issue was talked about openly, and ultimately a meeting for interested parties to discuss the matter was arranged and held at the Crown and Anchor Tavern in the Strand in April 1791. Clearly Mr Sewell's dismay echoed the views of many others, as a 'multitude' of the great and the good attended, and amazing to report, the Duke of Clarence presided. With effective royal patronage, a new organisation entitled the Society for the Improvement of Naval Architecture was set up with 134 persons enrolled (including several peers of the realm) and others including the renowned Sir Joseph Banks and the naval architect **Marmaduke Stalkartt**. Several of the constructors of the Royal Navy (including **Seppings**), and the Chief Shipwright of the Hon. East India Company were conspicuous by their absence. The Society grew rapidly and within a year membership topped 300, and by now Mr Sewell was publishing papers resulting from their deliberations. Awards and medals were instituted, and the decision taken to support what we now know as ship model testing. Model testing was not a new idea. Between 1650 and 1850, many attempts had been made to solve the riddles of powering and sea-keeping, ranging from Samuel Fortrey's early experiments right through to the water and turpentine tank of Alexander Hall of Aberdeen in the early nineteenth century.

Mark Beaufoy was enthused by the prospect of testing and joined the small sub-committee charged with this task, and shortly after was appointed their experimentalist in full charge. The first tests on skin friction were made by comparing the times of pendulums first swinging freely in air, and then compared to the times when passing through fluid, an ingenious innovation for which Isaac Newton should take some credit. However, the idea of measuring comparative pulls and speeds of geometrically-shaped blocks through water gained support, and came about when the owners of Greenland Dock at Rotherhithe made their open water facility available for a considerable period each year (presumably when the whaling fleet was in the north). The sundry models (which were a series of geometric shapes) were pulled across open water by towlines attached to pulley arrangements operated by falling weights. In keeping with the spirit of scientific enquiry of the age, the work was recorded meticulously. Sadly as everything was empirical, a full understanding of hydrodynamics theory had to await the later breakthrough of **William Froude**. One real benefit came from a greater awareness of the difference between wave making and skin friction. The sheer magnitude of the task cannot be under-rated when one learns that between 1793 and 1798, over 1,700 experiments took place, with Beaufoy presiding over nearly all of them. The cost of the experiments was assessed as between £20,000–£30,000, mostly paid for by Mark Beaufoy personally.

Beaufoy, along with other scientists from the Royal Society then turned his attention to the earth's magnetic field and to astronomy. He became a member of the Royal Astronomical Society and of the prestigious Linnaean Society based at Uppsala in Sweden, and was to win some scientific medals and awards. He died at Bushey in Hertfordshire in May 1827. After his death his son Henry spent £3,000 printing and freely distributing the results of his father's experiments.

SOURCES:

Stoot, W F
'Some Aspects of Naval Architecture in the Eighteenth Century'
Transactions of the Institution of Naval Architects
Vol 101 (1959)

Wright T
'Mark Beaufoy's Nautical and Hydraulic Experiments'
The Mariner's Mirror
Vol 75 (1989)

Sir Robert Seppings
1767–1840

THE FIRST FOURTEEN years of the life of Robert Seppings, an early nineteenth-century Surveyor of the Royal Navy who introduced considerable reform, were hard. Living at Fakenham in Norfolk, his family, like many in rural areas, suffered acute poverty, and to supplement the household income Robert developed a small delivery business taking letters and messages around the neighbourhood. Just before his fourteenth birthday, everything was shattered by the death of his father, resulting in Robert being adopted by an uncle, a retired naval captain living in Plymouth. According to reports, Robert was happy and joined cousins also adopted in the same household. Clearly the aunt and uncle did their work well, as within a few years – mostly through ability but with the help of 'good' marriages – this same family were to produce a Comptroller of Revenue Cruisers, a Vice Admiral, an Admiral, a Field Marshal, an Inspector of Shipping for the Hon. East India Company and in the case of Robert Seppings, a Surveyor to the Royal Navy. In 1795, Seppings married his cousin Charlotte.

Within a few months of arriving at Plymouth, Seppings commenced a personal apprenticeship under John Henslow, then the master shipwright at Plymouth Dockyard. Even in those times, such an arrangement was unusual and Seppings was especially lucky in receiving excellent training (as well as kindness and encouragement) from a shipwright destined to become a knight of the realm. By 1790 he had started to rise through the ranks, ultimately becoming a foreman in Plymouth Dockyard. At the age of thirty he was appointed Assistant to the Master Shipwright (then Joseph Tucker). In this capacity he was instrumental in introducing many labour-saving techniques to the Dockyard, something of immense importance to the Navy during the years of hostility with France. It is alleged that he invented a means of easing keels from keel blocks to enable local repairs to take place (something now done by hydraulic jacks). However, as he and colleagues did produce many improvements, innovations and inventions, and as his capacity for work and organisation was obvious to all, in 1803 and while still in his mid-thirties he was appointed Master Shipwright of the great Dockyard at Chatham.

For the following ten years, and at a time when the Navy remained on high alert, Seppings addressed the problems of diminishing stocks of long timber, of rot in timber structures, poor shipboard defence when gunfire was coming from ahead or astern and also the structural problems induced by the racking of ships in a seaway. He was responsible for the introduction of the round bow and the round stern, not necessarily liked by all seamen, but which were adopted in later years, innovations which saved timber and allowed better all-round gun positioning.* In the early nineteenth century, a shortage of lengthy timber developed (indeed it is a problem

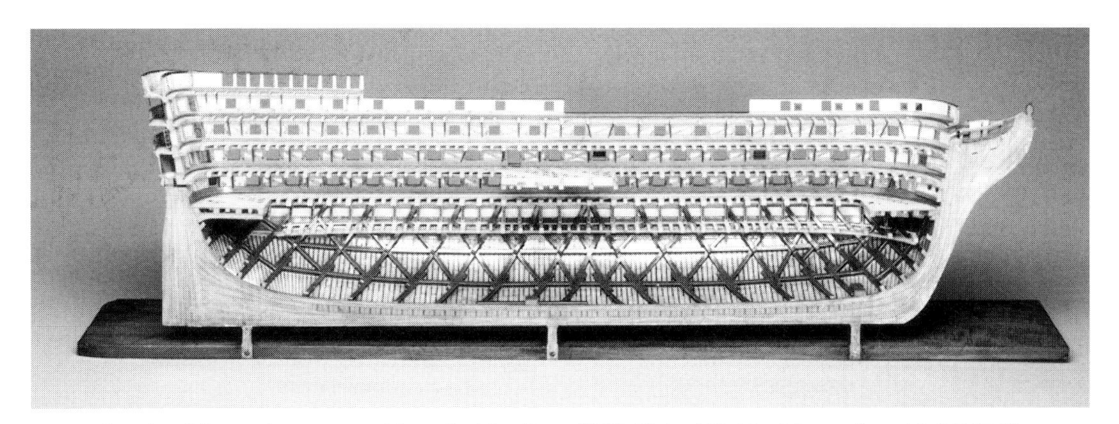

Seppings' frames incorporated into the First Rate. (© *The National Maritime Museum, Greenwich, D4069-5*)

that has remained with us since). Seppings introduced the use of diagonal planking on decks and other parts, enabling shorter pieces to be used on much of the hull. This in turn led to diagonal bracing in way of floors, a system that conferred strength and gave resistance to flexure of the hull.

To prevent the racking of ships, he brought in iron hanging and lodging knees in place of the grown knees which were prodigal with timber and not always effective. Decks were supported throughout their length on each side by beam shelves and the framing either braced with diagonals or by timber packing between floors and frames in the bottom of the ship. In these cases, the ceiling over the floors was dispensed with. During experiments in dockings, it was found that these modifications reduced the 'break' or change in hogging or sagging from dry-docking to afloat by over 50 per cent. The clearest example of diagonal bracing and iron bracing following Sepping's proposals is seen aboard the frigate *Unicorn* (Chatham 1824), now preserved in Dundee.

In 1813 he became Surveyor to the Navy, a position equivalent to the later Director of Naval Construction, remaining in post until 1832 and into his mid-sixties. Seppings was instrumental in carrying out fundamental changes in ship design and also in the organisation of all the Royal Dockyards. The timber shortages exercised his mind and new types of wood were tried, some good quality scrap material was re-used and especial efforts were made to reduce the incidence of rot by improved methods of timber storage and by experimentation on methods of scarfing timber joints. It has to be appreciated that on taking over as Surveyor he inherited not only the largest navy in the world, but one which was continuing to grow at a time when easily available stocks of raw materials were dwindling. The defeat of rot in timber was to elude him and indeed also his successor **Captain William Symonds**, a successful career seaman but not a trained ship constructor. Seppings's views were that careful storage of timber, construction work carried out with accuracy and attention to the seasoning of timber would yield the best results, and he believed that these points along with the structural changes introduced had reduced the mass of timber in sailing ships of the Navy by 10 per cent. These views hold good to this day. Strangely, in the early 1800s the Navy had reduced the amount of timber stored in ponds of sea water.

In 1819, he was knighted in an appropriate manner – by the Prince Regent while on the deck of the yacht *Royal George* at sea. His other great honour was election as a fellow of the Royal Society as well as receiving the Copley medal of this distinguished organisation. He retired to Taunton in 1832 and died there in 1840.

SOURCES:
Bjerg, H C, and Erichsen, John
Danske Orlogsskibe 1690–1860 (2 vols)
Copenhagen, 1980
Fincham, John
A History of Naval Architecture
1851
Packard, J J
'Sir Robert Seppings and the Timber Problem'
The Mariner's Mirror
Volume 64 (1978)

* The first known example of a ship with 'rounded corners' was the Danish 36-gun frigate *Najaden*, built at Holmen, Copenhagen, in the late 1790s. She was designed by Frederic Hohlenberg (1765–1804), Constructor in Chief to the Royal Danish Navy, who was a former student of **Henrik Gerner**. After begin seized by the British following the Bombardment of Copenhagen in 1807, the *Najaden* was taken to the United Kingdom and there inspected by Sir Robert Seppings, who introduced the innovation of rounded bows and sterns to ships of the Royal Navy.

James Watt

1736–1819

JAMES WATT, THE ENGINEER whose flash of inspiration touched off the Industrial Revolution, was born in Greenock, then a new port serving the lower reaches of the Firth of Clyde, and a town that was to have an illustrious shipbuilding history. The Watt family were fairly well to do, with the father James Watt (senior) running a general business which included housebuilding and of course the then associated trade of undertaker. James was the sixth of a total of eight children of whom only two survived childhood; he was of sickly indisposition and was to suffer from poor health all his life.

However, he had inherited his father's trait of longevity and his death (which was in Birmingham) would not take place until eighty-four years had passed.

He attended the local grammar school, but did not shine and was drawn to practical matters as his ability to work with his hands was more than impressive. After working with his father for some time, he made his way to Glasgow with a view to obtaining training as an instrument maker, and despite having good introductions in the city and at the University, there appeared to be no suitable openings and he made his way to London. Here at the age of twenty he worked for a year learning this trade, with many difficulties stacked against him such as his advanced age for an apprenticeship, and worse the fact that as a Scotsman he was seen as an intruding foreigner. The experience may well have been the making of him, as not long after he returned to Glasgow, was appointed instrument maker to the University and in 1757 was allowed to open a workshop on the premises.

At Glasgow he enjoyed friendly relationships with many of the academics, including the economist Adam Smith and Joseph Black, the professor who had defined the principles of latent heat. It was in 1764 that there came a turning-point in his life when the natural philosophy department tasked him with the repair of a working model of a Newcomen steam engine. This proved a lengthier and more difficult job than anticipated and taxed Watt's patience and skills. One Sunday in May while walking on Glasgow Green, he had a flash of inspiration (a moment that has become world-famous) when he realised that the problem with this model engine, as with almost all others, was the lack of a separate condenser. It being the Sabbath, he had to wait with patience during the day of rest, but on returning to the University the next morning, he commenced making the necessary adjustments which set the model back to work, but of greater importance, Watt realised that his path in life was to be that of engineering. A commemorative stone stands in Glasgow Green reminding the citizens that at this place, one of the most important events at the start of the Industrial Revolution took place.

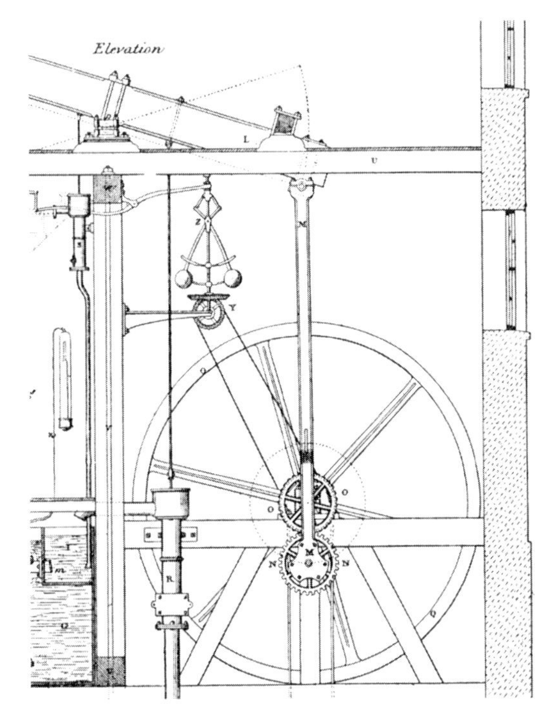

The bulk of machinery from Boulton & Watt of Birmingham was for stationery use. However, their work did enable the transition of engineering from land to marine purposes. This drawing of a 1780s double acting rotative engine shows Watt's Ball Governor and his innovative Sun and Planet gearing system. *(Author)*

Watt now went through one of the most difficult periods of his life. In an old warehouse on the banks of the River Clyde, he planned and then manufactured what was to be the world's first steam engine with separate condenser. There were many difficulties, some foreseen and others unforeseen, such as poor workmanship on most subcontracted parts, but worst the death of a trusted journeyman. Ultimately the new engine was completed and worked. Joseph Black was supportive and even lent Watt money that in 1769 he was able to register a patent in London. As he became better known, James Watt was asked to take on many consulting roles, including that of surveying routes for new canals which then were spreading throughout Britain. The first was the Monklands Canal designed to bring coal from the North Lanarkshire coalfield to Glasgow, and he remained in the Canal Company's employ as supervisor of the whole undertaking at the then substantial salary of

£200 per year. Survey work was carried out also for the Caledonian and the Forth and Clyde Canals. Just at the time he was becoming known and more affluent, his wife died in childbirth.

A further misfortune arose in that the mechanical side of his business came under the new partnership formed with John Roebuck from West Lothian. They worked together from 1768 until 1772, during which time Watt expanded his business and made a name in the repair and maintenance of mine pumping machinery, especially in the West Country. Sadly, little new business of this sort came from the Glasgow Region, but when Roebuck went bankrupt around 1772, providence played a major role in that an entrepreneur by the name of Matthew Boulton, the owner of the Soho Engineering Works near Birmingham, came on the scene. He knew Watt and had admired his workmanship, tenacity and honesty. Boulton tried to buy his way into the Watt/Roebuck partnership, but was rebuffed by Roebuck, and succeeded only after the financial situation worsened and Roebuck was forced to sell his share of the steam engine patent. Following the transfer of interests (around 1775) the well-known name of Boulton and Watt appeared for the first time: Watt dismantled the current experimental engine at Roebuck's home in Kinneil, moved it to Birmingham and made the Midlands his home for the rest of his life.

Watt was the engineer in the partnership, while Boulton was the businessman, and without his level-headed approach it is doubtful if Watt's genius for mechanical and heat engineering would have made real money. Watt maintained that he had been unable to recoup his costs for the first patent and quite surprisingly by Act of Parliament his original patent was extended for some years. He was not kindly disposed to competitors and with steam engines being a novelty at the beginning of the nineteenth century spent considerable time, effort and finance in disputing alleged patent infringements. Other well-known Watt inventions – or developments – included sun-and-planet motion, the ubiquitous Watt ball-governor and the introduction of 'cut-off' allowing the maximum use of steam expansion in a cylinder.

His official retirement came in 1800 when he and Boulton handed over responsibility for the business to their sons. Watt continued to manufacture advanced equipment on a private basis and spent much time in the workshops attached to his elegant home. Along with his FRS he was awarded an LL.D by Glasgow University, most probably the first such honorary degree ever awarded to a practising engineer. These honours were justified; they were given to the man who had invented the power system that drained mines, rolled hot metals, drove looms and propelled ships across the oceans. Furthermore he was the man who had defined the horsepower, the unit that was to remain in vogue for well over a century. Now by-passed by fundamental units of the SI System, it is pleasing to note that the international unit of power is the Watt.

SOURCES:
Dickinson, H W
A Short History of the Steam Engine
Cambridge, 1938
———, and Jenkins, R
James Watt and the Steam Engine
London, 1927
Smiles, Samuel
Lives of the Engineers
London, 1861

Joshua Humphreys

1751–1838

REMEMBERED AS THE FIRST constructor in the United States Navy and as the designer of the USS *Constitution*, Joshua Humphreys is assured of his place in American history. The family, who were Quakers, had migrated from Wales in the late seventeenth century and settled in Pennsylvania. Joshua was a second-generation American, and served an apprenticeship as a shipwright in Philadelphia. Following the death of his employer just at the completion of his indentures, he had full responsibility for a shipbuilding undertaking thrust on him. This opportunity was grasped with both hands and Joshua was on his way, soon to be recognised as an up-and-coming east coast shipbuilder.

Following the Declaration of Independence, consideration was given to the raising of an American navy. Humphreys was consulted and gave thoughtful support to the idea; he followed this up with detailed correspondence on the types of ship he felt appropriate for work on coastal protection as well as out in the oceans. He proposed that the first ships should have a keel length of not less than 45m (147ft), should carry around forty guns and have scantlings* equal to those of the best European 74s. Humphreys was instructed to design and to superintend the construction of six of these 'super-frigates' and to oversee their construction. In this task he was assisted by Josiah Fox (1763–1847), then a draughtsman trained in Britain at Plymouth Dockyard, who would rise to the rank of Master Constructor in the US Navy.

The hull shape was quite full forward and the displacement was surprisingly high at 2,250 long tons. These ships were designated frigates, but in reality were larger than British frigates and smaller than 74s. This size was unique at that time, and was to prove successful in many naval actions. Alexander Magoun, a lecturer at the Massachusetts Institute of Technology said '... Humphreys' design ... balances the conflicting claims of speed, armament and protection to a nicety'. Considerable use was made of a timber native to the southern states of the USA known as Live Oak – *quercus virginiana*, a member of the beech family. With great inherent strength and with a specific gravity far greater than unity, this timber was ideal for strength members and was chosen for the frames, futtocks, floors, knees and breast hooks of the new ships. There was a downside, however, since this timber, already becoming scarce through over-harvesting, was to be found only in inaccessible places like the disease-ridden marshes of Georgia. This logistical problem was handed over to his son Samuel Humphreys, who had to face long journeys in conditions of extreme heat and then select wood to be cut and transported over boggy terrain. Joshua Humphreys maintained that while ships built of American white oak and traditional material might last only ten years, those with their strength members of Live Oak should remain seaworthy five times longer. The first group of super-frigates would not disappoint him. They were *Constitution*, *President*, *United States*, *Chesapeake*, *Constellation* and *Congress*.

This is the earliest accurate depiction of *Constitution*, Humphreys' realisation of a large frigate which was designed to be superior to any European frigate and a match for far larger ships. Great hull strength and longevity came through the choice of Live Oak for frames, futtocks, and other key hull components (*US Navy*)

The *Constitution* was built by Edmond Hartt at Boston, Massachusetts in 1797 and is still afloat nearly two and a quarter centuries later. Thirty years after her launch she was laid up at Boston and in 1830 it was decreed she should be broken up. This so upset a young law student, Oliver Wendell Holmes, that his poem *Old Ironsides* stirred patriotic citizens and funds were raised for her preservation. The *Constitution* has been preserved as a unit of the United States Navy, the first ship in the world to be accorded such status. She has had major reconstructions in the 1920s and again in the 1990s, but remains afloat at the former Boston Navy Yard. Each year, at a well-publicised ceremony, she is towed into Boston Harbor and turned before being returned to her berth, in order that each side of the ship weathers equally. Joshua Humphreys would be pleased with her.

SOURCES:

Magoun, F Alexander
The Frigate Constitution and other Historic Ships
New York, 1928

Wood, Virginia Steele
Live Oaking: Southern Timber for Tall Ships
Boston, 1981

*The scantling is the official and regulated dimension for each important structural part of a ship's hull.

Part 2
Iron and Steam
1800–1850

The first half of the nineteenth century saw two of the most significant developments in maritime history. Arguably the more important, was the introduction of iron as a shipbuilding material, a change that enabled naval architects to be free of the design constraints of timber and to plan larger and more complex ships. The second was the adoption of steam power for propulsion. In this fifty-year period, longshoremen would cease to be surprised by tall funnels, smoke, steam and noise, whilst seafarers accepted that hulls were lengthening and changing in form, and that they had to learn new skills of ship operation. Experimentation was becoming the norm. While wooden sailing ships continued to come off the building slips for another hundred years and their design was improving, it became clear that their days were numbered.

Timber supplies

At the conclusion of the Napoleonic Wars (in which Britain had 600 ships available for service) there was a severe dearth of oak in all parts of the United Kingdom and new sources of supply had to be found. For a while the teak forests of India were opened up, and similar attempts made over the years to import hardwoods from the Dutch East Indies and latterly from West Africa. On the cessation of hostilities, difficulties with the Scandinavian countries were overcome and softwoods started to flow again from Norway, from Russia and the Baltic. Nothing however, could compare with the massive exports of softwoods to Europe and Britain from Quebec and the Maritime Provinces of Canada. Shipyards sprang up in New Brunswick, Nova Scotia, Prince Edward Island and Quebec, all of which sent great numbers of ships across the Atlantic and many with holds packed tight with lumber. During this period, when deck hatches were small and constricted by rigging and deck gear, it was found convenient to moor ships end-on to the quay and load long lengths of timber through hatches cut into their bows and sometimes the stern.

During the Napoleonic Wars, the Royal Navy, despite the constraints of a continental blockade, had been successful in keeping a massive fleet at sea for lengthy periods through cladding the underwater hull of their ships with copper. This cladding of around 1mm in thickness was instrumental in slowing the growth of weed and made the hull impervious to the ravages of borer worms like the teredo and the gribble.

Sailing ship hull form and construction

The introduction of fast hull forms, a development leading to the clipper ships and the extreme clippers, stretched the length of vessels to close to 65m (210ft) on the waterline. (In earlier times the dimensions of sailing ships were often quoted as: Length of keel: the maximum length of the straight part of the keel.) Such vessels had a Length to Beam ratio of just over 6, giving them a beam of 10 metres. The period of the Yankee clippers was from the 1830s to the late 1850s and they amounted to no more than 400 ships which worked on the United States East to West Coast trans-continental trade, a business later fuelled by the Californian gold rush. The British clippers were of a different type, built for the tea trade (and a few for opium). They amounted to around 300 ships and the years of building were from 1850 to 1870. In the tea trades these fast ships rarely were loaded to their marks owing to the very low weight of cased tea. In many cases great physical force was used to pack the tea for maximum stowage and every available locker and unused corner would be pressed into use.

The carrying capacity (or deadweight) of most wooden sailing freighters seldom surpassed 2,000 tons, and coupled with slow speed they were not efficient carriers. Indeed, the vast bulk of the sailing colliers on the British east coast were bluff-bowed brigs or barques seldom carrying more than 400 tonnes of sea coal.

Introduction of Iron

The introduction of iron in 1819 was the most significant event ever in ship design, and it is detailed in the biography of **Thomas Wilson**. The outstanding successes of the *Vulcan* were first her longevity and second that her mode style of building was adopted by all iron and steel ships and has remained in vogue, subject to minor changes for the subsequent nineteen decades. The length of iron ships increased at a more than steady rate, indeed in a mere fifty-four years there was a sevenfold increase in length with an even more impressive increase in cargo capacity.

Vulcan	1819 Glasgow	Length bp	66ft 6in or	20.27m
Great Britain	1843 Bristol		322ft	98.15m
Persia	1855 Glasgow		376ft	114.60m
Germanic	1875 Belfast		455ft	138.68m

The benefits of iron – longevity and strength – were discovered quickly, but there were drawbacks such as iron plates below the waterline attracted marine growths unless coated with anti-fouling composition, a study that is now a special preserve of chemical science. A further, and unexpected problem arose in the early years with ships losing their bearings owing to faulty compass readings – examples being the disappearance for several days of **Fairbairn**'s *Lord Dundas en route* from Manchester to the Clyde and the running ashore of **Brunel**'s *Great Britain* at Dundrum Bay on the Irish coast. The problem was recognised quickly, but the search for a long-term solution was more protracted and depended on the work of Sir George Airey and **Lord Kelvin**. They recognised that during construction iron ships absorbed a magnetic field which caused deviation in the ship's compass. It had to be neutralised by corrective irons and magnets placed near the ship's compass, a system known to this day as compass correction.

In the middle years of the nineteenth century, there was a short-lived fashion for fast sailing ships to be built on the composite system, which is an iron skeletal structure covered with wooden planking. This had the effect of enabling the ships to be slightly longer and have increased cargo capacity. The greatest benefit was for clipper ships, where composite construction enabled the largest vessel to be built whilst avoiding iron hulls which generated condensation on the inside of the holds in tropical conditions. The ultimate clippers were not only of composite construction but had copper sheathing below the waterline, a winning combination provided the copper and the iron were kept well apart.

Iron and Steel Manufacture

During the construction of the *Vulcan* of 1819, every shell plate and every angle frame had to be beaten to shape by blacksmiths using red-hot forged iron on the anvil. Such labour-intensive systems have no place in modern industry and mechanised iron works were set up in many parts of Europe and North America, designed to supply iron (and later steel) plates of pre-arranged thicknesses and dimensions. Similarly sections, that is lengths, of angle, girder and other geometrical conformations could be supplied from rolling mills to previously-agreed dimensions.

On examining the plating on SS *Great Britain* (now restored and open to visitors in Bristol), one is surprised by the variation in plate size and the 'patchwork' quality of the shell ironwork. The plates used in the hull construction had been forged by hand from puddled steel, and as there was no real standardisation, the builders in an *ad hoc* manner used the largest plates available that were free of blowholes, interstitial and other faults.

One hundred and eighty years later shipbuilding steel is manufactured in several ways, including the continuous casting process where the end product is monitored continuously by inspectors from Lloyd's Register or some other classification society.

Steam

From the 1780s there were many experiments with steam machinery aboard small ships. The key dates now accepted are 1803 for the successful steaming of PS *Charlotte Dundas II* on the Forth and Clyde Canal, 1807 for the successful inauguration of

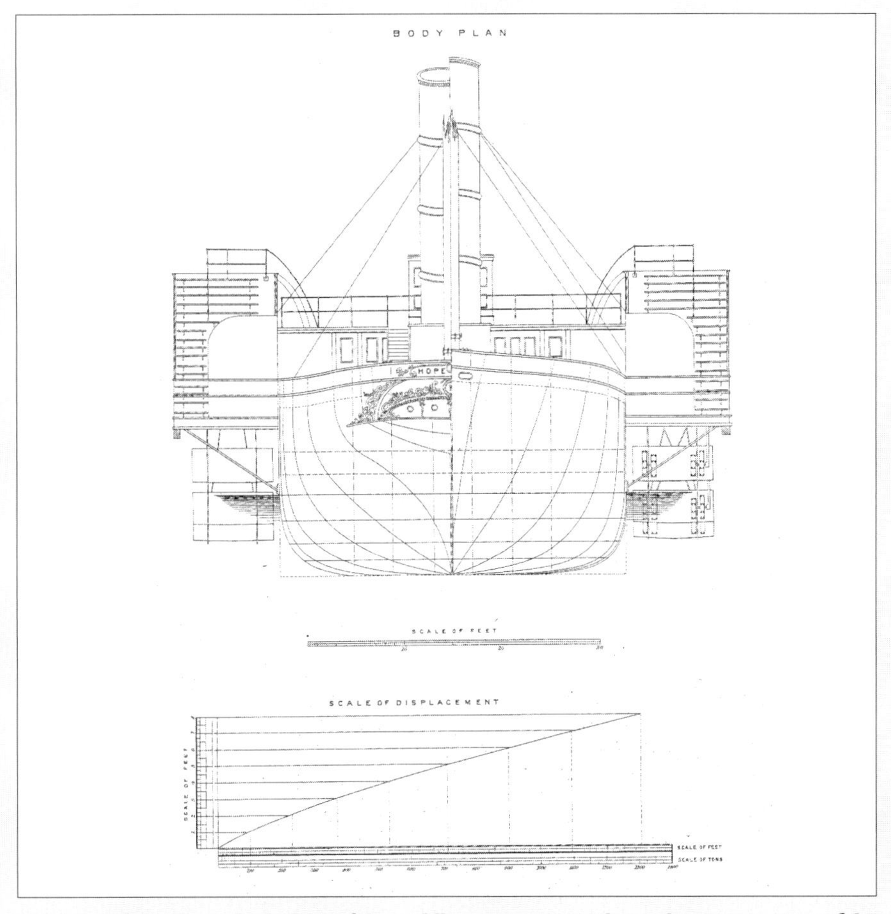

This beautifully-drawn body plan of the paddle steamer *Hope* shows the cross sections of the hull at each of the ten 'stations' from stern to bow – after sections shown on the left and forward on the right. The lower graph shows the seawater displacement against draft, necessary information for the ship's officers. This paddle ship was built by Jones, Quiggin and Co of Liverpool around 1850. (From Shipbuilding, Theoretical and Practical, London 1866)

steam navigation on the River Hudson in New York State by **Robert Fulton**'s *Clermont* and then in 1812 the commencement of commercial operations in Europe with the PS *Comet* steaming from Glasgow to Helensburgh on the Clyde, a marketing ploy to ensure a steady supply of guests at **Henry Bell**'s Hotel.

Steamboats were built in large numbers in the years leading up to 1820, and proved useful for short journeys carrying high-value cargoes, which almost always meant passengers or mail! The thermal efficiency was low, possibly just 1 or 2 per cent – in other words for every 100 tons of coal used, the energy from 98 tons would be lost in radiated heat, friction, noise and so on. Small hulls with limited bunker capacity, coupled with low thermal efficiency, placed pressure on shipbuilders to increase ship size and engine capacity.

Propulsors

With the successful application of the screw propeller on SS *Great Britain*, the side paddle wheel was to become redundant and latterly was used only on small vessels operating in shallow water. One of the last large transatlantic liners with side paddle wheels was the iron-hulled *Persia* built by **Robert Napier** in 1855. From then on most deep sea traders had propellers, although most ships carried auxiliary sail right up till the 1880s, for the simple reasons that steam condensers were the 'Achilles heel' of the engine room, regularly breaking down and leaving the ship bereft of fresh water for the boilers, and also the metallurgical problems associated with early tail shafts which fractured only too frequently.

Education

This period is distinguished by having the 'First' School of Naval Architecture at Portsmouth from 1811 to 1832 and the 'Second' School from 1848 until 1853. In both cases this forward move was negated by the reactionary Sir James Graham, then First Lord of the Admiralty

North of the Border, the University of Glasgow following deep heart-searching decided to accept a Regius Chair of Civil Engineering and Mechanics, making it the first chair in engineering in the world. The problem was two-fold; engineering was not recognised as a 'proper' university subject and secondly Regius Chairs had the perceived disadvantage of possible Government or Crown interference in university affairs. The incumbent from 1840 to 1855 was the brilliant and outgoing Lewis Gordon, who retired quite young in order to concentrate on consultancy work. His place was filled ably by his deputy **Macquorn Rankine**.

KEY DATES

1801	France adopts the metric system. Battle of Copenhagen.
1803	PS *Charlotte Dundas II* steams on the Forth and Clyde Canal.
1805	Battle of Trafalgar.
1806	Rafting of timber for export to Europe commences in Canada.
1807	PS *Clermont* commissioned on the Hudson River, USA. The Bombardment of Copenhagen.
1808	Setting-up of the Royal Navy slavery suppression flotilla in African waters.
1811	'First' School of Naval Architecture opens at Portsmouth (closed in 1832).
1812	PS *Comet* on the Clyde opens commercial steam navigation in Europe.
1812–15	'War of 1812' between USA and Great Britain.
1813	Seppings introduces widespread use of iron for knees, brackets etc, in shipbuilding.
1816	PS *Regent*, engined by Maudslay, Sons and Field, is first Thames-built steamship.
1817	Emigration Acts start to control conditions on passenger/emigrant ships.
1818	Invention of the Patent Slip Dock by Morton of Leith.
1819	World's first properly-built iron ship *Vulcan* launched near Glasgow.
1828	Bureau Veritas (Classification Society) founded in Antwerp (later moved to Paris).
1832	Muntz metal introduced for hull sheathing.
1835	John Scott Russell introduces longitudinal framing.
1836	Trinity House given powers to acquire privately-owned lights and lighthouses.
1838	SS *Archimedes* tours UK showing the effectiveness of the screw propeller. Grace Darling and her father of Longstones Lighthouse make famous sea rescue.
1840	Schooner *Scottish Maid* built in Aberdeen – forerunner of the clipper ship form. The world's first Chair of Engineering instituted at Glasgow University.
1843	SS *Great Britain* built at Bristol.
1844	Iron collier *QED* built Newcastle with structural tanks for water ballast.
1845	Board of Trade (UK) institutes examinations for sea-going masters and mates.
1847	Accepted date of potato blight in Ireland, and start of large-scale emigration.
1848	'Second' School of Naval Architecture opens at Portsmouth (closed in 1853). Discovery of gold in California.
1849	Report to British government on Fishing Boat Losses by Captain John Washington RN.

Patrick Miller

1731–1815

THERE IS CONSIDERABLE uncertainty regarding the date of the world's first voyage by a steam powered vessel, as there is regarding the names of those who may have arranged the financing, building or sailing of this ship. From a multitude of candidates including Jonathan Hulls of Gloucestershire (1699–1758), the French Marquis de Jouffroy d'Abbans (1751–1832) and the American John Fitch (1743–98), it may be impossible to decide on the person entitled to this laureate crown. However, recent research, backed by strong local tradition, indicates a high probability that this significant craft was the Dalswinton Loch steamship of 1788, with the funding and hull construction being the responsibility of Patrick Miller and machinery supply by **William Symington**.

Patrick Miller was typical of the wealthy country gentlemen of the late eighteenth century. He was a director of the Bank of Scotland and was to rise to the position of Deputy Governor. He had a country seat at Dalswinton in south Dumfriesshire, moved in Edinburgh society at the time of the Enlightenment and his sound investments included a holding in the Carron Company, the great Scottish ironworking firm then producing ordnance for the international market.

Like other men in his position he had a great interest in agricultural improvements, in artillery and other ordnance, and in the development of new forms of ships. Unsubstantiated reports indicate he had invented or at least had a major hand in the development of the carronade, which was a short-barrelled, large-calibre cannon widely used at sea. Miller was born in 1731 and for almost all of his life was resident in Scotland. He was a friend of the portrait painter Alexander Nasmyth and of the poet Robert Burns.

In 1787 Miller was responsible for the building and testing on the River Forth of a man-powered triple-hulled ship named *Edinburgh*. This vessel was 22m (72ft) long and had an overall breadth of just under 7m (23ft). The three hulls were held together by transverse beams and propulsion was by a pair of 2m (6ft 7in) diameter paddle wheels (one between each hull) driven by manual power applied to capstans. In his report to the Royal Society of Edinburgh in December 1787, Miller indicated that the crew of five could drive the *Edinburgh* at 8km/h (5mph). This ship, rigged with three masts, was reputed to be a good sea-keeper with adequate stability. Miller is known to have presented her later to the King of Sweden, and we must assume that this was Gustaf III, one of the most fascinating Scandinavian monarchs and a patron of the arts and sciences.

The following year saw the steam trial on Dalswinton Loch near Miller's home. Miller, an advocate of multi-hull construction supplied a catamaran and contracted with William Symington to furnish a two-cylinder simple steam engine. The ship was 8m (26ft 4in) long and had an extreme width of 2m (6ft 7in) and draft of about 0.65m (2ft) and with about five persons aboard is reputed to have travelled in calm conditions at 8km/h (5mph). The engine was made of two open-topped cylinders not unlike a Newcomen type, but with a condenser, and can be inspected to this day at the Science Museum, London. In correspondence with Boulton and Watt, Miller suggested some form of co-operation to develop steam navigation. **James Watt**, who was touchy about his patents, especially that of the separate condenser, refused to become involved and sadly the Dalswinton steamer was relegated to history. However, Miller and Symington had one further and very important adventure, which will be described in the following biography of William Symington.

One small mystery remains: several authorities maintain that both Alexander Nasmyth and Robert Burns were aboard the Dalswinton steamship on 14 October 1788. This cannot be confirmed, but it is more than likely that Burns (who was a tenant of Miller) was standing in the small crowd on the shore.

SOURCES:

Harvey, W S and Downs-Rose, G
William Symington: Inventor and Engine Builder
London, 1980

Spratt, H Philip
The Birth of the Steamboat
London, 1958

William Symington

1763–1831

IT WAS UNUSUAL for men of the late eighteenth century to describe themselves as engineers; with his excellent education and first-class practical experience, William Symington could make that claim. However, had it not been for his fortuitous meetings with **Patrick Miller** and Lord Dundas, he would not have been remembered as a pioneer of steam navigation. William Symington was born and brought up in the small Lanarkshire mining town of Leadhills, some 64km (40 miles) south of Glasgow. The once-sylvan county was becoming peppered with a few mines and many pits, all with their accompanying slag heaps. The industrial importance of the area was complemented by the discovery of black band ironstone, a mixture of coal and iron ore, which gave a competitive edge to iron-smelting in the Scottish central belt. All pits and mines in the area had severe drainage problems, and almost all were equipped with steam pumping engines and had mechanics and engineers permanently on site to maintain these vital but unreliable machines.

William Symington grew up knowing about machinery and mining as his father was mechanic and superintendent of the mining company at Leadhills. He was educated at the local school, which despite being in a fairly deprived area was a centre of excellence; he was destined for university and intended studying for the ministry. However, in his teens he decided to follow in his father's footsteps and started working in the nearby Wanlockhead mine.

Wanlockhead had had drainage problems since 1779 and the manager had approached **James Watt** for one of his engines to be installed by Symington's father. The arrangements with Boulton & Watt proved unsatisfactory, and the financial settlement took more time than had been anticipated. Young Symington realised there was an opening for a skilled engineer to produce his own steam engine, provided he could avoid running foul of the patent. Benefiting from the vast knowledge accumulated by his father, he started work and by 1787 was applying for a patent for a steam engine in his own name. He created such a good impression with the manager that he was encouraged to attend Edinburgh University, where he spent one session studying a wide variety of matters including anatomy. In later years this period, coupled with his working credentials, enabled him to rightly claim the title 'Civil Engineer'.

Most of his life was spent working on the steam machinery required at pitheads, but his private inclinations were for steam-driven transport. Around 1784 he designed and built a steam-driven

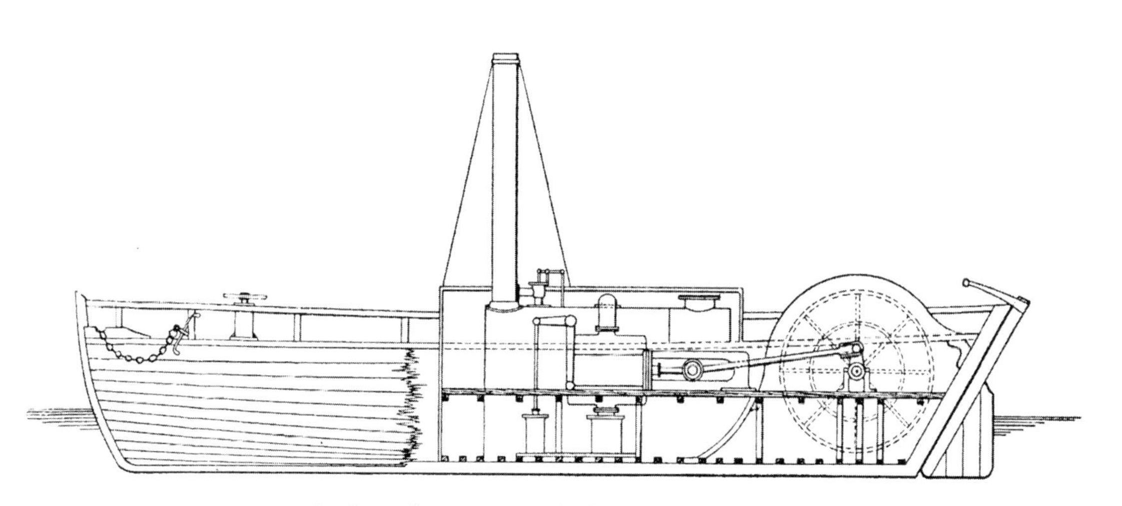

Symington's pioneering *Charlotte Dundas II.* (Author)

carriage, an elegant coach body suspended above a four wheeled chassis and with a small steam engine fitted at the pillion seat. It was displayed in Edinburgh giving Symington publicity of the best type. A press review said 'Five pence worth of coals will serve it twenty four hours and the velocity will be ten miles in an hour'. In 1787 he met **Patrick Miller** and they discussed the trials of his triple-hulled man-powered ship *Edinburgh*. Miller had realised that using seamen for motive power was inefficient and persuaded Symington to design a small steam engine for the trial on Dalswinton Loch in October 1788.

Miller felt that while the Dalswinton trial had been successful, it had not taken the public by surprise. Something on a larger scale was needed and he decided to attempt towing barges by steamship on the Forth and Clyde Canal. An order for machinery was placed with the Carron Company and Symington was involved. The hull chosen was an old canal gabbart. At the time Symington's hands were full with a troublesome pumping engine and his estimate of the cost of the machinery was inexact. Added to this the ship was slightly late, there was a cost overrun and worst of all the trial in 1789 was unsuccessful for a variety of reasons including a broken paddle float. All this was rectified quickly and at the second trial in February 1790 the ship steamed at 11km/h (7mph). Miller, probably unwisely, having brought guests to the first trial, felt so let down that he was absent from the second and gave instructions for the engine and hull to be sold – at best! This took time, but his wishes were carried out.

Lord Dundas, the Governor of the Forth and Clyde Canal, was interested in the 1789/90 trials, and after consulting with his co-director **Captain Schanck**, ordered a hull from Hart in Grangemouth (later the Grangemouth Dockyard) and machinery from various sources but under Symington's instruction. It is believed the ship, known as the *Charlotte Dundas*, had two paddle wheels and a horizontal engine. The machinery cost without boiler was £175 1s 7d, while that of a contemporary pit winding engine was £192 15s 5d. The overall cost of the project exceeded £858, then a considerable sum. Difficulties abounded on both the operational and the legal front and in 1802 the new ship was abandoned at Grangemouth.

Symington had patented a new engine in 1801 and under a cloak of secrecy another ship was authorised by the canal company and built at Grangemouth. Known nowadays as the *Charlotte Dundas II* she was 18m (59ft) long and 5.5m (18ft) broad. There was a single paddle wheel positioned in a cut-away in the middle of the transom again powered by a single cylinder horizontal engine. On completion the ship was taken to Glasgow and in January 1803 towed two barges for 29km (18 miles) at approximately 3km/h (2mph). The occasion may have been historic, but the canal company decided it was time to withdraw from steamships. The story that the directors were concerned that the wash of the tug might damage the banks is less than credible: they withdrew because the cost for the two ships had escalated to £1,463. The *Charlotte Dundas II* lay abandoned until 1808 when she was converted into a dredger.

Symington was paid little, but it is believed his real losses came from litigation. He worked for a few more years in Scotland, and then fell upon hard times. He and his wife moved to London where he died in 1831 and was buried in St Botolph's Church in Aldgate. While his name is remembered as that of a great pioneer in steam propulsion, it is sad to think that truly great success just eluded him.

SOURCES:
Harvey, W S, and Downs-Rose, G,
William Symington: Inventor and Engine Builder
London, 1980
Spratt, H Philip
The Birth of the Steamboat
London, 1958

Robert Fulton

1765–1815

ROBERT FULTON WAS THE prototype of the successful and pragmatic American engineer; a man able to watch, to listen and to adapt. In 1807 he built the world's first commercially successful steamship.

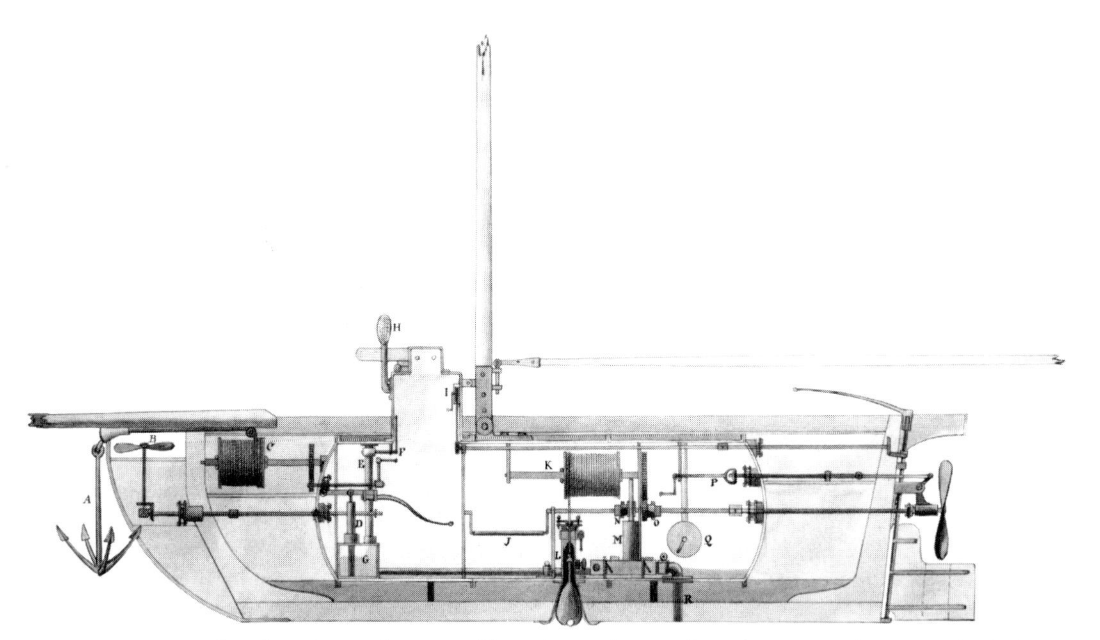

Arrangement of a submarine craft proposed by Robert Fulton in the early nineteenth century. *(Author)*

Born in Pennsylvania, Fulton moved to London in 1786. As his profession had been that of painter (miniatures held by the Historical Society of Pennsylvania are ample evidence of this), the transatlantic journey was to enable him to study and further his career. Sadly while his skills may have eked out a living for him in Pennsylvania, they were not good enough for the more sophisticated London market, and soon he was living on the edge of poverty. However, painting was soon forgotten as he became engrossed in British industrialisation and in particular the development of the steam engine and the building of canals. Here the artist's powers of observation, a retentive memory and sheer determination enabled him in later years to become a developer of steamships and also submarines.

Taking advantage of a lull in the Napoleonic Wars, he left Britain after an eleven-year stay and made his way to Paris. There he met some of the French pioneers of steam navigation including the Marquis de Jouffroy d'Abbans whose remarkable steam-powered ship *Pyroscaphe** had been tried on the River Saône in 1783. The full story of Fulton's work is difficult to unravel, particularly as there are conflicting versions, something which is understandable when the rival and pioneer steam ship and engine builders were staking their claims on originality. However, it is believed that in 1803 he was involved, indeed he may even have built, a 23m (75ft 5in) hull for the Seine with a single vertical-cylinder engine driving side paddles.

His feelings towards his former hosts the British were ambivalent, as within months of settling in France he had designed and offered a man-powered submarine, the *Nautilus*, to help break the British blockade. A working boat was built and tested in the Seine, but it was rejected by authorities, on the grounds that should France so arm itself, then the United Kingdom would follow. He also designed a fairly simple system of mines tethered to float just beneath the surface of the water, so as to detonate when ships passed over them. Again another rebuff, but according to one authority the idea was then offered to the British Prime Minister William Pitt and then to the US President Thomas Jefferson. Clearly national loyalty came second to the raising of revenue.

It is not clear where his financial backing was coming from, but by now Fulton was friendly with

Robert Livingstone, the American Ambassador to France. Livingstone had previously purchased shipping concessions for the Hudson River in America and had been hunting around to find a builder of steam ships. Soon Fulton was back across the English Channel inspecting as many workshops building steam engines as possible, and it is known that he had meetings with **James Watt** at Boulton & Watt's factory in Birmingham. There is anecdotal evidence that he visited **William Symington** and sailed on the *Charlotte Dundas II* on the Forth and Clyde Canal, but while this is uncertain, it is quite clear that he had the opportunity of seeing the plans of the ship's machinery. Before leaving Britain he tried to interest the Admiralty in a spar torpedo fitted on the bow of a submarine – but again without success.

On returning to the United States, he had built a wooden hull of around 100 tons displacement and powered it with machinery imported from Boulton & Watt. This ship was the *Clermont* and starting in 1807 this ship would work the 241km (150-mile) stretch of the Hudson between Albany and New York, on a voyage lasting thirty-two hours. It was a significant step forward in inland navigation and made Fulton a wealthy man. He built several very fine ships including one named *Chancellor Livingstone* after his old friend and benefactor, and then in 1815, the year of his death, the USS *Demologus*, the first steam-powered warship in the world.

SOURCES:
Flexner, James Thomas
Steamboats Come True
Boston, 1944
Spratt, H Philip
The Birth of the Steamboat
London, 1958

* A model of the *Pyroscaphe* can be seen in the Musée de la Marine, Paris. Incidentally, the earliest steamships operating as excursion vessels between St Petersburg and Kronstadt in Russia were known as *Pyroscaphes*, as at that time French was the second language, and the language of the Court, in Russia.

Henry Bell
1767–1830

ON THE NORTH BANK of the Clyde at Dunglass, halfway between Glasgow and Greenock, there stands an obelisk, now partly shrouded in trees, but visible from the river. At the base of this monument is carved the name Henry Bell. Bell was a hotel owner who, by commissioning the pioneer steamship *Comet*, was instrumental in introducing the first commercial steam navigation to both Britain and Europe.

Henry Bell was born at Torpichen Mill near Linlithgow in 1767, the fifth son of Patrick Bell, a millwright. After leaving school at the age of twelve, he spent several years learning two very different trades, one of the mason and the other of millwright. In 1786, he joined the firm of Shaw and Hart, shipbuilders at Borrowstoneness on the east coast of Scotland. His experiences there must have been inspiring, as these shipbuilders later were to produce the first effective steam-powered hull in the world, the Forth and Clyde Canal steamer *Charlotte Dundas*, and the ship which so inspired **Robert Fulton** of the United States. After twelve months working at Bellshill near Motherwell, later to be the centre of steel production in Scotland, he moved to London to gain experience at the works of John Rennie first at Blackfriars and later at Greenwich.

After eighteen months he returned to Glasgow and it is known that he spent seven years as a contractor based at the Trongate, working on various mechanical engineering projects – among these it is believed he designed a river dredger for the Clyde and machinery for the printing industry. It is reputed that he approached Henry Dundas, the first Viscount Melville, chairman of the Forth and Clyde Canal Company and later to become First Lord of the Admiralty, with a view to showing him the benefits of steam navigation. This overture was turned down, although it is also reported that Lord Nelson commented that Mr Bell should be supported and encouraged. In 1808, his name appeared as Provost of the up-and-coming commuter town of Helensburgh, just west of Dumbarton, and he was also the proprietor of the newly-opened Baths Hotel which offered protected sea bathing in that elegant watering-place. It was important to attract visitors from Glasgow and elsewhere, and for this reason Bell arranged a horse-drawn coach service (operated by a member of his family) three times a week between Glasgow and Helensburgh.

Clearly, being what is now known as an entrepreneur, he looked around and decided that the best way to attract customers to the hotel would be by providing transport direct from Glasgow on a steam-driven ship, then a novelty without parallel. Following negotiations and detailed planning, he placed two contracts: first for a 13m (42ft 7in) wooden hull with **John and Charles Wood**, the shipbuilders of Port Glasgow; second with John Robertson of Glasgow for a single cylinder 3hp steam engine and a boiler (costed at £27) from the company owned by the father of David Napier. The cost of the engine has been given as £165, but it is believed that after modifications this rose to £365. There has been controversy for years over the boiler invoice, but recent research indicates it must have been paid. For all of this Bell was reliant on his own funds.

The *Comet* went into service in August 1812 and on trials steamed the 32km (20 miles) from Greenock to Glasgow in three hours and thirty minutes. This was very good timing, as according to Sir James Marwick (1828–1908) the former Town Clerk of Glasgow: 'Glasgow to Greenock . . . prior to 1812 ... was on wherry built nutshells designated 'flyboats', the justice of which appellation will be sufficiently apparent when it is considered they generally completed their voyage in the short space of ten hours.'

Initially the *Comet* had two sets of paddle-wheels, each on a transverse shaft and driven by pinions meshed to a gear wheel on a third shaft positioned between them. Later the ship was converted to what became the conventional form of one shaft with paddle-wheels port and starboard; a change which gave a significant increase in speed. The engine was on the port side and the boiler on the starboard, with the tall funnel (which also acted as the mast for the single square sail) abaft. The remarkably low thermal efficiency of the pioneer steamships made passenger carriage their only profitable work. The *Comet* had many interesting trips on the Clyde, and regularly became stuck on the shoals off Bowling. It was not uncommon for passengers to be asked to step overboard to lighten the ship and to help push her into deeper water, while on other occasions they had nothing more to do than move from one side of the deck to the other to loosen the keel from the sand.

In 1819, the *Comet* was moved from the Clyde to the West Highlands, and on 15 December 1820 was wrecked at Craignish while on a voyage from Fort William. The engine was salvaged and is now displayed at the Science Museum, London.

Henry Bell received few financial rewards for his pioneering work. He died in 1830 at Helensburgh and is buried at nearby Rhu in Dunbartonshire. While the proprietorship of the Baths Hotel changed after Bell's death, his wife remained the manager and hostess until her death in 1856. Henry Bell has never been forgotten as one of the world's steamship pioneers, and his name is held in especial honour on the River Clyde.

SOURCES:
Marwick, Sir James D
The River Clyde and the Clyde Burghs
Glasgow, 1909
Morris, Edward
The Life of Henry Bell
Glasgow, 1843
Osborne, J Craig
The Comet and her Creators
Gourock, 2007
Smart, H Philip
The Birth of the Steamboat
London, 1958

John Wood

1788–1860

THE WOOD FAMILY built small ships in Greenock from 1780 until 1810 and then moved the few miles to Port Glasgow where they continued ship construction until 1853. The business was founded by John Wood senior, a man destined to make history, in that he contracted to build the hull of the first steamship to operate commercially in Europe.

Unfortunately he died before construction began, when responsibility for this work was taken over by his able son John, then in his early twenties. For many years the shipyard in East Port Glasgow was managed by both John and his brother Charles.

The *Comet* – John's first ship, a diminutive 13m (42ft) in length and 3.7m (12ft 1in) in breadth, and displacing under 30 tonnes – is remembered now as one of the world's most historic ships. She had a single tall smokestack which doubled as a mast, and on either side were sponsons incorporating large paddle boxes with double paddles on two transverse shafts driven by gearing from a central athwartships crankshaft. The single-cylinder engine produced no more than three horsepower, enabling the ship to move at just a few miles per hour under power. The machinery was built and supplied by a John Robertson of Glasgow, the first example of the now-universal system of subcontracted machinery supply. While the *Comet* had limited success – her double paddles proved impractical and were reduced to one each side, and while her low speed and high fuel consumption were a severe hindrance – she did usher in a new form of transport before being wrecked in 1820. In these eight years, steam propulsion was developed, and John Wood and Co of Port Glasgow took the lead, with close on sixty steamers being produced by John and Charles (both jointly and independently) before the 1850s.

John Wood is known to have been a kindly and approachable man, one willing to share his unique knowledge and experience with both friends and commercial rivals alike. He was interested in hull design, and presumably arranged the recording of lines of all ships constructed, as the design and layout of his steamers are fairly well understood, at least by the standards of the early years of the nineteenth century. He did not believe in the traditional hull form known as 'cods head and mackerel tail', where the station of maximum cross-sectional area was well forward of the midships section. All his ships had maximum breadth and cross-sectional area close to amidships. An unsolicited testimonial was given by no less than **John Scott Russell** in his 1861 paper to the Institution, and as Russell had been manager of the nearby Caird shipyard in Greenock and had worked closely with the brothers Wood, one must assume he spoke from the heart and with assurance.

On completion of the *Comet*, there was no looking back and a succession of wooden hulls with steam paddle machinery came from the Port Glasgow works. Their seventh steamer was then the largest yet built, being nearly 30m (98ft) in length. Named *Caledonia*, she had a short and unsuccessful career, first on the Clyde and later on the Thames. In 1817, James Watt, the son of the pioneer engineer, purchased her for experimentation, and then following re-engining and remarkably comprehensive sea trials was sold to a Danish company which operated her between Copenhagen and Kiel for some years. The *Caledonia* has two claims to fame, first being Denmark's first steamship and remaining under the Danish flag until broken up in 1843, and secondly being the subject of the most comprehensive sea trials of the early part of the century.

Significant ships produced by the young John Wood included a 21.3m (70ft) vessel for towing duties in the port of Leith named *Tug* in 1817. This appellation was given thereafter to all towing ships produced world-wide. Another interesting ship was the *Tracker*, a work boat built in 1844 for the Union Canal near Edinburgh, which had one of the earliest propellers, but fitted at the bow.

The high taxes on imported North American timber had been a cause of dissatisfaction in British shipyards, and had encouraged the massive imports of Canadian-built timber hulls into the United Kingdom during the first half of the nineteenth century. John Wood's brother Charles was commercially minded and became involved in a project designed to circumvent these rules. He went over to Canada, and built two massive ships on the Island of Orleans in Quebec. The first, *Columbus* of 1824, was of 3,690 tons and more than one-third longer than the then-largest ship in the Royal Navy and this was followed slightly later by the much larger *Baron Renfrew* built of timber with massive reinforcements throughout and indeed with every available space taken up by constructive material. On arrival in the UK the first ship was broken up and the material found a ready market, but whether this venture was profitable or not is unrecorded. The second ship which was 93m (305ft) long and 19m (62ft 4in) broad ran aground on the coast of France and became a total loss.

In the late 1830s, **Robert Napier** of Glasgow received the contract to build four steamships for Samuel Cunard's new North Atlantic passenger service. The four hulls were subcontracted out as follows: *Acadia* to John Wood, *Britannia* to Robert Duncan of Port Glasgow, *Caledonia* to Charles Wood, now acting on his own at Dumbarton, and *Columbia* to Robert Steel of Greenock. Despite being 'lead ship' *Acadia* was not the first to sail, that honour going to the appropriately-named *Britannia* from Duncan's which inaugurated Cunard's Liverpool to Halifax and Boston service.

In 1847, John Wood sold his yard to John Reid, and while the historic name ceased to be used, the shipyard continued in production for many years and built some very excellent sailing ships. The *Comet* has not been forgotten in her birthplace of Inverclyde, as a full-sized working replica was constructed in 1962 and now is on display close to the site of John Wood's shipyard.

SOURCES:
Bellamy, Martin
'P.S. *Caledonia*: Denmark's First Steamship'
The Mariner's Mirror
Vol 80 (1994)
Marcill, Eileeen Reid
The Charley-Man: A History of Wooden Shipbuilding at Quebec 1763–1893
Kingston, Ontario, Canada, 1995
Scott Russell, J
'On the late Mr John Wood and Mr Charles Wood, Naval Architects of Port Glasgow'
Transactions of the Institution of Naval Architects
Vol 2 (1861)

Peter Barlow

1776–1862

UP UNTIL ABOUT forty-five years ago it would be hard to find any naval architect who did not acknowledge a debt of gratitude to Peter Barlow, a mathematician and physicist who served for forty-six years on the staff of the Royal Military Academy, Woolwich. While few naval architects knew much about the man and his work, it is more than likely that they used his book of mathematical tables daily in the ship design office.

Born in Norwich in October 1776, Barlow had various commercial appointments as a young man until he organised and ran a small school, during which time he pursued academic interests, as well as being a regular correspondent to the journal *Ladies' Diary*. It was at this period of his life that he became interested in the then fashionable pursuits of science, mathematics and in particular the theory of numbers. This interest, coupled with his widening knowledge of natural philosophy, encouraged him to apply for the post of assistant mathematics master at the Royal Military Academy, Woolwich, an appointment which he won in 1801, despite fierce competition. Within ten years he had commenced his prodigious output of publications covering matters as diverse as magnetism, compass correction, the theory of numbers and the strength of timber, all of which led to his appointment as Professor. In 1819, while ships were still built of timber, he started work on compass deviation as this effect was beginning to be noticed through the slow but quite significant introduction of ferrous parts and fastenings. This led to the invention of a small specially-designed iron plate to neutralise compass deviation, and thereby paving the way for further work on compass correction by Airy and **Kelvin**. The Board of Longitude gave him a prize of £500 (a then not-inconsiderable sum) for this invention and Tsar Alexander I of Russia presented him with a gold watch.

Barlow's greatest assistance to naval architects was undoubtedly his book *New Mathematical Tables*. For all integers between 1 and 10,000, he listed their square, cube, square root, cube root, reciprocals and other functions. Few mechanical means were available to assist in this work which was labour-intensive and time-consuming. In the preface to the first edition, Barlow described the work as an unprofitable exercise, but went on to say: 'If I have succeeded in facilitating any of the more abstruse arithmetical calculations, and thereby rendering mathematical investigations more pleasant, I have obtained the object in view.' The *Book of Tables*, now

No. n	Square n^2	Cube n^3	Square root $\sqrt{n}$		Sq. rt. of 10n $\sqrt{10n}$		Cube root $\sqrt[3]{n}$		Reciprocal $\frac{1}{n}$	
			97·		309·		21·		0·000	
9550	91 20 25 00	870 983 875 000	724101	5117	030743	16179	216209	741	1047120	109
9551	91 22 16 01	871 257 511 151	729218	5116	046922	16178	216950	740	1047011	110
9552	91 24 07 04	871 531 204 608	734334	5116	063100	16178	217690	741	1046901	109
9553	91 25 98 09	871 804 955 377	739450	5115	079278	16177	218431	740	1046792	110
9554	91 27 89 16	872 078 763 464	744565	5115	095455	16175	219171	740	1046682	110
9555	91 29 80 25	872 352 628 875	749680	5115	111630	16175	219911	741	1046572	109
9556	91 31 71 36	872 626 551 616	754795	5115	127805	16174	220652	740	1046463	110
9557	91 33 62 49	872 900 531 693	759910	5114	143979	16174	221392	740	1046353	109
9558	91 35 53 64	873 174 569 112	765024	5115	160153	16172	222132	740	1046244	109
9559	91 37 44 81	873 448 663 879	770139	5113	176325	16172	222872	740	1046135	110
9560	91 39 36 00	873 722 816 000	775252	5114	192497	16170	223612	740	1046025	109
9561	91 41 27 21	873 997 025 481	780366	5113	208667	16170	224352	740	1045916	110
9562	91 43 18 44	874 271 292 328	785479	5114	224837	16169	225092	740	1045806	109
9563	91 45 09 69	874 545 616 547	790593	5112	241006	16169	225832	740	1045697	109
9564	91 47 00 96	874 819 998 144	795705	5113	257175	16167	226572	739	1045588	110
9565	91 48 92 25	875 094 437 125	800818	5112	273342	16166	227311	740	1045478	109
9566	91 50 83 56	875 368 933 496	805930	5112	289508	16166	228051	740	1045369	109
9567	91 52 74 89	875 643 487 263	811042	5112	305674	16165	228791	739	1045260	109
9568	91 54 66 24	875 918 098 432	816154	5112	321839	16164	229530	740	1045151	110
9569	91 56 57 61	876 192 767 009	821266	5111	338003	16163	230270	740	1045041	109
9570	91 58 49 00	876 467 493 000	826377	5111	354166	16162	231010	739	1044932	109
9571	91 60 40 41	876 742 276 411	831488	5110	370328	16162	231749	739	1044823	109
9572	91 62 31 84	877 017 117 248	836598	5111	386490	16160	232488	740	1044714	109
9573	91 64 23 29	877 292 015 517	841709	5110	402650	16160	233228	739	1044605	109
9574	91 66 14 76	877 566 971 224	846819	5110	418810	16159	233967	739	1044496	110
9575	91 68 06 25	877 841 984 375	851929	5110	434969	16158	234706	740	1044386	109
9576	91 69 97 76	878 117 054 976	857039	5109	451127	16157	235446	739	1044277	109
9577	91 71 89 29	878 392 183 033	862148	5109	467284	16157	236185	739	1044168	109
9578	91 73 80 84	878 667 368 552	867257	5109	483441	16155	236924	739	1044059	109
9579	91 75 72 41	878 942 611 539	872366	5108	499596	16155	237663	739	1043950	109
9580	91 77 64 00	879 217 912 000	877474	5109	515751	16154	238402	739	1043841	109
9581	91 79 55 61	879 493 269 941	882583	5108	531905	16153	239141	739	1043732	109
9582	91 81 47 24	879 768 685 368	887691	5108	548058	16152	239880	739	1043623	108
9583	91 83 38 89	880 044 158 287	892799	5107	564210	16151	240619	739	1043515	109
9584	91 85 30 56	880 319 688 704	897906	5107	580361	16151	241358	738	1043406	109
9585	91 87 22 25	880 595 276 625	903013	5107	596512	16149	242096	739	1043297	109
9586	91 89 13 96	880 870 922 056	908120	5107	612661	16149	242835	739	1043188	109
9587	91 91 05 69	881 146 625 003	913227	5106	628810	16148	243574	738	1043079	109
9588	91 92 97 44	881 422 385 472	918333	5106	644958	16147	244312	739	1042970	108
9589	91 94 89 21	881 698 203 469	923439	5106	661105	16146	245051	738	1042862	109
9590	91 96 81 00	881 974 079 000	928545	5106	677251	16146	245789	739	1042753	109
9591	91 98 72 81	882 250 012 071	933651	5105	693397	16144	246528	738	1042644	109
9592	92 00 64 64	882 526 002 688	938756	5105	709541	16144	247266	738	1042535	108
9593	92 02 56 49	882 802 050 857	943861	5105	725685	16143	248004	739	1042427	109
9594	92 04 48 36	883 078 156 584	948966	5105	741828	16142	248743	738	1042318	109
9595	92 06 40 25	883 354 319 875	954071	5104	757970	16141	249481	738	1042209	108
9596	92 08 32 16	883 630 540 736	959175	5104	774111	16141	250219	738	1042101	109
9597	92 10 24 09	883 906 819 173	964279	5104	790252	16139	250957	738	1041992	108
9598	92 12 16 04	884 183 155 192	969383	5103	806391	16139	251695	738	1041884	109
9599	92 14 08 01	884 459 548 799	974486	5104	822530	16138	252433	738	1041775	108
9600	92 16 00 00	884 736 000 000	979590		838668		253171		1041667	
			97·		309·		21·		0·000	

0 193

A page from *Barlow's Tables*, first produced in 1814 and which had multi-editions right up until 1965 when made redundant by the advent of the hand-held calculator and the universal adoption of the computer for complex engineering and ship design calculations.

By painstaking manual means, Barlow prepared these tables giving functions of all numbers from 1 to 12,500 and thereby saving engineers and designers incalculable time and effort in complex tasks.

Over the years, hand-operated design tools were developed to reduce the tedium of 'number crunching' and to improve the accuracy of calculations. Such instruments are now collectors' items and the National Maritime Museum, Greenwich, was the recipient in the early 1980s of the priceless collection of naval architecture instruments once held by the Admiralty. It is hoped these will be placed on public display in the not too distant future. (*Author*) known as *Barlow's Tables*, has continued through four editions and a multitude of impressions. The impression of 1965 incorporated minor changes and the integers were increased to 12,500 enabling more accurate work on either side of unity.

The study of timbers and their properties kept him employed both intellectually and physically; he carried out numerous experiments in the Woolwich Dockyard, publishing the results in 1817. This information was used to good effect by the great civil engineer Thomas Telford during the final examinations for the design of the Menai Suspension Bridge. Barlow was not finished there, as he carried out experiments on optical matters, and all based on a mathematical background, showing his philosophical approach to the science of engineering.

Barlow remained at Woolwich until 1847 when he retired laden with honours and in receipt of his full professorial pay in recognition of his work for the country. He had been elected FRS, received the Copley Prize of the Royal Society and had been made an Honorary Member of the Institution of Civil Engineers. Unsung perhaps, but a man who had contributed much to science, and in practical terms one who had eased the complexity of heavy 'number crunching' ship-design calculations well before the days of calculators or mechanical counting aids.

SOURCES:
Barlow, Peter
Mathematical and Philosophical Dictionary
1814
———,
Essay on Strength of Timbers
1817
Smiles, Samuel
Lives of the Engineers
London, 1861

Antoine Nicolas François Bonjean
1778–1822

THIS GENTLEMAN HAS ONE of the best-known names in naval architecture. Every student knows the uses and advantages of 'Bonjean Curves', an invaluable tool for many operations, especially the many calculations required for dynamic ship launching. However, few naval architects know about the background and life of Monsieur Bonjean. The author is especially indebted to his friend Larrie D Ferreiro for having tracked Antoine

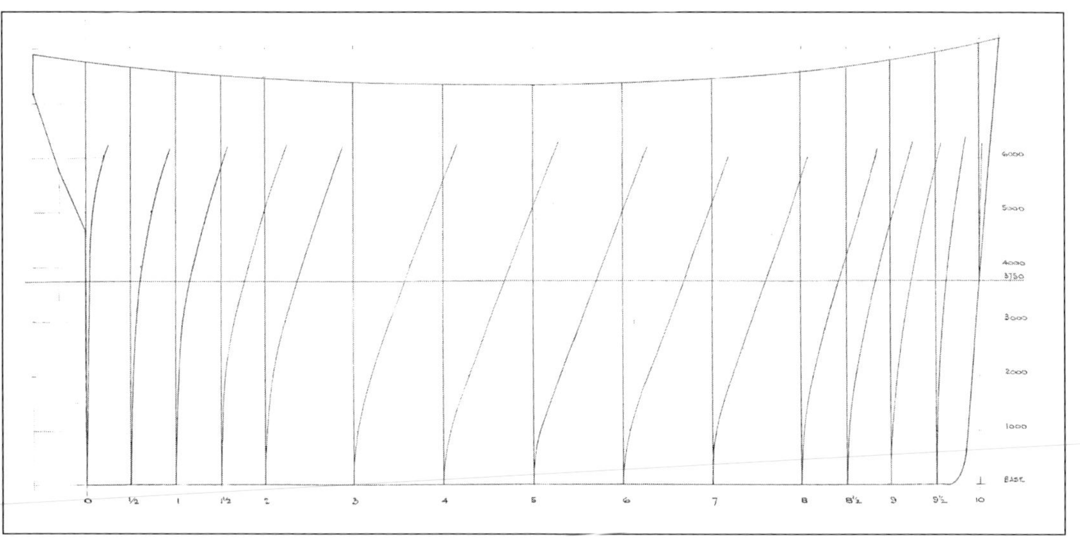

Bonjean Curves. Drawn for a recently-constructed three-masted sailing barque, each curve shows the increase in area of each cross section as the ship's draft increases. (*Author*)

Bonjean and made his story accessible to those interested in the history of ship design.

Antoine Bonjean was a constructor in the service of the French Navy. He was born in Paris and after having studied engineering, he joined the Corps of Maritime Engineering when he was twenty and then served afloat on a frigate fighting the British in Egypt. In 1801 he returned to France and worked for some years in different naval dockyards, and then in 1808 wrote a paper entitled *Nouvelles Echelles de Deplacement* describing the curves of cross sectional area which can be drawn for any convenient cross-section of a ship, and which have been invaluable to all naval architects ever since. Bonjean served for a while on Napoleon's Rhine flotilla, but retired around 1815 on health grounds, and is believed to have died in 1822 while still in his thirties.

SOURCES:
Ferreiro, Larrie D
The Birth of Naval Architecture in the Scientific Revolution 1600–1800
Cambridge, Mass., 2007

John Wilkinson

1728–1810

WILKINSON WAS A COLOURFUL eighteenth-century iron founder, whose drive and inventiveness brought him into national prominence at a time when the iron trades were expanding in the United Kingdom. His birth was remarkable, being on a farm cart, while his mother was taking produce from their farm to the local market. As well as farm work, his father, Isaac Wilkinson, acted in a supervisory position at a haematite iron ore furnace, of which there were then several in the Workington area of Cumbria. John (and his brother) received good secondary school education, and at the age of seventeen, John went to Liverpool to serve an apprenticeship in an ironmonger's business.

At the time of Wilkinson's birth, iron smelting was little more than a cottage industry, and almost totally dependent on charcoal supplies, hence the denuding of the great forests in south-east England, the Lake District and elsewhere. By the beginning of the nineteenth century, the turnover in iron had increased fifteen-fold, charcoal was almost redundant, new ore fields had been exploited, and more efficient methods of smelting had been developed.

Returning from Liverpool, Wilkinson learned as much as possible about iron smelting, before moving to Staffordshire, then the acknowledged centre of the trade. In a few short years, both by careful management and the shrewd choice of a wealthy bride, he had amassed sufficient capital to buy works at Bradley, and commence the career which made him known as 'Iron-mad Wilkinson'. Clearly he had a real love of iron and iron-founding, and, once established financially, broadened the scope of his business. Among the more unusual products were house construction items such as columns and window frames, church pulpits, and even cast iron coffins. It is said that he had a stock of these at home, to be shown to shocked house-guests with the offer of a free one made to their measurements! It is also claimed that he kept one for himself, but that on his death, his increased girth made it too tight a fit and it had to be discarded for another.

His wife died shortly after their marriage and about eight years later (in 1763) he married another lady, with whom he had a poor relationship, but who brought him further wealth. To avoid going into sordid detail, it may be best to quote one of his biographers, who described Wilkinson's domestic life as 'ill regulated'. On the positive side, his management of the foundries was good and his relationship with supervisors excellent. As was allowed at the time, he minted his own coins for payment of the workforce, and for a while considered printing his own financial promissory notes. Long-serving and trusted employees were given pensions, something almost unheard-of in the eighteenth century.

Throughout his working life he was responsible for new techniques and the introduction of innovations, like the production of cog wheels, iron rolls and pipes – then quite a novelty. While not responsible for the world's first iron bridge which spans the Severn at Ironbridge, he was involved in this undertaking. One important task was the design and manufacture of a horizontal boring mill for cylinders and similar items, which led to a long standing business relationship with **James Watt** and Matthew Boulton. Boulton and Watt required accurate machining for cylinders, sleeves and similar items, and also good quality solid castings. In 1792 he patented a rolling mill, for the manufacture of bars from blooms of puddled iron; this was not successful, but it did establish Wilkinson at the very forefront of the mass production of iron. One less-successful venture was experimenting with peat as a fuel for iron-smelting.

Like all industrialists in the Midlands, Wilkinson used canals for the transportation of fuel, raw materials and finished products. The canals were of the traditional English type: relatively shallow and narrow. It is said that after a dispute with barge builders during a period of timber shortage, he decided to by-pass this bottleneck and to manufacture barges in his own right. He decided to experiment with iron, and the first such barge, believed known as *Trial*, was manufactured of iron plates bolted to a framework of elm. Whether the plates were of cast or of forged quality is uncertain, and indeed they may have been 'hammer welded' on the blacksmith's anvil. The dimensions have been recorded as 21.34m (70ft) long and 2.05m (6ft 8.5in) broad and of similar dimensions to current narrow-boats on English inland waterways. The plate material was 8mm ($^5/_{16}$in) thick. The vessel is unlikely to have been shaped beyond swim ends, but is again recorded as being 8 tons lightweight and with a deadweight capacity of 30 tons.

In the twenty-first century it is difficult to comprehend the antipathy to iron boat building, and the woeful misunderstanding of the public with regard to floating iron structures over 200 years ago. One blacksmith asked Wilkinson to witness a horseshoe being thrown into a water trough, and the inevitable sinking was taken as proof that his master had gone mad! On 6 July 1787, *Trial* was launched, and if the lightweight figure is correct, she must have had a draft of no more than 20cm (8in).

There are reports of other iron barges built by Wilkinson, but historic evidence is sketchy. Thirty-two years were to pass before the first proper iron ship, *Vulcan*, was built by **Thomas Wilson** at Coatbridge. She was launched on 14 May 1819, the date on which iron shipbuilding commenced in earnest.

SOURCES:
Bailey, W H
'The First Iron Boat, and its inventor John Wilkinson, the Father of the Iron Trade'
Proceedings of the Manchester Association of Engineers
1886

Thomas Wilson
1781–1873

This biography of the originator and true pioneer of conventional iron and steel ship construction must begin by reporting that at the St Alban's Tavern in London on 14 March 1768, the Duke of Queensberry chaired the first general meeting of the Forth and Clyde Canal Company and one of Britain's most significant and profitable civil engineering ventures was incorporated. Within two years the 'cut' had commenced of a deep-water canal, and by 1790 it was open from sea to sea, and able to take fairly substantial vessels: indeed the dimensions of the traditional Clyde Puffer were defined by the size of locks on the waterway. The success of the undertaking is reflected, first by the share dividend which climbed to 25 per cent in the year 1816, and second by the vast numbers travelling by barge between Edinburgh and Glasgow, a figure which reached 198,000 by 1836.

The Canal Company had always sought the advice of outsiders on technical and other matters, and over the years its consultants sound like a Who's Who of eminent early nineteenth-century engineers. The list includes **James Watt**, **Vice Admiral John Schanck**, and Professor Joseph Black, the investigator of latent heat, and an early mentor of James Watt at Glasgow University. The Admiral in turn had been involved with the trials of the pioneer steamship *Charlotte Dundas* on the Canal at the turn of the century.

In the years after 1810, the runaway success of the Canal brought problems in its wake, the most

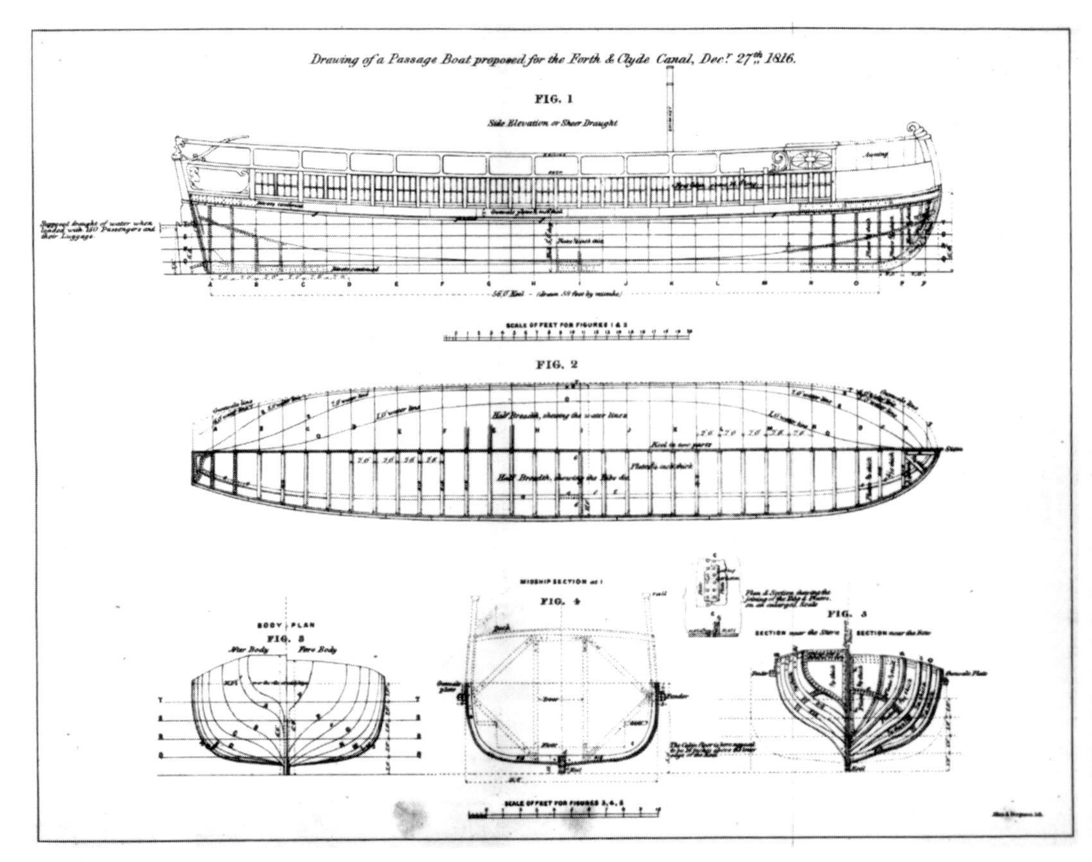

Sheer draught of the world's first properly-built iron ships, the passenger barge *Vulcan*, launched in 1819. Her length was limited to just over 20m (66ft 6in) in order that she could operate on the highly successful Forth and Clyde canal. It is interesting to note that the draughtsman realised an error was incorporated in the drawing, as under the profile the dimension reads 58'-0" keel – (drawn 56 feet by mistake). (Institution of Engineers and Shipbuilders in Scotland)

serious being congestion. The result of this was increasing levels of damage to the ships of the Canal Company and ever-rising costs for damage repair and maintenance. Again, the company appointed a committee to consider the matter and make recommendations, the group included the ship designer Henry Creighton of Soho and Sir John Robison of Edinburgh, an eminent scientist and member of the influential establishment of that city. After considering various options, their proposals were straight and to the point: Design and build an experimental fast passage barge of iron, then a completely unknown material for serious ship construction. The 'gestation period' for the barge was fairly lengthy, being nearly three years, during which time the designs were assessed carefully and a shipwright appointed to take charge of this revolutionary venture. Surprisingly, none of the established iron masters were considered, and the work was placed with a young shipwright Thomas Wilson, a man with no previous experience of working in this new medium.

Wilson was born in 1781 at Dunbar, but moved to the Clyde and served a shipwright apprenticeship at the then village of Bowling, about 24km (15 miles) west of Glasgow and on the north bank. The development of the river was only starting, and he must have lived and worked in primitive but sylvan surroundings. On completing his indentures, he moved to the Monkland Canal and at Blackhall became involved in building lighters and scows for inland work. He must have been known to the Canal Company, and as the Monklands was then the centre of the iron trades in Scotland, the choice of shipwright is more understandable.

Wilson started the construction in 1818 and employed two excellent blacksmiths, John and Thomas Smellie, who completed the work in time for her launch on 14 May 1819. They must have formed a good working team, as every detail of this ship was an innovation, requiring thorough planning coupled with a courageous approach to a new technology.

The new passenger passage barge, appropriately named *Vulcan*, was laid down just outside Coatbridge on the bank of the Monkland Canal, a feeder waterway for the cross-Scotland link. She was 20.2m (66ft 6in) long and 3.3m (11ft) broad and built throughout with plates and sections, forged from puddled iron blooms. As there were no iron-rolling mills, every item had to be forged by the two blacksmiths on the anvil, making *Vulcan* probably the most labour-intensive ship of all time. The constructional technique differed little from all later iron and steel vessels, with keel, keelson and angle iron frames at 61cm (24in) centres. Everything was riveted, with plates also being 61cm (24in) broad and fitted vertically up round the frames and flush butted. The only appreciable change in construction came in later years when plates became longer as quality standards improved and then they were fitted in longitudinal strakes.

The new vessel was an outstanding success, working first as a horse-drawn passenger vessels between the two main Scottish cities. In keeping with the passage barges and also some of the fast 'fly-boats' she had two cabins as well as a small galley and the modern convenience of two toilets – one for ladies and the other for gentlemen – which flushed directly into the canal! In later years, passenger numbers fell as the influence of the railways began to be felt. The *Vulcan* was stripped down and became a cargo carrier and was to be seen not only on the canal, but also on the River Forth and the River Clyde. After over half a century of service, she was broken up in 1873, clear proof of the longevity of wrought iron in the marine environment.

Thomas Wilson was appointed Inspector of Works for the Forth and Clyde Canal Company in 1822. He was regarded highly by all who knew him, and before his death moved to Grangemouth where he superintended the building of the dock system. He died in 1873, the same year that his masterpiece *Vulcan* was broken up. Few men can claim such a vital part in our maritime history, and Thomas Wilson deserves to be remembered and honoured for as long as iron and steel ships are constructed.

SOURCES:

Gilchrist, A
Early Examples of Iron Shipbuilding
Scottish Shipbuilders' Association, 1864–5

Walker, Fred M
'Early Iron Shipbuilding – a reappraisal of the *Vulcan* and other pioneering vessels'
Transactions of the Institution of Engineers and Shipbuilders in Scotland
Vol 133 (1989–90)

Henry Eckford

1775–1832

Henry Eckford was a notable shipwright, a superb designer and a man who became renowned for teaching apprentices destined to make their mark in American shipbuilding. According to **H I Chapelle** (the noted naval architect and historian) his most important attribute was being 'a master of the art of high speed production of ships'. Born in Ayrshire, Scotland, Henry Eckford spent sixteen years in the small village of Kilwinning before setting off across the North Atlantic for Canada. His destination was Quebec where he would join his uncle John Black, and serve a shipwright apprenticeship under him. In the 1790s and the following decades, Quebec was a significant shipbuilding area with a growing number of yards. Skill levels were high, raw material was to hand and export work for Britain and other parts of Europe kept employment at consistently high levels.

Clearly Eckford had little mind to settle down, as by 1796, aged about twenty-one, he had made his way to New York where he took employment from time to time in various shipyards, then in 1799 he married and shortly after took out American citizenship. For the next few years he worked as manager of the shipyard of Christian Bergh (1763–1843) and also operated under his own name. His ability to design, to build well and best of all to deliver at speed and on time made his name on the East River. Demand for ships fell in the latter years of the Napoleonic Wars owing to the American embargoes on trade, but as soon as these were dropped in 1809, business picked up and Eckford opened another yard in New York.

Clearly his time with the Quebecois and the New Yorkers had made him feel less disposed towards the United Kingdom and in 1812 when the USA declared war on Britain, Eckford felt able to accept a major project for his new country. Fearing invasion from Canada, the American government decided to build fleets to protect their shores in the Great Lakes. A yard was to be set up on the southern shore Lake Ontario, and men, equipment and raw materials were dispatched with Eckford in full charge. It was said that the US Navy Secretary could not have made a better decision regarding the man in charge. Two further yards, under Eckford's overall supervision were set up at Lake Erie and at Lake Champlain.

For this task Eckford recruited men from all over as well as a goodly number from his own yard, including an apprentice, Isaac Webb, the father of the future shipbuilder and philanthropist **William H Webb**. They travelled part of the way up the River Hudson on one of **Robert Fulton**'s steamships. At Lake Ontario, a shipyard was laid out and the positions of launchways settled. Their first ship, the USS *Madison*, named after the President, was launched on 1 November 1812 just nine weeks after her timbers had been felled as lumber. In times of war, building with green timber was not regarded as serious, and as is now known is less disadvantageous than believed previously. Having promised two 'line of battle ships' in sixty days the yard was geared for an immense effort. With 1,200 workmen, the *New Orleans* of 130 guns had been built high enough for eighty gun ports to show before work was stopped when peace was declared. The *New Orleans* lay on the shores of Lake Ontario until 1884, when broken up.

On his return to New York, Eckford continued shipbuilding under his own name, but in addition carried out both production and design tasks for the nearby New York Navy Yard. Assignments included the design of a 'no-frills' 26-gun sloop and the design and oversight of several gun vessels where emphasis was on the largest possible pieces of ordnance. His most famous ship, launched in May 1820 was the 74-gun USS *Ohio*, regarded by many as one of the United States Navy's finest sailers – she is even mentioned in Rudyard Kipling's great novel of the sea *Captains Courageous*! In the late 1820s Henry Eckford was invited to Turkey where he designed and built several ships of the line and frigates for the Ottoman Empire.

SOURCES:

Beach, Edward L
The United States Navy: a 200-year history
New York, 1986
Chapelle, Howard I
The History of the American Sailing Navy
New York, 1949

Sir William Symonds
1782–1856

William Symonds, Surveyor of the Navy from 1832 to 1848, is both a controversial and enigmatic figure. The two main contributions to the Royal Navy during his time at the helm were first experimentation in hull shapes to ensure higher sea speeds through the introduction of sharper entries, steeper floors and elliptical sterns, and secondly the badly-needed standardisation of rigging 'establishments'. In almost all other matters he was ultra-conservative and prejudiced against scientific thinking. William Symonds took over the post of Surveyor at the beginning of Sir James Graham's tenure as First Lord of the Admiralty. Many changes were afoot including the abolishment of the old Navy Board, and the much less welcome closure of the 'First' School of Naval Architecture at Portsmouth. The outgoing Surveyor was **Sir Robert Seppings**, a first-rate shipwright with wide experience and an active interest in the improvement of the fleet. For the next sixteen years development would be limited and dealt with in an amateur and dilettante manner.

Symonds was born at Taunton in September 1782. His family were from the local aristocracy. When aged fourteen, he joined the Royal Navy, served in many theatres, witnessed the mutiny at the Nore in 1797, and rose to the rank of Captain. He married twice; his first wife died in the West Indies. It is interesting to note that following his death, a Memoir – akin to an autobiography – was, on the direction of his will, prepared from his papers, edited by a Mr Sharp and published in 1858.

On reading the many reports of this controversial period, one finds several vastly differing opinions on the effectiveness of William Symonds. He had cultivated a name as an amateur naval architect and had designed (or possibly overseen the designing) of some small fast craft, including the fast and elegant HMS *Columbine* which had brought him to public attention. The position of Surveyor to the Navy was almost a natural development for a man who was politically aligned with the Whig (but deeply conservative) Sir James Graham, First Lord of the Admiralty.

The positive aspects of Symonds' work include the design of fast hulls, work which was overseen by John Eyde, the Assistant Surveyor and a properly-trained and educated shipwright. Here Symonds had success and the ships proved excellent provided they were handled by good commanders with drive and verve. On the administrative side, enormous improvements came through the review of the Rigging Establishments; these were the standards laid down for rigging ships of which there had been eighty-eight in 1832, but happily only twenty when Symonds retired. He changed the design of the 'waist' of ships of the line, closing as far as possible the opening amidships on the weather and gun decks, but most surprisingly he introduced steam assistance for deck work on ships of the line. For the lovers of the sailing navy designs of the time he is held esteem for the beautiful and effective brigs and hermaphrodite brigs of the 1830s. These ships, with their lower prismatic coefficients, had poorer inherent stability.

Clearly the First Lord and Symonds saw 'eye-to-eye' on many matters, and the closure of the Portsmouth School of Naval Architecture must have pleased the amateur ship designer who was Surveyor of the Navy. Clearly he disliked not only the young students, but also the school. As he wrote in his memoirs: 'It is said that its members were too proud of their own theories, of which they held a monopoly, to listen with deference to the suggestions of seamen of experience and practical information [*sic*].' How many older graduates in naval architecture can remember while apprentices being at the receiving end of similar jibes from older shipbuilders?

Symonds opposed all new shipbuilding methods; he hated steam power and described iron ships as 'monstrous'. However, he accepted election as a Fellow of the Royal Society in 1835 and promotion to Rear Admiral in 1854. Most remarkable of all, he authorised the laying-down at Devonport of HMS *Sans Pareil* in 1843 using the lines of the ship of the same name captured from the French on the First of June 1794, some forty-nine years earlier.

Symonds was eventually ousted and his place taken by another career seaman, Captain Baldwin Walker, who was in post from 1848 to 1860. The atmosphere changed, old enmities were healed and Walker, an able manager was supported fully by a qualified shipwright Isaac Watts who took over from him later with the designated title of Chief Constructor. As a final irony, the *Sans Pareil* was recalled to the Dockyard and retrofitted with a steam engine and screw.

SOURCES:

Clowes, Sir William Laird
The Royal Navy: A History from the Earliest Times to 1900, Volume 6, London, 1901

Symonds, Sir William (ed J A Sharp)
Memoirs of the Life and Services of Rear Admiral Sir William Symonds etc London, 1858

Sir William Fairbairn
1789–1874

FAIRBAIRN WAS ONE of the first industrialists to manage an engineering concern based on iron fabrication. His birthplace was Kelso in the Scottish Borders, and he spent most of his first fourteen years there. Of farming stock, his father was a pioneer of crop rotation, deep ploughing and agricultural drainage, which were new concepts at the end of the eighteenth century. William was interested in scientific matters and this coupled with a good classical education, ensured he stood out from his peers. At the turn of the century, the family fell upon bad times and William, aged just fourteen, left home on obtaining a millwright apprenticeship at the Percy Main Colliery near North Shields. In his memoirs Fairbairn indicates that with his 'foreign' accent and good education he had a struggle to be accepted, but equally he made many lifelong friends including his up-and-coming contemporary George Stephenson. On completion of his training he set off for London, travelling to the capital on one of the traditional collier brigs. After three difficult years there, he set off for Manchester, the city he was to adopt as his own.

Sir William Fairbairn, 1789–1874. (From The Life of Sir William Fairbairn, London 1877)

With a little luck and some basic engineering skill one could make a living in Manchester, as the mills were developing and required well-motivated staff. Iron was the material of the future and Fairbairn became one of its strongest advocates. Meeting up with a former workmate James Lillie, they agreed to work together and ultimately formed the partnership known as Fairbairn and Lillie. Their first job was an iron conservatory, but work of ever-increasing complexity followed for all parts of the United Kingdom and overseas; some interesting tasks included water wheels and mill machinery. One particularly fortunate contact was with the principal of Messrs Eschers of Zurich, a connection that would remain positive for years. Sadly the relationship between Fairbairn and his partner Lillie deteriorated and around 1830 their business affairs were separated, both men going their own way.

The vast improvements in railway travel were beginning to give canal proprietors cause for concern and one company in particular, the very go-ahead Forth and Clyde instituted tests with various forms of fly boats to improve passage times between the two main cities in Scotland. Around the time of separation from Lillie, William Fairbairn became interested in iron ship construction, and as he travelled great distances it was inevitable that he had visited many of the iron shipbuilding sites in Glasgow, Birkenhead, Staffordshire and London. Working with the Forth and Clyde Company, various experiments were carried out, and although understood imperfectly, it was clear that Fairbairn and the Canal Company were aware of the 'Wave of Translation'. All parties worked towards ensuring the new craft took advantage of this phenomenon and an order was placed with him for a new cross-Scotland passage boat named *Lord Dundas* after their chairman. In June 1831 this new but very small steamer was completed in Manchester and shortly after left Liverpool under her own power for the Clyde. The subsequent story is now part of the rich heritage of British shipbuilding. The *Lord Dundas* was noted overdue at Greenock and after a frantic search was found miles off course, sheltering in the Isle of Man. Fairbairn surmised that the problem was compass deviation caused by a magnetic field having been formed in the hull during construction, and following some empirical tests, he fitted a network of magnets which enabled the compass to give fairly accurate readings. The *Lord Dundas* then proceeded in safety for the Clyde and the entrance to the Canal at Bowling Harbour.

The successful outcome of the delivery voyage of the *Lord Dundas* gave confidence to the new shipbuilder and he proceeded to build a larger vessel, the *Manchester* for use in the North West. Shortly thereafter orders started to flow from many parts of the world for iron steamships to be used in lakes, harbours, rivers and canals. Fairbairn hit upon the idea of erection in the Manchester works, dismantling and then transportation in parts, thereby becoming another of the builders in the 'knockdown' market for which Britain developed a great reputation in the nineteenth century.

The Manchester Works became highly successful and Fairbairn found himself advising clients in every walk of life including heads of state. Despite his previous experiences in London, he felt drawn to the city again and in 1835 land was purchased on the Isle of Dogs with a view to setting up what was named (rather prosaically) the Millwall Ship-Building Factory. This was in operation for a mere ten years during which time over one hundred ships were constructed. During the final two or three years experimental work on structures was carried out. The Isle of Dogs was a financial drain on the resources of Fairbairn and his other companies and the premises were dismantled in 1848 and the land sold. Shortly thereafter it was taken over by **John Scott Russell** who went on to build **Brunel's** *Great Eastern* on the site.

It is of more than passing interest that Fairbairn was able to attract Admiralty orders to his Millwall Factory. He must have made friends and influenced decision-makers as well as ensuring engineers understood the high level of his competence as at that time the Royal Navy placed few orders with new companies, private individuals and few people resident well north of London! One of Fairbairn's main Admiralty jobs was the iron steam frigate *Megaera* (1849) as well as engines for several other frigates. Commercial clients included the Hon. East India Company and the P & O Company, whilst among the prestigious personal customers were the Tsar of Russia and the King of Denmark.

William Fairbairn died in Surrey in August 1874 while visiting close friends. He kept his home base in Manchester till the end. He had honorary doctorates from Edinburgh and Cambridge, as well as the Presidency of the Institution of Mechanical Engineers and of the British Association. In the final analysis, it is probable he would have regarded the use of his name on the riveted swan-necked cranes seen throughout the world as his most appropriate memorial. Fairbairn cranes are now protected structures in the United Kingdom and elsewhere.

SOURCES:

Fairbairn, William, and Pole, William
The Life of Sir William Fairbairn Bart
London, 1877

Robert Napier

1791–1876

ON 21 AUGUST 1815 the Incorporation of Hammer-men of the City of Glasgow admitted the 24-year-old Robert Napier to their fellowship. In later years, while speaking to several thousand employees, the man destined to be known as 'the Father of Clyde Shipbuilding' admitted this to be the proudest and the most important moment of his professional life. In a period of over fifty years Robert Napier left an indelible mark on British shipbuilding; he was one of the first in the north of Britain to build ships for the Hon. East India Company and later for the Admiralty, he was instrumental in enabling Samuel Cunard to form the British and North American Steam Packet Company, he introduced systematic testing of ferrous products, and what gave him the greatest

Robert Napier, 1791–1876, the Father of Clyde Shipbuilding. (From The Life of Robert Napier of West Shandon, *Edinburgh* 1904)

pleasure was that his Govan shipyard trained over twenty men who were to set up new shipyards in the late nineteenth century.

The Napier family were established blacksmiths and millwrights. The grandfather Robert Napier was married to Helen Denny (of the famous shipbuilding family); he had three sons, the oldest and the youngest being John and James who operated a blacksmith business in Dumbarton, and the middle son Robert who was blacksmith to the Duke of Argyll at Inveraray. All three men in turn had sons who rose to eminence in the engineering profession.

While not the subject of this short biography, it is important that mention be made of David Napier, the son of the oldest brother John, as he had a great influence on his cousin. David was born in Dumbarton in 1790, but moved later to Glasgow, where his father set up a foundry. The management of this business fell on his young shoulders on the death of his father, and remarkably for a man in his early twenties, received from **Henry Bell** in 1811 the order for the boiler and castings of the pioneer steamship *Comet* then under construction at Port Glasgow. This placed him at the forefront of marine engineering, a position that he and his cousin Robert were to hold for half a century. With increased business he built works at Camlachie and later at Lancefield Quay, both of which produced many fine engines (the hulls being subcontracted), arguably the most successful machinery being for the large timber-hulled paddle steamer *United Kingdom* of 1826, which sailed from Glasgow to Leith with 150 passengers in sixty-five hours. Incidentally, he instituted early model hull testing procedures at the Camlachie Burn in Glasgow. A serious boiler accident in 1835 led to health problems and, deciding to move south to London, he leased Lancefield to Robert Napier and transferred his interests to a site on the Isle of Dogs. He continued to produce engineering work of excellence until his death in 1869.

Robert was also born in Dumbarton* in 1791. Originally destined for the Church, by the end of his schooling he decided to serve an apprenticeship under his father. There were no formal documents drawn up until a Royal Navy press gang suddenly appeared in Dumbarton, and then indentures as a blacksmith and millwright were organised rather hurriedly. The Church was not denied a minister as Robert's brother Peter graduated in 1810 and was ordained into the Church of Scotland.

Robert Napier's real work began in 1821 when he leased Camlachie from his cousin; with little capital and few machine tools he set up an engine works. He was fortunate in employing David Elder as manager, a man who was to remain with him for years (his son founded **John Elder** and Company, later known as Fairfield and then Govan Shipbuilders and whose widow endowed the first ever university chair of naval architecture). Napier had various engine works in the Glasgow district, but in 1841 purchased land in Govan where he commenced building both ships and engines. In a life as colourful and diverse as that of Robert Napier it is possible only to touch on two or three incidents, each of which led to the coming of age of the River Clyde.

A dispute at the august Royal Yacht Squadron created a situation in which Napier became the main beneficiary. In 1827, the Northern Yacht Club (now the Royal Northern and Clyde Yacht Club) offered a cup for the fastest steam vessel on a three-hour course on the Firth of Clyde, and two ships engined by Napier came first and second. This intrigued a member of the Royal Yacht Squadron, Mr T Assheton Smith, who petitioned the Squadron to admit steam vessels but to no avail, and the said gentleman then resigned his membership. After two brief meetings with Napier he ordered a steam paddle yacht *Menai* which was delivered in 1830, and was to be the first of nine yachts, both paddle and screw for this intrepid steam enthusiast. Through introductions and recommendations from Assheton Smith, Napier received an order from the Hon. East India Company for their 646-ton paddle steamer *Berenice*, which was delivered in 1836. This was a major break through, being the first 'quasi-government' contract to be placed away from the rather protected shipyards and dockyards of southern England. Being a successful ship, the Admiralty took notice and decided to entrust new construction work to Napier. The first orders came in 1839 for steam machinery to be fitted in the wooden paddle sloops *Vesuvius* and *Stromboli*, which had been built at Sheerness and Portsmouth respectively. Work soon followed from the governments of Turkey, France, Denmark and Russia, as well as from overseas dominions.

In 1839, negotiations commenced between Robert Napier and the charismatic 'bluenose'** Samuel Cunard for the construction of a class of ships to carry the Royal Mail from the UK to Canada and the United States. The outcome is well-known, with the building of the hulls of *Acadia*, *Britannia*, *Caledonia* and *Columbia* at various Clyde shipyards with machinery supplied from Napier. As in all matters, work does not always go to plan and the second ship in the series, *Britannia*, had the honour of commencing the Cunard Line's illustrious 150-year history. In some ways it is surprising that the line is known by the name Cunard, as 80 per cent of the equity was raised by Robert Napier and his friends, the bulk coming from business associates in London, Liverpool and Glasgow. Napier is remembered however by the Cunard funnel markings of red with black bands, as this was the trade mark of Robert Napier and Company, following on the established Clydeside tradition that funnels were an engineer's supply item.

Shortly after the first four Cunarders were completed, Napier tried his hand at shipbuilding using a small site in Dumbarton. However in 1841 he acquired ground in Govan shipyard, and from then until his death in 1867 over 160 ships were built and engined, vessels that included the magnificent Cunarder PS *Persia* of 1855 and the Dutch navy's ironclad *De Buffel* which remains afloat to this day. In 1850 additional ground was acquired becoming known as the New Yard and more and more work was channelled there. The Old Yard passed to the London and Glasgow Engineering and Iron Shipbuilding Company and later was sold to Harland and Wolff. On Robert Napier's death the New Yard became part of the Beardmore Group, but continued under the name of Robert Napier until 1900. One of the directors was **Dr A C Kirk** and with his guidance some wonderful ships were produced including the ground-breaking SS *Aberdeen* of 1881 and the luxurious Orient Liner *Ophir* which was used as a Royal Yacht in 1900.

Robert Napier's wife Isabella (who was David Napier's sister) died in 1875 after fifty-seven years of very happy marriage. From then on Robert withdrew from many of his interests and after a short illness died the following year. Thousands of people lined Dumbarton's streets for the funeral and 1,500 workmen travelled from Glasgow by train to pay their respects. Fittingly he was buried in the churchyard of Dumbarton Parish Church, a few metres from the River Leven and close to the Shipyard of Denny's. It has been remarked that while he received many foreign honours (including the Danish honour of Knight Commander of the Dannebrog), no British award was forthcoming. Napier was a fairly humble man, but it is more than likely that he would have accepted an award from the Queen – possibly the political climate in the United Kingdom in the mid-nineteenth century, and possibly to this day, cannot recognise the real men of merit.

SOURCES:
Bowen, Frank C
'The Govan Yard – "Shipbuilders of Other Days"'
Shipbuilding and Shipping Record
15 February 1951
Napier, James
Life of Robert Napier of West Shandon
Edinburgh, 1904

* The 'Ancient Capital of Strathclyde' is a Royal Burgh. The name is spelt: 'Dumbarton'. The surrounding county covering some of Scotland's most beautiful parts is 'Dunbartonshire'.
** 'Bluenose' – the name given to a native of Nova Scotia.

William Henry Webb
1816–1899

IN A RECENT TRIBUTE to this great naval architect and shipbuilder, one of the alumni of the Webb Institute said that William Webb's life had three distinct periods; first the years of training, second the years spent establishing himself in his profession and finally the period when he returned all that he could to the community that had supported and nurtured him.

William H Webb, 1816–1899. *(Author)*

William Webb was born in New York in 1816, the son of the well-known shipbuilder Isaac Webb, proprietor of Isaac Webb and Co., a yard later renamed Webb and Allen. William's parents had high aspirations for him, and it required much determination on his side to be allowed to serve an apprenticeship (of six years) at his father's yard. At school and in the shipyard he displayed an above-average understanding of mathematics and scientific matters which ensured that by the end of his training he was recognised as an eminent designer and calculator. In 1840, he set off on the equivalent of a 'gap year', a prolonged visit to Scotland and in particular to the shipyards of the Clyde. Here disappointment awaited him, as this eagerly-anticipated visit had to be curtailed owing to the untimely death of his father.

William returned to New York and on examining the shipyard records discovered that Webb and Allen was virtually insolvent. With great courage, he met all the creditors, satisfied them with his future plans and then re-organised the shipyard and made arrangements for all debts to be paid off. In 1843, he bought out his late father's partner John Allen, and then renamed the yard William H Webb and Co. This shipyard was to continue building ships in timber for the next twenty-six years, when Webb decided that the days of timber construction were over and closed the yard. Between his father's death in 1840 and the closure in 1869 a total of over 130 hulls were constructed, many of which held the record for being the largest or longest ship in the world at the time of launch.

The Californian Gold Rush was an impetus for East Coast shipowners and shipbuilders, as there was no direct rail link to San Francisco from New York until 1869. Indeed many ship owners had more vessels than needed as often they had ships anchored in San Francisco, their crews having deserted. A large number of Webb's ships were clippers, designed and built for the speediest possible voyage from New York and the east coast to California. On reading through the lists of Yankee Clippers, it is amazing to see the name Webb appear time after time for ships described as 'clipper', 'medium clipper' and then the 'ultimate extreme clipper'. The use of the prefix 'extreme' indicates a hull with unusually fine endings or rise of floor. It has never been defined officially, but is most easily explained by describing such ships as having an unusually low prismatic co-efficient.

One remarkable product of the yard was the medium clipper *Intrepid*, launched in 1856 for American owners who placed her on both the Californian and Chinese routes. On her third and last voyage, she left Macao on 17 March 1860 and was making a good passage when she went aground in the Dutch East Indies. Shortly thereafter she was attacked by Malay pirates, and battles ensued over several days, with one crewman being lost and many pirates killed. Ultimately the crew were saved and put ashore while a salvage vessel from Singapore protected by two Dutch gunboats salvaged a tiny part of the cargo valued at $2,000. Nothing much has changed in that part of the world!

Webb built several steamships including a paddle vessel which was the first to trade with New Orleans on the Mississippi delta, and the yard built the US ironclad *Dunderberg*, then the largest wooden hull in the world. The end of the American Civil War lead to the mass disposal of surplus ships – a mistake the United States Government did not repeat in 1946. In 1865 and for some years, the market for ships was flat and all the yards including Webb's were hard pressed to find work, even at bargain basement prices. In 1869, William Webb built his last ship, the wooden steamship *Charles H Marshall* named appropriately after his oldest and most respected client. The downturn in the market coupled with clear indications that wooden shipbuilding was in decline decided William to end the shipbuilding part of his life.

Here the third 'chapter' started: at the age of fifty-three, Webb was now a very wealthy man, and started to invest (with mixed results) in transport, real estate and other trades including that of the extraction of nitrates from guano. On several occasions he was asked to stand as Mayor of New York, but declined, although he did serve on several committees including a key one aimed at local political reform. As the years passed he concentrated his mind on setting up an academy for aspiring naval architects and shipbuilders, and this was inaugurated in 1894, and as we know remains a successful college to this day. Premises were obtained in the Bronx, and the Webb Academy founded with the objective of giving free tuition to carefully selected American students, as well as free accommodation for 'old shipbuilders'. The original numbers of academic staff, students and pensioners amounted to about 400. Webb had many other feathers in his cap including being a founder of the Society of Naval Architects and Marine Engineers. He died in New York in 1899.

Shortly after the Second World War, the college, now named the Webb Institute, moved to a site more suitable for expansion at Glen Cove NY and at that time the retention of retired shipbuilders was phased out. The Institute now has about a hundred undergraduates working on a four-year Bachelors course on ship sciences.

SOURCES:

Chapelle, Howard I
The Search for Speed under Sail 1700–1855
New York, 1967

Howe, O T and Matthews, F C
American Clipper Ships 1833–1858
Marine Research Society, Salem Mass, 1926–7
(since republished).

Frederic Sauvage

1786–1857

THE PRINCIPLE OF THE screw propeller was debated for many years, and as so many claims for its invention were made it is difficult to apportion credit to the many names involved. By chronological precedence, the honour should go to the Frenchman Frederic Sauvage, but in terms of historical impact, the real contenders are John Ericsson and Sir Francis Petit Smith, whose biographies follow.

Frederic Sauvage was a boatbuilder in Honfleur on the coast of Normandy and facing across the Seine to Le Havre. At his own expense, tests were carried out in 1832 on a screw propeller of which few details survive. The French navy indicated they had no interest in the matter and sad to relate Sauvage found himself destitute and for a while was incarcerated in a debtors' prison. He died in 1857.

A small plaque on the wall of a house in Honfleur has the inscription: '*A la memoire de Frederic Sauvage qui inventa à Honfleur et en fit Les Premiers Essais dans le vieux basin 1832.*' In 1909 a book *The Screw Propeller* by A E Seaton a former lecturer at the Royal Naval College, Greenwich, was published. It records about a dozen screw propellers, but sadly does not record the work of Sauvage.

SOURCES:
Seaton, A E
The Screw Propeller
London, 1909

John Ericsson

1803–1889

JOHN ERICSSON IS remembered as one of the greatest inventors and researchers of the nineteenth century. While it is almost impossible to ascribe the invention of the screw propeller to any one individual, Ericsson must take his place as one of the two or three great leaders in this endeavour. In eighty-six years he left a string of discoveries and a legacy of innovative engineering.

Born at Farnebo in south-eastern Sweden, at the age of thirteen Ericsson enlisted as a cadet in a military engineering unit then working on the Göta Canal. His work was good and he was noticed by his superiors, including Thomas Telford who was advising on the construction. On good recommendations he joined the Swedish army four years later, ultimately becoming an engineer officer. His wide-ranging experience in canal construction marked him out and his first posting was as a surveyor in the military cartographic unit. In 1826, while still a very young man, he resigned his commission and set off for London to pursue a career in mechanical engineering, which from the very outset involved him in a wide range of state-of-the-art engineering developments.

It is recorded that his first invention was an engine. While unsuccessful, this work awakened an interest in steam engines which led to his involvement in the Rainhill Locomotive Trials held by the Liverpool and Manchester Railway Company over seven days in October 1829. The three best-performing entries were Stephenson's *Rocket*, Hackworth's *Sans Pareil* and the *Novelty* entered by Ericsson and his colleague Braithwaite. The *Rocket* won the competition on account of its reliability, but it and Ericsson's *Novelty* regularly achieved the then unheard-of speed of upwards of 32km/h (20mph). Further experiments took place in 1834 with the development of a design for a hot air engine, although the fate of this invention is not known.

In 1836, John Ericsson took out a patent for a marine screw propeller, just a few weeks after his great rival **Francis Pettit Smith** had done the same. The two men were now in open competition and both were wooing the Admiralty for its custom. Smith's first propeller was in the form of an Archimedian screw fitted in an aperture of the skeg or deadwood, whilst Ericsson's first offering was of twin contra-rotating discs on a single shaft, each with helical blades. It was from these similar ideas that the modern propeller with independent blades developed. Ericsson demonstrated his invention to the Admiralty Board in 1837 by using a small screw-propelled vessel to tow the 600-ton ship *Toronto* against the Thames tidal current, and then the Admiralty barge (with a suitable party on board) from Somerset House to Blackwall and back; he demonstrated that with a low line of shaft, the main engine could be below the waterline and the propeller would have some limited protection in action. In the initial design, Ericsson's propeller was abaft the rudder, and the shaft passed through a fore and aft tunnel constructed into the rudder. This reduced the maximum rudder angle and with an unimpeded propeller race going directly aft, reduced the quality of the steering. In general, Smith's rival campaign was the more successful and shortly thereafter Ericsson set off for America where he hoped to interest their government in armour plating, screw propulsion and other matters concerning ordnance.

American involvement in screw propulsion had been evident in 1837, when a Captain Robert F Stockton came to Britain to take delivery of a 21.3m

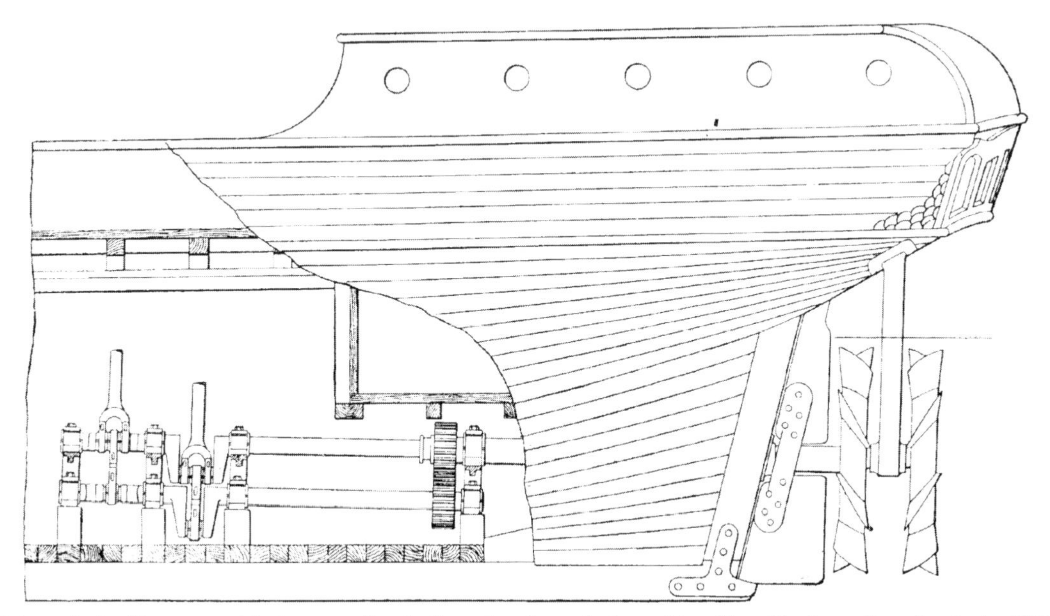

Ericsson's double screw with the propeller shaft passing through the rudder. (From *The Screw Propeller*, London 1909)

(70ft) steamer with an Ericsson-type propeller. This ship crossed the Atlantic unaided and then was put into service on the Delaware Canal. Stockton and Ericsson teamed up and remarkably were given a free hand to construct three warships, the first of which, the USS *Princeton*, is regarded as the first screw-propelled warship in the world. Two ships followed in later years, including the USS *Monitor*, a vessel which would later give its name to a new breed of warship built for coastal bombardment.

The design of the *Monitor* came through Ericsson's proposals to the French for a near-watertight and armoured floating battery with enclosed turrets to be used in the Crimean War. The French rejected the scheme and the idea had time to mature until 1861 when Ericsson persuaded the United States Government to build just such a ship. The *Monitor* was 'ground-breaking' in every way. She was mastless, had a flat-bottomed hull, drew about 2.5m (8ft 2in) with about 0.5m (1ft 7in) of free-board. She had reciprocating steam machinery and was screw-propelled. The construction was mostly of iron, although there was some timber, mostly supporting the heavy band of armour around the waterline. The most revolutionary idea was that of a revolving gun turret enabling her to fire in any direction without altering course. Her encounter in 1862 with the Confederate ironclad *Merrimac*, a cut-down and armoured wooden frigate, is one of the most celebrated battles in naval history.

In later years Ericsson turned his attention to the development of heavy guns and on a more contemporary note he studied renewable energy as well as alternative national energy sources. One of his most ingenious inventions was a gauge that could be dropped over the side to measure depth. At the end of a long and productive life, he died as an American citizen in New York in 1889. In 1891 his body was returned to Sweden aboard the cruiser USS *Baltimore*.

SOURCES:

Church, W C
The Life of John Ericsson
London, 1891

Hovgaard, William
Modern History of Warships
London, 1920

Seaton, A E
The Screw Propeller
London, 1909

Smiles, Samuel
Lives of the Engineers
reprinted London, 2006

Sir Francis Pettit Smith

1808–1874

IT CAN BE SAID WITH fairness that the ubiquitous screw propeller came about through the imagination and the efforts of three men, namely the luckless Frenchman **Frederic Sauvage**, the Swedish émigré to America **John Ericsson** and the Man of Kent **Francis Pettit Smith**. Smith and Ericsson worked independently of one another, and came up with similar solutions at exactly the same time. Smith's patent for a screw propeller was registered on 31 May 1836, a mere six weeks before Ericsson's!

Francis Smith was born in Kent, where his father was a postmaster. His education was good but rudimentary, and on leaving school he worked as what has been described as a 'grazing farmer', first in the beautiful Romney Marsh and later at Hendon in Middlesex. From his earliest years he had been fascinated by ships and it is said that in 1834 he built a small self-propelled model with some form of screw turned by a clockwork spring. One has to admire his dedication and conviction, as in the following year he carried out more advanced model experiments and in 1836 applied for his patent on screw propulsion. Sadly, there are no known records of his tests, but as his story will tell, he was one of a very small number of men who influenced ship design in a significant way.

Smith was a devoted researcher with a single-minded desire to find a method of driving ships that would be an improvement on side paddle-wheels. His enthusiasm was contagious, and soon he had sufficient financial support from friends and admirers for serious experimentation to commence. His test bed was a 6-ton launch powered by a single-cylinder steam engine with stroke of

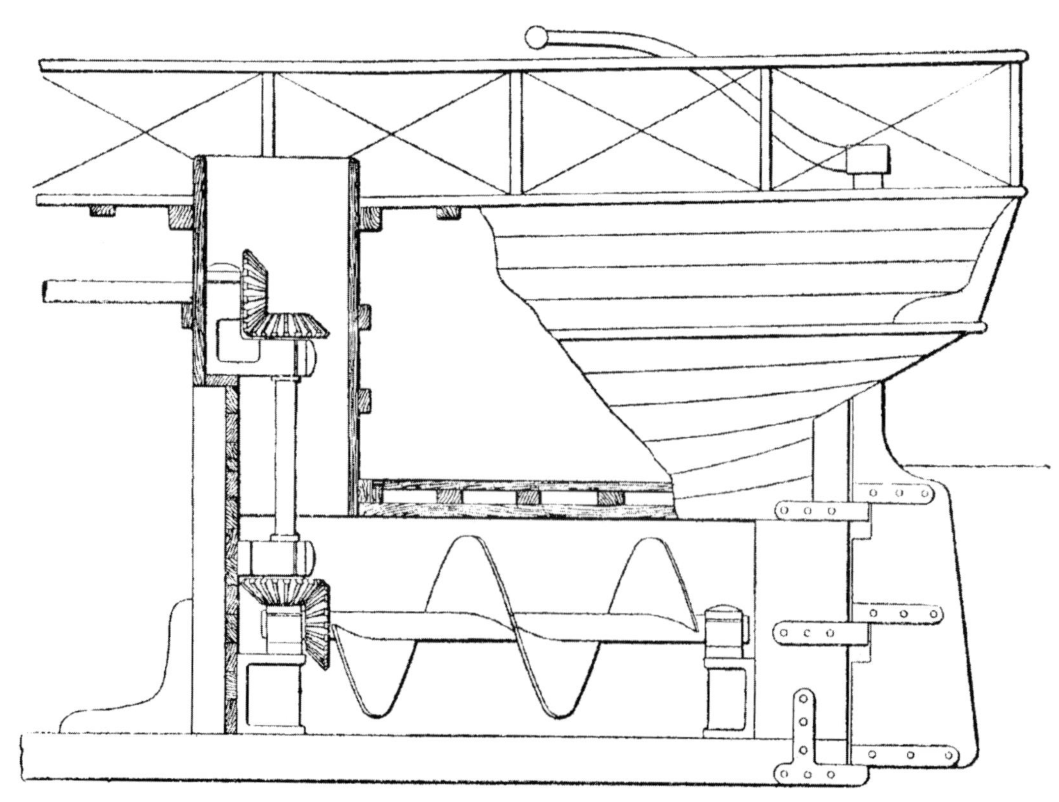

Francis Pettit Smith's first attempt with a screw propeller, which harked back to Archimedes' screw.
(From The Screw Propeller, London 1909)

375mm (14.7in). It had a threaded screw of two revolutions manufactured of wood, and it operated regularly on the Paddington Canal, where unexpectedly, an accident broke off half the propeller. This was fortuitous as it enabled the ship to travel faster, and was the birth of Smith's consideration of a two- or three-bladed propeller where the blades generated a helix in the water as they turned. This little steamer, aptly named *F P Smith*, made one or two lengthy voyages, one being an adventurous coastwise trip from London to Folkestone, a distance close on 160km (100 miles).

In 1839, Smith joined with a group of investors who purchased his rights to the screw propeller, under the name of the Screw Propeller Company. In November 1838 they launched a most elegant but fairly small steam yacht (a mere 39m [128ft] overall) named *Archimedes*. It was designed at first to have a single-thread screw just over 2m (6ft 7in) in diameter, but later was changed to a new configuration of two propeller blades. The propeller was placed in an aperture in the skeg, anticipating twentieth-century practice. The machinery operated at 26rpm, but the propeller was geared up and turned at 139rpm. This must be about the first demonstration ship ever built; it was a great success and toured the United Kingdom introducing shipbuilders and owners to the screw. Particular attention was paid in Glasgow and on the Mersey, but of especial importance was the reaction of **Isambard Kingdom Brunel** who decided that the *Great Britain*, then under construction at Bristol, should be changed from side paddle to screw propeller.

The *Archimedes* had at least one international voyage, to Oporto, but overall she was not a commercial success, and the Screw Propeller Company ran at a loss. Smith was retained as an adviser by the British Government until 1850, but being in financial difficulties was granted a small stipend by Lord Palmerston. His position recovered over the years and by 1860 had become curator of the Patent Museum in South Kensington and lived in considerable style in Dulwich in South London. He was knighted in 1871, and moved to South Kensington where he died in 1874.

Postscript

Many people in the late eighteenth and early nineteenth centuries suggested new means of driving ships, including De Quet, Daniel Bernoulli and Bramah. William Lyttleton patented a triple-headed screw in the 1790s and in 1800 a two-bladed propeller was invented by Edward Shorter. It is known that a small twin-screw launch operated successfully in New York around 1804, having been designed and built by a Colonel John Stevens.

SOURCES:
Penn, Geoffrey
'Up Funnel, Down Screw!'
London, 1955
Winchester, Clarence (ed)
Marine Engines and their Story (Shipping Wonders of the World Volume 1)
London, c1938

Richard Green

1803–1863

REFERRED TO IN THE biography of **William Pile** of Sunderland, Richard Green was a remarkable man who has been described variously, but correctly, as shipowner, shipbuilder and philanthropist. As Richard Green had come from a wealthy and privileged background, quite different from that of William Pile, it is clear that their friendship and mutual respect must have grown out of professional admiration coupled with the fact both were decent men.

The Blackwall Yard on the Thames had a long and distinguished history, and by the beginning of the nineteenth century it had become the largest private shipyard in the world. Through various commercial transactions, aided and abetted by for tuitous marriage settlements, the yard was owned by two families – the Wigrams and the Greens, and they continued together as Wigram and Green until 1843 when the yard was divided, the western part becoming Wigram and Sons, while the less historic eastern part became R & H Green. In 1910 this became R & H Green and Silley Weir Ltd which merged with the London Graving Dock in 1977 becoming River Thames Shiprepairers and part of British Shipbuilders. The company was closed and

John Lynn's illustration of the East Indiaman *Vernon*, built and owned by Richard Green of Blackwall, outward bound and off the Isle of Wight in 1839. The *Vernon* was an early example of a sailing vessel fitted with auxiliary steam power to assist with deck work, and the smokestack from her 30hp engine is clearly visible. (*© National Maritime Museum, Greenwich, PT2634*)

the yard had discontinued all work by the late 1980s, bringing to an end a 350-year tradition of shipbuilding.

Reverting to Richard Green, he joined the Blackwall yard as a young man, and later along with his half-brother Henry managed first Wigram and Green, and latterly R & H Green. They built the last ships for the Hon East India Company and then developed vessels for the long-haul trades of the then expanding British Empire. The restrained style and high quality of their ships earned them the name 'The Blackwall Frigates'. As a shipowner he took an especial interest in the Australian trade and just before his death had started to study the possibilities of running regular voyages to China.

His work and gifts to the Merchant Navy and to East London are legendary, and include the endowment of the Sailors' Home at Poplar as well as the Merchant Seaman's Orphan Asylum. The gifts included funding for the Dreadnought Seaman's Hospital at Greenwich, an organisation now subsumed within the National Health Service. Another matter that exercised his mind and time was the setting up of a training school for Merchant Navy Officers, and just one year before his death the Thames Marine Officer Training School was established, an organisation which in the 1870s became known as HMS *Worcester*.

SOURCES:
Green, H and Wigram, R
Chronicles of Blackwall Yard
London, 1881

John Laird
1805–1874

IN 1810 WILLIAM LAIRD of Greenock moved south to Birkenhead to found a small ship repair business at Herculaneum Dock, and in 1824 this was extended by the establishment of the Birkenhead Ironworks in the West Float area. His two sons, John Laird and Macgregor Laird, took professional training before joining the firm and going on to make successful careers, one in shipping and the other in shipbuilding. Macgregor Laird, the younger brother, studied at Edinburgh University before joining the company for a short time, but left to devote his life to West Africa and the shipping companies serving the Guinea Gulf. His endeavours helped to form the Liverpool shipping company of Elder Dempster, where the **Elder** part of the name was from the well-known Glasgow shipbuilding family.

The founder of iron shipbuilding on the Mersey, John trained as a solicitor before joining his father in 1828 and was to remain with the company until around 1861 when his political activities forced him to sever connections with the industry. The first 'new buildings' came with an order in 1829 for three iron barges for the Inland Steam Navigation Company of Ireland, and delivered within a couple of years – greatly to the credit of the fledgling shipbuilders as the first ever iron ship, the *Vulcan*, was less than ten years old. In 1833, the same owners entrusted them with the paddle steamer *Lady Lansdowne*, which with a length of 40m (131ft 3in) and breadth of over 5m (16ft 4in) was just too big to enter the Irish canal system. She was built at Birkenhead, launched and tested on the Mersey, and then dismantled and delivered to the banks of the River Shannon for re-erection and subsequent launching. It is probable that this example of 'knock-down' iron shipbuilding, was the first in the world, and was the precursor of what became later an important constituent of British shipbuilding output.

John Laird's enthusiasm for iron construction knew no bounds and further knock-down jobs followed including a vessel called *John Randolph* which was the first iron steamer to operate in the United States. In the 1830s, the Hon. East India Company ordered two vessels named *Tigris* and *Euphrates* which were taken to the Persian Gulf to test the feasibility of taking the Indian Mail up the rivers instead of the Red Sea. While unsuccessful, they served a useful purpose in introducing prestigious owners to the shipyard now run by John Laird. Watertight iron transverse bulkhead were introduced on the innovative cross-Channel steam packet *Garryowen* which was built in 1834 for Dublin owners, and which confirmed Laird's as a market leader in this form of construction.

Despite considerable effort, the Admiralty were slow to adopt iron construction and to the great frustration of John Laird placed no work with him until the late 1830s, when he was asked to build the cross-Channel mail steamer *Dover*. (In those days, ships for the Royal Mail were under the control of the naval authorities.) Following the construction of three small expedition ships, the Admiralty decided to build a larger vessel in the North West of England and asked Laird to design and price an auxiliary steam frigate, which culminated in the order for a 1,400-ton vessel to be named *Vulcan*. The damage done to iron warship hulls during gunnery trials had shocked observers and orders were given for the *Vulcan*, then on the building berth, to be re-classified as a steam paddle troopship and renamed *Birkenhead*. Troop accommodation was fitted throughout, and more significantly accesses cut through the watertight bulkheads. On the night of 25 February 1852 with 638 persons aboard she struck a rock 50 miles from Cape Town and sank quickly with the loss of 445 lives. The '*Birkenhead* story' has become one of the legends of the British Army as through the determination of the officer commanding troops Lieutenant Colonel Seaton of the 74th Highlanders (now the Royal Highland Fusiliers), the surviving soldiers manned pumps and helped launch the lamentably few lifeboats. All the children and women aboard were saved, but almost every soldier died at his post.

Another well-known vessel was the 23m (75ft) Zambezi river steamer *Ma Roberts* built for Dr David

Livingstone's work in Central Africa. From the outset it was controversial, being built of steel which suffered from the corrosive effect of the river waters and the constant abrasion when running aground. Several reasons for this have been mooted, but without doubt the demands on this vessel were too high bringing about her short life of a mere eighteen months.

The Crimean War enabled Lairds to re-establish themselves with the Royal Navy and at one time they were producing either a new gunboat or mortar-boat (both of iron and of wood) at the rate of one per week. Shortly thereafter, and no doubt through family connections, work began to flow from the various companies operating on the UK to West Africa trade, and John Laird took the opportunity to extend the ground of the shipyard taking a lease from the Harbour Board for land at Monk's Ferry. The Birkenhead shoreline began to change as the new shipyard, complete with five dry-docks, started to come into operation in 1858, and Birkenhead began to be recognised as a community in its own right, achieving borough status in 1861. This change enabled the town to return a Member of Parliament, and few will be surprised to learn that John Laird was returned to Westminster for the Conservatives.

Around that time negotiations had commenced for the building of the Confederate commerce raider *Alabama*, another ship destined to become world-famous. Whether it was through pressure of parliamentary duties, or (more likely) an embarrassing conflict of interest with a ship being built for the Confederacy is debatable, but Laird resigned from the shipyard management, handing authority over to his sons at around that time. He died in Birkenhead in 1874 following a riding accident and while still an MP.

SOURCES:
Branigan, Denis
'John Laird: Iron Shipbuilder'
Sea Breezes
(October 1974)
Davies, P N
The Trade Makers: Elder Dempster in West Africa 1852–1972
London, 1973
Hocking, Charles
Dictionary of Disasters at Sea during the Age of Steam
2 vols (Lloyd's Register, London, 1969)

Sir Marc Brunel

1769–1849

AFTER SOME ADVENTUROUS years, Marc Isambard Brunel was to invent a machine that was of incalculable service to the Royal Navy. His background was remarkable; born in Normandy, he joined the French Navy when he was around seventeen and served six years as a junior officer. In 1793 he set off for the United States, where in less than six years he became a land surveyor, took American citizenship and then was appointed Chief Engineer to the City of New York.

At a dinner party he learned that the Royal Navy had an annual requirement for 100,000 blocks for use in the rigging of its ships. At that time all of these were manufactured by hand. After only a brief period of consideration, he resigned from his job in New York and sailed for Britain, arriving early in 1799. There he discussed the idea of a block-making machine with the manufacturer Henry Maudslay of London and ultimately placed an order with him for manufacture. The machine was a success and in the course of time several were made for supply to the naval dockyards, and some are preserved today by the Science Museum, London.

The Maudslay and Brunel families were to have a long and friendly relationship, and the two Brunels, father and son would place work with Maudslay, Sons and Field. Marc Brunel had a long and eventful life which included inventing a machine to mass-produce boots for soldiers (it was operated by disabled veterans) and he invented the system of tunnelling using a shield. This idea was conceived while studying the teredo worm, *Teredo Navalis*, which gnaws its way through ship timbers and then lines the tunnel or worm hole with its own hard-setting excreta. From this, the system of digging with a shield and then back-lining was developed and used with conspicuous success in the construction of the Rotherhithe Tunnel.

Marc Brunel married a British lady, Sophie Kingdom, whom he had first met in Rouen and they had one son, the redoubtable **Isambard Kingdom Brunel**.

SOURCES:
Gilbert, K R
The Portsmouth Blockmaking Machinery
Science Museum, London, 1965
Steel, David
Steel's Art of Rigging
London, 1818

Isambard Kingdom Brunel

1806–1859

IT IS SAID THAT THE young I K Brunel was told by his father that 'the alphabet of the engineer' was the art of rapid and accurate drawing. Judging by the scale and quality of his work Brunel took this lesson to heart.

Brunel has both adulators and detractors. On the one hand he was difficult to work with, he observed the social conventions of the Victorian age, and was distant and authoritarian whilst at all times ensuring that his public image was one of confidence and self-assurance. He was inflexible with both his rivals and his clients, which at times was to the detriment of financial survival. On the other hand he was a dedicated engineer showing considerable humanity towards those associated with him at work, and, almost single-handed, he oversaw some of the most complex engineering feats of the mid-nineteenth century. A most admirable quality was loyalty to the profession of engineering; he regarded membership of the Institution of Civil Engineers (then the sole engineering institution in the United Kingdom) as a badge of honour. It is interesting to note that he never sought patent protection for his ideas: he regarded the engineer's work as one of service to the community.

His father **Sir Marc Isambard Brunel** was a Frenchman who had later taken American citizenship and his mother Sophie (née Kingdom) was British. To ensure proper identification, the convention has arisen to call the father Sir Marc Brunel and the son Isambard Kingdom Brunel. Born in Portsea, Hampshire his early years were in the south of England with education for some years at a private boarding school in Hove. At the age of fourteen, he was sent to college at Caen, France and later to the Lycée Henri-Quatre in Paris. An apprenticeship with Louis Breguet, a renowned maker of chronometers and watches, followed. On returning to Britain in the 1820s he worked both in his father's office and also that of the engineers Maudslay, Sons and Field, all leading to the great task he held between 1825 and 1828 as resident engineer for his father's monumental work of driving a tunnel under the Thames at Rotherhithe. This task, which lay dormant for some years was not completed until 1843, and undoubtedly it was the 'finishing school' in practical engineering that would make I K Brunel a giant in his field.

Writers have found that what with Brunel's works being so numerous and wide ranging, it is difficult to decide on whether to deal with them in a chronological, geographic or subject basis. Here the matter will be dealt with differently, but with the ships discussed at the end. In 1831 Brunel was appointed engineer for the Clifton Suspension Bridge in Bristol; he completed his design work, but for various reasons the bridge was not finished until after his death. This enabled him to feel confident about bridge design and many were to be built according to his drawings as far apart as Chepstow in Wales to the Royal Albert Bridge at Saltash in the west of England. The Saltash Bridge was of tubular design, an idea that Brunel must have adopted from the work of George Stephenson, the 'father of the railways'. Brunel also designed several timber bridges which were used along the railways, these have been documented and are superb designs showing his understanding of working in wood. His connections with Bristol would remain for the rest of his life, and among them was work for the improvement of Bristol Docks, an organisation with the strange appellation of the Floating Harbour.

In 1833 his work with railways commenced with his acceptance of the post of engineer to the Bristol Railway, an organisation later to become the Great Western Railway (GWR). By 1838 the first westward 'road' was open from Paddington in London, and just six years later the track from London to Exeter was open. Brunel not only designed and supervised the civil engineering

The celebrated 1857 photograph of the building of the *Great Eastern* at the Isle of Dogs, London. It is believed that the man in the top hat is John Scott Russell, the shipbuilder. Her gross tonnage was not surpassed until 1901.
(© National Maritime Museum, Greenwich, B1699-A)

work, but he was in full charge of mechanical engineering and even the architecture of stations and other railway facilities. He believed in large scale operations and instituted the broad gauge of 7ft 0in (2.13m) for the railways under his control: Gauge is the dimension between the inside faces of railway tracks, which for reasons of tradition in the United Kingdom is 4ft 8½in (1.43m). The GWR was broad gauge throughout, and there is no technical fault in this, but it did cause problems at the interface with other railway companies. Such problems do not go away and finally the British government had to act. A Royal Commission was appointed to investigate the matter and their decision, ratified by Act of Parliament in 1846 required all railways to adopt the standard gauge. In time the Great Western Railway had to comply and quite amazingly most railways throughout the world now use the standard gauge which (for reasons unknown) was first introduced in the coal pit sidings of north-east England.

The railway work re-introduced Brunel to tunnels, and one of his most remarkable undertakings was the Box Tunnel of the GWR. Here a two-mile tunnel driven on a fairly high declivity had to be cut and part of it lined with bricks. It is known that 5,500 bricks were required for every foot of advance, and assuming three quarters of the tunnel requiring lining, then over 35 million bricks were required. Brunel took this in his stride and employed 100 men to make them locally. He accepted services and logistics as part of the role of the engineer. One other railway venture that must be mentioned is the 'Atmospheric Railway' in South Devon, an unsuccessful attempt at pulling rolling stock along a railway line using the suction from a vacuum tube placed between the rails.

In addition to all the work above, Brunel found time to design three steamships, all for an offshoot of the Great Western Railway Company which was planning to extend its reach across the Atlantic. The first was the wooden paddle steamer *Great Western*, produced by Patterson and Mercer of Bristol in 1836, a soundly-built vessel with iron diagonal strapping on the inside of her frames and with side lever machinery supplied by Maudslay, Sons and Field of London. It had been hoped she would be the first vessel to cross the Atlantic under steam, but through bad luck, was beaten by just days when the slower *Sirius* arrived in New York from Cork. His second ship the *Great Britain* of 1843 was a masterpiece, and is now almost fully restored in her original building berth in Bristol. Built of iron a mere twenty-four years after **Thomas Wilson**'s *Vulcan*, the *Great Britain* proved the efficacy of iron in seagoing craft, and paved the way for larger ships and therefore more efficient trading by sea. No ship before or since has so proved the value and longevity of iron, as first she was aground at Dundrum Bay in Ireland for the best part of a year, and despite fears of her loss on this shore, she stood up to the battering of the seas and was salvaged without serious damage. In later years, she withstood a similar battering when beached as a store hulk on the Falkland Islands. Incidentally the grounding at Dundrum Bay was caused by compass error. In the 1840s compass deviation was not yet understood, and it was through accidents of this sort that **Lord Kelvin** and Professor Sir George Airy were motivated to improve the mariners' compass.

It is sad to relate that Brunel's third ship, the *Great Eastern*, can only be described as a professional disaster. The ship, designed by Brunel but built by **John Scott Russell** at the Isle of Dogs, London was controversial from the outset. Larger by far than any previous ship, she moved well beyond the bounds of normal extrapolation, and was to be the largest ship in world for another forty years. The relationship between Scott Russell and Brunel deteriorated, and the shipyard started to make serious financial losses through Brunel's sometimes unreasonable demands; it has to be borne in mind that both men were working at the limits of known ship design and ship production experience. Clearly Brunel had responsibility for ship design and this was accepted in the shipyard. It is difficult to understand how Scott Russell allowed him to interfere with shipyard procedures, however, and in particular the use of cast iron plates on the fixed and sliding faces of the launchways – and which were without camber, a sure recipe for disaster – which indeed it became. After weeks of effort the ship floated on 31 January 1858, but thereafter enjoyed only a lacklustre career.

Scott Russell suffered severe financial losses and Brunel's health broke down. Despite a restful holiday in Europe in the winter of 1858/9, Brunel returned to Britain. On the morning of 9 September 1859, there was an explosion aboard the *Great Eastern* during her sea trials. Brunel was ill and at home, but this news so devastated him that he died a few days later.

SOURCES:

Caldwell, Professor J B
The Three Great Ships, part of *The Works of Isambard Kingdom Brunel*
The Institution of Civil Engineers, London, 1976

Corlett, E
The Iron Ship
Bradford-on-Avon, 1975

Forbes, Donald A
'Launch of the Great Eastern and the Aftermath'
Transactions of the Institution of Engineers and Shipbuilders in Scotland
Vol 136 (1992–3)

Griffiths, Denis
Brunel's Great Western
Wellingborough, 1985

———, Lambert, Andrew, and Walker, Fred
Brunel's Ships
London, 1999

Rolt, L T C
Isambard Kingdom Brunel
London, 1957

Part 3
Naval Architecture Comes of Age
1850–1900

The America's Cup

1851 was the year of the Great Exhibition, for the British a year of optimism and patriotic pride. The annual regatta of the Royal Yacht Squadron at Cowes saw the American 170-ton schooner *America* win the newly-presented One Hundred Guinea Cup for a race round the Isle of Wight. The cup became known as the America's Cup and resided in the New York Yacht Club for the next 132 years. The *America* had been designed by an up-and-coming naval architect, George Steers, who would die just five years later aged only thirty-six. The importance of this event has to be emphasised; it inspired many wealthy people to take to yachting, which in turn supported the naval architecture profession and a dozen or so important yacht-building yards on both sides of the Atlantic. The sport encouraged the 'Corinthian' sailors – the men and women who cruised the Scottish Hebrides, the Baltic and the New England coast, as typified by the hero Carruthers of the yacht *Dulcibella* in Erskine Childer's masterpiece *The Riddle of the Sands*.

The Suez Canal

With the opening of the Suez Canal in 1869, the length of voyages from Europe to the Far East was shortened dramatically. This coincided with the introduction of the compound steam reciprocating engine into long-distance ships with the corresponding reduction in coal consumption, and immediately shipping companies commenced liner services (that is, scheduled departures) using the new waterway. In turn this led to an immediate drop in demand for sailing ships, constrained as they were to sail round Cape Horn or Cape of Good Hope. The Suez Canal was a contributory factor to the demise of the deep-water sailing ship.

Formal education for naval architects and marine engineers

After two thwarted attempts, the Royal Navy opened the (third) Royal School of Naval Architecture at South Kensington in 1864, an organisation that would transfer to the Royal Naval College, Greenwich upon the founding of the Royal Corps of Naval Constructors in 1883.

In the last two decades of the century, the teaching of naval architecture and ship design commenced at several schools (some are listed under their current names):

Ann Arbor, University of Michigan.
The Massachusetts Institute of Technology.
The Webb Institute, New York.
The University of Strathclyde, formerly the Royal Technical College of Glasgow.
The University of Newcastle upon Tyne.
The University of Glasgow.

Naval architecture schools were also founded in Germany, Japan and many other countries.

Hydrodynamic studies

This period saw the introduction of scientific hull testing and the ability of naval architects to predict speed, power and ultimately fuel consumption for almost any kind of ship. The foundations laid down by **William Froude**, a man born in 1810, fifty years before the Royal Institution of Naval Architects was founded, stand good to this day.

In 1871, the Admiralty authorised the construction of a ship experiment tank at Torquay, where the non sea-going part of the *Greyhound* tests was carried out. Froude used the tank for experiments on ship stability and it was there that he noticed the effect of ram bows which in the late twentieth century developed into the almost ubiquitous bulbous bow. Incidentally, **Kelvin** (then Sir William Thomson) also noted this and it is believed the two men corresponded on the matter. In 1883 the **Denny** shipyard in Dumbarton commissioned a slightly larger tank which was the first such commercial undertaking in the world. Since then tanks have been constructed in almost every maritime country in the world, and at almost every university where the teaching of naval architecture takes place. The Denny Tank was de-commissioned in 1983, and it is now the only museum of hydrodynamics in the world.

Bulk cargoes and dedicated cargo carriers

The full potential of iron was realised when ships began to be built for dedicated trades. The best example is the humble collier, which became a profitable tool for the delivery of coal once it had a hull of iron, was endowed with a steam engine and fitted with effectively-positioned water ballast tanks. Such ships could make round trips laden from the British east coast coalfields to London and back in ballast in as short a time as four days, instead of the indeterminate number of weeks required by the collier brigs in previous centuries. The hulls were longer and more capacious and the London power stations could depend on nothing short of a 'liner' service to their doorsteps.

The shipbuilders of the north-east of England, mainly situated on the three rivers of the Tyne, the Tees and the Wear, produced enormous numbers of cargo ships and one – 'the three island tramp' – could be described as one of their specialities. These vessels had a basic outfit which included a triple expansion steam engine, Scotch boilers and fairly simple cargo gear enabling them to work in almost any part of the world. Few were left under the British flag after the Second World War, but under other flags some were to be seen carrying coal and ore right up until the 1960s.

The classic three-island configuration seen here on *Alfalfa*, built as *Indradevi* by J Blumer & Son, Sunderland, in 1898. (Ambrose Greenway)

Such vessels might, on delivery from a British port, sign on a crew and then call at Cardiff in South Wales for a coal cargo bound for an overseas coaling station. Thereafter the ship would work on the cross trades, possibly never reaching her country of registry, and would hope to arrive at the River Plate empty and ready to take part in the massive annual grain shipments to Europe. Only after arrival at a British or European port would the crew articles be ended and the men released to make their way home.

The Learned Societies

The most important contribution that a professional society or institution can make is to publish learned papers which have been presented, and as necessary defended, in public. This great tradition ensures the widest dissemination of professional knowledge, and creates an archive of historic development. In the nineteenth century there was a genuine willingness by engineers to share their hard won experience with their peers.

The Institution of Civil Engineers covered all branches of engineering, but in 1857 the first specialist institution was formed in Glasgow, the Institution of Engineers and Shipbuilders in Scotland, and just three years later it was followed by the Institution of Naval Architects. In 1884, the Scottish group was emulated by the shipbuilders of Newcastle and Sunderland with the North East Coast Institution, and in 1889, the marine engineers set up their own Institute in London. The Naval Architects obtained the ultimate seal of approval in 1960 when they became the Royal Institution. Sadly the North East Coast Institution was disbanded a few years ago. In 1893, the Society of Naval Architects and Marine Engineers was set up in North America and continues to this day with its headquarters in Jersey City.

Classification Societies

Lloyd's Register (LR), while almost a household name, is one of a very select group of organisations charged with ensuring that ships, their equipment and their cargoes are safe and that conditions are suitable for the safe transit of passengers and crew. To carry out these tasks, LR (founded in London in 1760) has a detailed and ongoing programme of inspections which include dry-dockings, and a worldwide team of expert surveyors numbering 7,500 in the year 2010. This service is independent of national politics and is for the benefit of the wider shipping community. LR is a Classification Society, that is an organisation that grants a 'class' to a ship which denotes her quality of construction and maintenance. Hence the famous phrase '100A1 at Lloyd's'.

Over the years, competitors emerged, starting with Bureau Veritas which was founded in Antwerp in 1828, but which subsequently moved its headquarters to Paris. Each society has a two-letter symbol which is placed on either side of the Plimsoll Mark if the Society has had the task of assigning the freeboard. The main societies and their founding dates are:

1828	Bureau Veritas	(BV)	founded in Antwerp and now based in Paris
1861	Registro Italiano Navale	(RI)	
1862	American Bureau of Shipping	(AB)	
1864	Det Norske Veritas	(NV)	founded in Christiania (now Oslo)
1867	Germanischer Lloyd	(GL)	of Hamburg
1899	Nippon Kaiji Kyokai	(NK)	of Japan
1913	Russian Maritime Register	(RS)	based in St Petersburg

... there are newcomers to the field ...

1960	Korean Registry of Shipping	(KR)
1975	Indian Registry of Shipping	(IR)

One other classification society deserves especial mention: the British Corporation (BC) which was founded in Glasgow in 1890 as a rival to LR, and in only a few years made great inroads into the industry by offering reduced steel scantlings with the same margins of safety. BC operated closely with American Bureau and with the Italian society. After two world wars, when LR and BC worked amicably, it was decided that the national interest would be served best by a merger, and this took place in 1949.

Whaling

Arctic whaling once was a major European industry, and for several hundred years Britain, Denmark, France, Germany, Norway, The Netherlands and the United States were all involved. The preferred catch was the Greenland Right or Bowhead Whale, but by the 1890s the numbers of these 'fish', as they were known to the whalers, had diminished in number. In 1850 there may have been as many twenty British whaling ports each with anything from half a dozen to as many as thirty whalers. The work was vital for the economy as whale oil was a necessity and the other whale products, such as baleen were highly profitable. However, as the northern industry died, fewer and fewer ports were involved and just before the First World War only Dundee in Scotland and Tønsberg in Norway had active fleets. In the twentieth century the whaling companies, using some of the gear invented by **Svend Foyn**, started to operate in the Antarctic, operations which were so badly-handled that the current whaling moratoriums had to be imposed.

The building of wooden whaling ships was highly specialised. The ships had massive structures to enable them to withstand the pressure when caught in the ice, and their shape was designed to assist them to break free when temperatures rose. The yards of **Alexander Stephen** and of **Colin Archer** typify the building places of these mighty ships. To help quantify the risks faced by the whalemen, it is instructive to look at nineteenth century statistics of Dundee: In that one century the Port had a total of eighty whaling ships, and of these ships fifty-nine were lost at sea, almost all in the northern latitudes.

Refrigeration

One of the greatest boosts came to world trade, and to shipping and shipbuilding, when the carriage of frozen meat started from Australia, New Zealand and South America. Experiments started in the 1880s and meat carriage was so advanced by 1890 that Lloyd's Register produced the first rules for refrigeration plant at sea. Refrigeration engineers had evolved suitable heat cycles for the refrigeration plant and they had overcame the health risks associated with the handling of bulk frozen carcasses. Lloyd's intervention was important as the value of cargo on a well-laden ship is astronomic.

* * *

In many respects, the year 1883 typifies the struggles of a profession that was coming of age. Two events symbolised public recognition and awareness of the importance of naval architecture. First, the move of naval architecture classes to the Royal Naval College Greenwich, and the founding of the Royal Corps of Naval Constructors. Second, an event more geared to the merchant shipbuilding sector was the founding of a Chair of Naval Architecture at the University of Glasgow.

That same year was to witness the greatest disaster in British shipbuilding, when the steam coaster *Daphne* capsized after launching in Glasgow with the loss of 124 lives. No event could be more appropriate in reminding naval architects of their primary duty of care for the safety of lives, of ships and cargoes and also of the environment.

KEY DATES

1851 The schooner *America* wins what is known now as the America's Cup.

1852 Loss of the troopship *Birkenhead* off South Africa.
Iron collier *John Bowes* built at Jarrow – arguably the first ship for a dedicated cargo.

1857 Sound Dues abolished for trade with the Baltic.
Institution of Engineers (later '& Shipbuilders') in Scotland founded in Glasgow.

1859 Launch of *Great Eastern* at Isle of Dogs, London.
France launches *Gloire*, the first ironclad warship.
Work commences on cutting the Suez Canal.

1860 Founding of the Institution of Naval Architects (later the Royal Institution).
First British iron warship HMS *Warrior* built by Thames Iron-works.
John Scott Russell publishes papers in *Transactions of INA* on his Wave Line Theory.

1861 First recorded carriage of oil in barrels by *Elizabeth Watts*.

1862 Forerunner of the American Bureau of Shipping founded.
Battle between ironclads USS *Monitor* and CSS *Merrimac* at Hampton Roads, Virginia, in American Civil War.

1863 *Spes et Fides* whale catcher built Nylands Værft, Norway (Foyn system).
Opening of Royal School of Naval Architecture, South Kensington (later at Greenwich).

1865 Passenger/cargo *Agamemnon* built Greenock with economic compound machinery.

1866 Skelmorlie Measured Mile opened off Ayrshire coast.

1869 Suez Canal opens.

1871 Opening of the Admiralty Test Tank at Torquay.

1871 William Froude commences the historic *Greyhound* experiments.

1874 SS *Propontis* retrofitted in Glasgow with triple-expansion machinery.
William Froude publishes 'Experiments with HMS *Greyhound*' in *Transactions of INA*.

1876 The Merchant Shipping Act.
French and British ships pioneer carriage of frozen meat from the Southern Hemisphere.

1878 City of Glasgow Bank fails: under Scots Law all directors imprisoned.

1879 Tay Bridge disaster.

1880 Launch of Russian Imperial Yacht *Livadia* at Glasgow.

1881 SS *Aberdeen* built at Glasgow and triple-expansion machinery becomes norm.
Naval architecture teaching commences at Ann Arbor, Michigan.

1882 Ship drawing classes commence at Glasgow (in later Royal Technical College).

1883 Founding of the Royal Corps of Naval Constructors at Greenwich.
Founding of the John Elder Chair of Naval Architecture at Glasgow University.
Capsize of SS *Daphne* after launching in Glasgow with loss of 124 lives.
Commissioning of first commercial ship model tank at Denny's Shipyard, Dumbarton.

1884 Washington conference decides that Greenwich identifies the prime meridian.

	Founding of North East Coast Institution of Engineers & Shipbuilders in Newcastle.
1885	Bofors produce their first whaling harpoon gun.
	Lloyd's Register merges with the Liverpool Registry.
1886	*Glückauf*, now accepted as the world's first tanker, delivered from Newcastle.
1887	Admiralty Experiment Works, Haslar opened.
1889	Founding of the Institute of Marine Engineers (now the IMarEST).
1890	The British Corporation (Classification Society) founded in Glasgow.
1895	Energy accumulators introduced in whale-catching systems.
1897	C A Parsons delivers a paper to INA on compound steam turbines.
1898	Delivery of pioneer Russian icebreaker *Ermack* from Newcastle.
	Opening of Kiel Canal (the Nord-Ostsee Canal).
	Lloyd's Register publishes rules for refrigeration machinery.
1899	Founding of the Schiffbautechnische Gesellschaft, Berlin.
	Paper to INA on 'Elswick Cruisers' by Philip Watts.
1900	Offshore oil wells operating for first time in Caspian Sea and off west coast of USA.

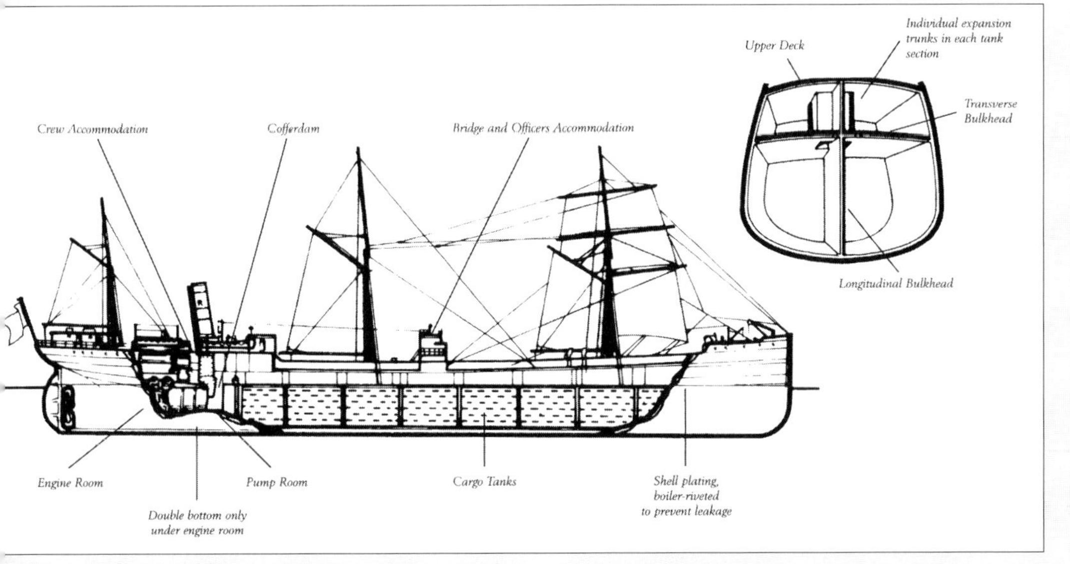

Glückauf was the first ship to be classified as a petroleum steamer, by the Bureau Veritas Registration Society. She was designed by Colonel Henry F Swan, a leading naval architect of his day; built by Armstrong Mitchell & Co Ltd on Tyneside as a speculative venture; and then acquired by the German shipowner Wilhelm Anton Riedemann. The cargo space was divided by both longitudinal and transverse bulkheads, creating eight separate compartments. She can be said to have been the forerunner of the modern tanker. (From *Liquid Gold Ships*, London 1985)

John Scott Russell
1808–1882

SINCE THE FOUNDING of the Institution of Naval Architects in 1860, many hundreds of great naval architects, academics, shipbuilders and other engineers have had their names inscribed on the membership list. In the event of a 'straw poll' being taken to indicate those of truly international importance, then it is likely that this cadre would drop to a few dozen, but it is inevitable that it would include an urbane and distinguished man of the nineteenth century, John Scott Russell, one of the most distinguished naval architects of his time, who had the benefits of both academic training and well-honed shipbuilding skills.

Described as a 'great Victorian Engineer and Naval Architect', Scott Russell was much more, being an academic, a practical shipbuilder and a man who throughout his life was to display great administrative and organisational skills. His memory has been ill-served by the passing success of his authorship in the 1870s of the Wave Line Theory. Then a great step forward in the philosophy of ship design, this theory later was discredited as the science of hydrodynamics moved forward, and Scott Russell's great services to the profession of naval architecture were overlooked. Happily his place is now assured in the history of ship design and construction.

John Scott Russell, 1808–1882.
(The Royal Institution of Naval Architects)

A son of the manse, Scott Russell was born in 1808 and brought up in Parkhead, then a garden suburb of Glasgow. He was to attend both St Andrews and Glasgow Universities, graduating from the latter in 1825 before moving to Edinburgh to become a teacher of mathematics. In this field he proved more than adequate and soon had additional work with the Leith Mechanics Institute as well as the Royal College of Surgeons in Edinburgh. Despite having been invited, he declined to apply for the Chair of Mathematics at Edinburgh, a decision which may have been a loss to the University, but would be advantageous to the profession of ship science. For some years he designed and assisted in the operation of steam-propelled road vehicles, and is known to have been consulted by the Trustees of the Forth and Clyde Canal and also of the Union Canal Company of Edinburgh. Maritime transport interested him, and in 1837 he presented his first paper on Wave Line Theory to the Royal Society of Edinburgh, a theoretical treatise that would bring him their Fellowship, as well as that of the Royal Society of London some years later. It is believed the first ship designed (by Scott Russell) according to the Wave Line Theory was the *Flambeau*, constructed at Port Glasgow.

His practical enthusiasms took him back to the Clyde, and around 1840 he accepted appointment as Manager of the Greenock shipyard of Thomson and Speirs. This yard built hulls on sub-contract for larger engine builders, one of which was the mighty Caird and Company, latterly the main builders for the P & O Company. As the Cairds objected to losing out on the profits of hull construction, they bought out Thomson and Speirs and invited Scott Russell to remain as shipbuilding manager. He remained there for some time, but with several young Caird family members breathing on his coat-tails, Scott Russell realised that his future was not to be in Greenock. He resigned and then made London his home.

For some years his financial situation was far from secure, but sundry appointments kept his head above water, the most important being Secretary to the Commissioners of the 1851 Exhibition. This task launched him in London society and brought him into close and friendly contact with Albert, the Prince Consort. In the late 1840s, **Sir William Fairbairn** decided to sell his shipyard at Millwall on the Isle of Dogs, and the lease was taken on by Robinson and Russell, an operation shortly thereafter renamed John Scott Russell and Company. In about ten years the new shipyard produced slightly less than thirty iron ships, the most notable of which was the *Great Eastern*, the ship which destabilised Scott Russell's finances and broke the health of **I K Brunel**. The Scott Russell/Brunel relationship was a nightmare, with no clear lines of demarcation existing between the two strong-willed men. Over and over again Scott Russell requested Brunel to use traditional, proven or at least well-tried methods of shipbuilding – but without success. One example was Brunel's insistence on using iron plates for the standing and sliding launch ways, and with the standing ways laid out in a straight line without any cambering. This proved to be one of the failures that caused deaths in the shipyard, brought the shipbuilders close to the point of bankruptcy and lead to Brunel's own death. The great iron ship hung over the River Thames from 3 November 1857 to 19 January 1858, with ways that had an unrealistically high coefficient of friction and had bumps and hollows, making movement almost impossible. With massive efforts, the hull was moved to the bottom of the ways and then left to float off on the incoming tide.

Once the *Great Eastern* debacle was over, Scott Russell was able to return to a more normal existence, and in the last years of his life undertook some fascinating projects. In 1859, he convened a meeting of great importance at his home in Sydenham in Kent. It was attended by the **Rev Joseph Woolley**, **Sir E J Reed** and **Nathaniel Barnaby**, and it resulted in a public meeting at the Adelphi in London on 16 January 1860, when over forty persons assented to the founding of the Institution of Naval Architects. This public approval enabled this great professional body for ship science to commence work in the United Kingdom.

It is recorded that John Scott Russell's last major professional task was that of designing a Swiss lakes steamer to be built by Escher Wys. It would be good to know which of the lovely Swiss Lakes steamers this was. He wrote an impressive book, in three volumes entitled *The Modern System of Naval Architecture*, a publication that now sells at the high end of the antiquarian book market. Until just before his death he was involved in the work of the INA where in all he presented fifteen papers in addition to several to the Royal Societies of London and Edinburgh. Like many other industrialists, he was interested in reform, but his writings were often criticised by right-wing newspapers (like *The Times* in the nineteenth century) as 'socialist propaganda'. Nothing has changed!

SOURCES:
Emmerson, George S
John Scott Russell – a great Victorian engineer and naval architect
London, 1977
Forbes, Donald A
'The Launch of the Great Eastern and the Aftermath'
Transactions of the Institution of Engineers and Shipbuilders in Scotland
Vol 136 (1992–3)
Scott Russell, J
'The late Mr John Wood and Mr Charles Wood, naval architects, Port Glasgow'
Transactions of the Institution of Naval Architects
Vol 2 (1861)
———, *The Modern System of Naval Architecture*
3 vols (London, 1865)

Svend Foyn
1809–1894

ON APPROACHING SIXTY years of age, and when most others are considering retirement, Svend Foyn surprised his friends by inventing a whaling harpoon gun, and going on to develop and market this new product. The Arctic whaling industry had one of the highest industrial mortality rates in the world, and this gun, coupled with Foyn's new system of whale-catching, was destined to save the lives of many whale men. On an equally positive note, this new piece of nineteenth-century ordnance was to revitalise the dying Norwegian and Scottish whaling fleets, but in the long term it was responsible for the ruthless butchery of whales in the Southern Ocean, a business which besmirched much of the twentieth century.

Svend Foyn was born in 1809 on a small island near Tønsberg in Norway, and having been brought up close to the sea, chose seafaring as his profession. Like many of his fellow countrymen of that period, he was deeply religious and a devoted member of the Norwegian Lutheran Church. At sea he rose through the ranks to become master and ultimately owner of a sealer working off Svalbard (then Spitsbergen) and the Greenland coast. This was a graveyard for American and European ships, an area where hundreds of vessels and thousands of men perished, such that by the latter part of the nineteenth century few ports, apart from Dundee and Tønsberg, were sending sealers or whalers to the area.

From early times whale-catching off Greenland was carried out by small teams of men working from open whaleboats, up to 12m (39ft) in length, and armed with a hand-thrown harpoon and several hundred metres of line. The premier prey was the Bowhead or Greenland Right Whale (which is now nearly extinct), chosen because it was docile, allowed boats to come near and most usefully remained afloat once dead. This whale is pelagic, that is a surface feeder living on plankton filtered through the baleen or long bone structures in the mouth. Other whales were equally good catches, but could sink on death or worse, like the Sperm Whale, attack the boat. The hunting required 'playing' the whale which had to come to the surface for air every fifteen minutes or so, and then had to be lanced in the final kill. Despite this horrendous manner of making a living, most of the whaleboat crews survived their ordeals, with the real loss of life coming when the mother-ships becoming beset in the ice of those inhospitable fogbound regions. Ships trapped in ice could wait up to two years before breaking free, but many were crushed, taking their crews to an unmarked grave.

What were the rewards? A whaler returning with several 'fish', as they were known in the industry, would enable the crew to have a year's cash and comfort, and the local industries enjoy the benefits of whale oil, baleen and possibly whale meat. Some whale men made scrimshaw, bones, teeth or tusks carved in ornate manners, usually as a gift for homecoming, but items which a century later are highly sought after. The Dundee jute mills required whale oil for their machinery (one of the reasons the Dundee whalers lasted until the end of the Greenland whaling) and the corset manufacturers of Europe needed whalebone or baleen for their millions of customers. It is reported that in 1900 the price of raw whalebone had reached the then astronomic figure of £1,500 per ton.

Svend Foyn had considered the system of catching and felt a more scientific method was appropriate; he accepted also that too many lives were being lost and that most whales suffered unnecessarily. His religious and humanitarian background came to the fore and he designed a small gun that could fire a harpoon fitted with a grenade that could kill a whale quickly, whilst minimising the risk to the crew. Furthermore, in 1862 Foyn commissioned the building of a small steamer *Spes et Fides* (Hope and Faith) at Nylands shipyard in Norway and with that inaugurated the dedicated whale-catcher and the Foyn System of whale-catching, which enshrined three principles:

(1) Shooting from a dedicated and safer catching craft.
(2) Using a harpoon with an explosive head.
(3) Employing a harpoon winch with the ability to absorb the shock load of one hundred tons of whale diving several hundred metres in its death throes.

The Norwegian Government were helpful in the granting of patents, and by the time of his death Svend Foyn was a wealthy man.

The *Spes et Fides*, at only 7 knots, lacked speed and in the course of time craft operating up to 15 knots were produced and armed with very efficient harpoon guns, initially manufactured by Bofors of Sweden, but latterly by the Kongsberg Company. The first catchers came from Norwegian yards such as Akers of Oslo, but more and more they were built in the UK at several shipyards including Hall Russell, Aberdeen and A & J Inglis of Pointhouse, Glasgow. However, the real market leader was Smiths Dock on the River Tees which produced scores of these beautiful and seaworthy craft, mostly powered by triple-expansion steam engines. It was from the Smiths Dock design that the plans of the ubiquitous Second World War 'Flower' class corvette was developed and then sent to builders throughout the UK and Canada.

As a postscript, whaling in northern waters had all but died out by the outbreak of the First World War. The organisation of whaling changed and with increased mechanisation, the Norwegian and British whaling companies targeted the Antarctic and were to be joined there by many other nations. Overfishing and lack of long-term accountability had their effect in bringing about the current moratorium on international whaling.

SOURCES:
Hardy, A C
Seafood Ships
London, 1947
Harland John H
Catchers and Corvettes – the steam whale-catcher in peace and war
Rotherfield, 1992
Jackson, C Ian (ed)
The Arctic Whaling Journals of William Scoresby the Younger
(19th Century) Vols 1–3
The Hakluyt Society, London, 2003–9
Watson, Norman
The Dundee Whalers
East Linton, 2003

Alexander Stephen, 1795–1875. (*Mr A M M Stephen*)

Alexander Stephen
1795–1875

THE STEPHEN SHIPBUILDING dynasty is unique in the history of world shipbuilding; for 218 years – from 1750 until 1968 – they operated six different shipbuilding sites in Scotland. To represent this illustrious family, we have chosen Alexander Stephen who witnessed shipbuilding in five of the sites and was the son of a man who served his apprenticeship at Burghead, their first yard in north-east Scotland. There are two embellishments to this story, the first that Alexander's grandfather had been conscripted into the Jacobite army and was a most reluctant attendee at the terrible battle of Culloden in 1746. If that were not enough, Alexander's brother William was captured at sea by the French during the Napoleonic Wars and not repatriated to Britain until 1814 when he returned to set up a shipyard at Arbroath in the County of Forfarshire, now known as Angus.

The complex life of this family at the end of the eighteenth and the beginning of the nineteenth century illustrates how hard it was to make a living in a deprived area. The story begins with the first family shipbuilding yard at Burghead, a small village on the Moray coast and a few miles west of the River Spey, an area noted now for whisky, but in the nineteenth century for excellent wooden ships. Here Alexander's father served his apprenticeship under his uncle, before moving south and setting up both home and another shipyard at the fishing village of Footdee in Aberdeen harbour. Here Alexander was born and here he served a shipwright apprenticeship. His brother William (who had been captured by the French) ran a small shipyard at Arbroath, but from 1826 until his death in 1829 had major problems, which included the loss of a son at sea and then serious financial difficulties which had been underwritten by a bond from his father. This led to both his and his father's death and Alexander found himself in charge of two shipyards. He wisely decided to give up one lease, namely the shipyard in Aberdeen where labour was becoming hard to come by. His management of the southern shipyard was successful and Arbroath expanded, thirty-two ships being built between the late 1820s and 1843. By then Alexander had set his sights on a larger yard in the City of Dundee, and making use of the opportunity afforded by a temporary lull in shipbuilding orders he moved his business to the Dundee site, leaving Arbroath in the hands of his brother William's son.

The Dundee yard was in operation under the name of Alexander Stephen and Sons from 1843 to 1893 and produced ninety-seven ships, all of which were recognised as world-class. They built in timber, in iron, in steel and produced also a handful of composite ships with iron skeletal structures planked with timber. Close to 25 per cent of production were whalers and sealers for the Arctic, wooden ships of enormous strength with larger than usual scantlings, reinforced by additional structures known as fortifications. Dundee, which was to be the last whaling town in Britain, continued building these ships until the end of the nineteenth century, and completed the RRS *Discovery* for Antarctic exploration as late as 1901. The yard had a covered building berth for quality tonnage, and the 800-ton *Amazon* was launched there in 1850, a ship classed at Lloyd's for fourteen years as the first ship in Scotland built under a roof. Another innovation (copied from the Royal Dockyards) was the introduction of hollow launching ways. The yard was destroyed by fire in 1867 but production was hardly affected with the genial Alexander bringing out the best in those around him. He and his wife were blessed with a most happy marriage, and produced an amazing eighteen children, sixteen of whom survived childhood. Two died tragically; one daughter, while playing in the shipyard, ran into a circular saw, and another was suffocated when a sleeping nanny rolled on top of her in bed.

In 1850 it was decided to expand, and a site at Kelvinhaugh in Glasgow was chosen, on the north bank and just a mile west of the city centre. In 1852, the first of the 147 ships from the new yard was launched. Apart from two fairly large wooden sailing ships and about thirty hulls described in the records as built of 'wood and iron', better known now as composite construction, all other ships were of iron. Kelvinhaugh remained active until 1870 when the lease ran out and the yard transferred to another site at Linthouse a further mile west and on the south bank of the river Clyde. By this time Alexander had retired and the purchase and setting up of the new yard at the once-sylvan Linthouse estate was carried out by his son, another Alexander.

Alexander Stephen retired to Broughty Ferry in Angus and enjoyed his last years, and was seen 'often in his shirt sleeves at six o'clock in the morning superintending, and lending a hand with some of the heavy operations'. In 1875, following a visit to the Dundee Shipyard, he returned home content and well but died shortly after. It is doubtful if any other man of his time had been involved in four family shipyards, and had immediate contact with one that was earlier and another that was later. He left a legacy of goodwill, a company that had witnessed steady innovation and a workforce that had increased from a few dozen men in Aberdeen to several thousands on the Clyde. He left a shipbuilding company that was poised in the twentieth century to be leaders in apprentice and student training and that would continue building good ships in Glasgow until 1968 when it merged into the larger grouping of Upper Clyde Shipbuilders.

SOURCES:

Carvell, John L
Stephen of Linthouse 1750–1950
Glasgow, 1950

Rev Joseph Woolley

1817–1889

DR JOSEPH WOOLLEY was a key figure in the development of naval architecture. Not only a gifted teacher but a man accepted by the profession as one of their spokesmen in the difficult political arena of the mid-nineteenth century.

Woolley was a well-established Cambridge don who found himself drawn in to the teaching of naval architects and the setting-up of the Institution of Naval Architects (INA) in 1860. The son of a physician, he had been born in the Hampshire village of Petersfield but moved with his family to London where he attended first Brompton Grammar School and latterly St Paul's. In the 1830s he studied at St John's College, Cambridge, where he was noted as a gifted mathematician. In keeping with the times he took holy orders, and was a curate first in Norfolk and later elevated to become vicar of Crostwich. He was married.

In 1848, the opportunity arose for him to become Principal of the 'Second' or re-opened School of Mathematics and Naval Construction at Portsmouth. From all reports from the graduating young men, he was an exemplary teacher and produced some great stars for the profession; men like **Frederick Barnes** and **Edward Reed** respected him not only as their mentor but also as one who made them aware of the current deficiencies in the theories of ship science. The School lasted a mere five years as once again the reactionary Sir James Graham was reappointed First Lord of the Admiralty. It is not recorded how Woolley spent the next couple of years; clearly he was not on the poverty line and it is possible he had a living within the Church of England. In 1858 he was appointed HM Inspector of Schools, a post he was to hold for many years.

In 1859 he attended the meetings which led to the setting-up of the INA, and in 1860 was appointed to the first council which included **John Scott Russell**. Indeed, in 1863 he and Russell were appointed joint executives to manage the INA during a period when a secretary was awaited. In 1860 Woolley gave the introductory paper to the INA entitled 'The present state of the mathematical theory of naval architecture'. No one was better qualified, and Woolley rose to the occasion, informing the Institution of the weakness of current theory and of the danger of too many established practices governed by rule of thumb. He mentioned also the Thames Tonnage Rule (a variation of the Builders' Old Measurement Rule), one of the most unsatisfactory ship measurements of all time.

In 1864 the new Royal School of Naval Architecture was opened at South Kensington, and while welcomed broadly by almost everyone there were lingering doubts that London was the wrong venue and that the course might prove too theoretical. Joseph Woolley was asked to present a paper on 'The Education of Naval Architects', and in doing so struck a firm blow on behalf of formal education at the highest level. To quote **Kenneth Barnaby** in the Centenary Volume of the Institution of Naval Architects: 'Woolley was himself a Cambridge graduate, so he delighted in pointing out that great improvements had been introduced in warship design by "Master **Phineas Pett**, gentleman, sometime Master of Arts at Emmanuel College, Cambridge". This was 250 years ago, so "it seemed the first recorded instance of bringing the results of education to bear on naval architecture".'

Woolley gave six papers to the INA and discussed many matters including the theory of rolling of ships. Following the loss of HMS *Captain* in 1870, he was appointed to Lord Dufferin's committee set up to advise (belatedly) on the design of ships of war. In 1881 he was instrumental in pointing out to the Royal Navy that the examinations at the Royal Naval College, Greenwich, were biased towards old-fashioned techniques and he reminded them that while Lloyd's Register of Shipping was involved with a total of 690,000 tons of shipping under construction, only 30,000 tons were timber-built. The naval authorities conceded this point and revised their examination procedures. It is interesting to note that Joseph Woolley's son, A Sedgwick Woolley, served as secretary of the INA from 1875 until 1878.

SOURCES:

Barnaby, K C
The Institution of Naval Architects 1860–1960
London, 1960

Donald McKay

1810–1880

THE STORY OF nineteenth-century wooden shipbuilding in the maritime provinces of Canada and the eastern states of the USA is not well known in Europe, having been overshadowed by the well-recorded history of contemporary British shipbuilding. In the mid-nineteenth century the finest timber ships in the world were produced in yards stretching south from Prince Edward Island in the Gulf of St Lawrence, through New England to Massachusetts and New York. Amongst the great builders, Donald McKay, builder of a remarkable number of the fastest Yankee clipper ships, stands head and shoulders above all others as a naval architect, shipbuilder and innovator. His seat of honour in the halls of American shipbuilding is assured. McKay was born in Shelburne, Nova Scotia, the son of a farmer and fisherman and the grandson of Captain Donald McKay, a highlander and officer in the British Army who emigrated to Canada after the American Revolution. Like many others, he settled to become a Nova Scotian 'Bluenoser'.

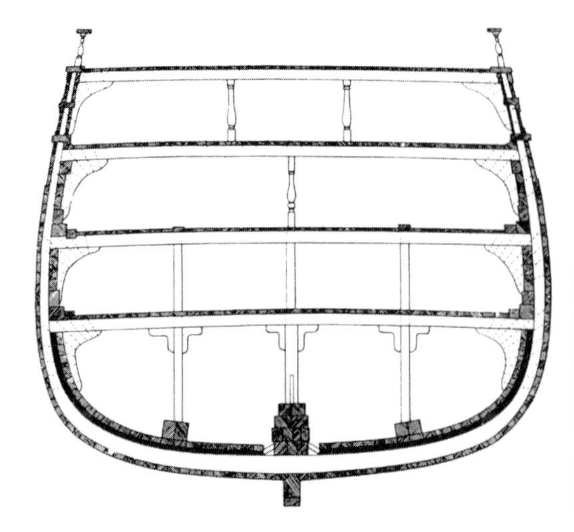

The midship section of *Great Republic*, showing the four decks, the massive keelson, and the marked tumblehome of this huge ship. The hull-form was well designed to carry a big cargo while the extra deck and high freeboard would have made her a dry ship. After the fire she was rebuilt with one fewer decks. (From Souvenirs de Marine, *Paris* 1875)

By 1826, the bitterness between the United States and Canada and the United Kingdom was receding. Donald McKay travelled south to New York looking for work, and in 1827 became apprenticed to Isaac Webb, one of the younger shipbuilders on South Street, the 'street of ships' in New York. (Ultimately, the business passed to **William Webb**, whose generosity helped found the Webb School of Naval Architecture, New York.)

From the outset, McKay and Webb had a good relationship, aided by their nearness of age and joint enthusiasms. While working in the shipyard, Donald McKay became aware of his lack of formal education and strove to better himself by study. He met a young lady, Albenia Boole, the daughter of a New York shipbuilder who not only taught him mathematics, but also won his heart as later they married and raised a family. Prior to completing 'his time', McKay was released from his indentures and was seconded to another yard for experience, and then as a shipwright joined the Brooklyn Navy Yard. Here he suffered harassment owing to his Nova Scotian connections. Around 1840, he moved north to Wiscasset in Maine, the 'Down-East' area that harboured little ill-feeling towards the British.

He joined John Currier, and in 1841 a new company Currier and McKay was set up which produced some fine ships including the 400-ton *Courier* designed and overseen entirely by Donald McKay. In 1844, he met the shipowner Enoch Train who ordered a ship within an hour of their meeting, and later encouraged McKay to come south to East Boston and even agreed to meet some of the expenses incurred by the move. A new company was formed in 1845 and the young man was on his way as a designer and builder. Between 1845 and 1850, Donald McKay completed a succession of very fine ships, establishing a reputation for quality, whilst amassing a small fortune. At this time, Albenia died, and after a while Donald married the woman who was his personal assistant in the shipyard.

Around 1850, an event took place which was to have a significant effect on the history of the

United States, and also was to make Donald McKay internationally known. The event was the Californian Gold Rush. The word 'clipper' conjures up many images, but in North America it was the name given to fast passenger and/or cargo sailing vessels, of which just over 400 were built. The discovery of gold and the need to transport people from the East Coast to California in the minimum of time, gave impetus to the design of clippers and ultimately the 'extreme clipper'. Naturally the word 'clipper' was used indiscriminately in advertising where shipowners had to maximise their passenger and cargo manifests, but on the whole the fleet racing round the Horn to California was composed of excellent vessels, and in almost all cases built of hardwood, not the normal American or Canadian softwoods. Twenty-four were built in 1850 in North America, a number rising to 120 in 1853, but falling to ten by 1857. The clipper period was short and colourful in both the United States and Britain, each country having about the same number of great ships, although built for completely different reasons.

Reputedly, the first Yankee clipper was *Anne McKim*, from Baltimore in 1833, while the first British clipper was *Scottish Maid*, built by Alexander Hall of Aberdeen in 1847. Until the introduction of composite shipbuilding, the length of clippers was limited by current timber technology to around 70m (229ft), cargo capacity and the potential for fast passages. McKay tried to maximise ship lengths and designed and built several large vessels including *Stag Hound*, *Flying Cloud* and the wonderful *Great Republic*, a monster 108m (354ft) long, in 1853 the largest ship in the world. He sailed on ships from time to time to study their behaviour at sea. His output included the full-rigged *Sovereign of the Seas* which broke all records between New York and San Francisco, and was immortalised in the words of the chantey men:

'Oh, Susanna, darling
Take, oh, take your ease!
For we have beat the clipper-fleet!
The *Sovereign of the Seas*'

In 1853, McKay produced the extreme clipper *Great Republic* which was over 100m (328ft) in length. Launched at Boston with a bottle of water, she was regarded at the time as the pinnacle of American shipbuilding, equipped with state-of-the-art equipment including a 15hp steam engine to assist in raising sail. While loading her first cargo at New York she caught fire, was severely damaged and had to be rebuilt. McKay tried to disregard this setback, but for the first time his enthusiasm and, more unfortunately, his financial position had been affected.

In the following years, he built slightly less glamorous but nonetheless highly profitable vessels for the North Atlantic trade, including *Lightning*, *Champion of the Seas*, *James Baines* and the appropriately-named *Donald McKay*, all for the Black Ball Line. They wore the Red Ensign and were the largest British ships of their time. Prime Minister Disraeli visited *Lightning* on the Mersey, and Queen Victoria went aboard the *James Baines* in 1857 to review 1,000 men of the 97th Regiment about to leave for India.

At the end of 1859, McKay toured the shipyards of Britain and Europe and on his return instituted iron shipbuilding and broadened the range of his products. However, he had lost his métier and within ten years had sold the yard. He retired to a farm, where he died in 1880. It is doubtful if any man will surpass Donald McKay's record of designing and supervising over seventy successful and extreme ships, many of which were to become record-holders.

SOURCES:

Howe, O T, and Matthews, F C
American Clipper Ships 1833–1858
Salem, Mass., 1926

McKay, Richard C
Some Famous Sailing Ships and their Builder Donald McKay
New York, 1928

Marcil, Eileen Reid
The Charley-man: A History of Wooden Shipbuilding at Quebec 1763–1893
Kingston, Ontario, 1995

William Froude
1810–1879

WILLIAM FROUDE IS remembered today not only as the greatest hydrodynamicist of all time, but as the man who first placed ship model testing on a systematic and scientific basis. Since his experiment tank was opened in Torquay in 1871, ship model testing basins have sprung up in almost every nation with a maritime heritage. When new tanks are inaugurated, there is an amusing traditional ceremony of pouring a small quantity of liquid into the new basin; this libation is of water from another tank and which has come in an 'apostolic succession' from the water used by Froude in Torquay. The author has a bottle of Denny Tank water – and he is willing to make this available to any prospective builder of a new tank, as it is safe to assume that just a few molecules of Torquay water will be present in the Dumbarton water!

William Froude, 1810-1879.
(The Royal Institution of Naval Architects)

William Froude was born at Dartington in Devon, one of several children, where their father was a Rector in the Church of England. The family had a comfortable lifestyle, William's parents were greatly respected and all the children made good progress in life. Froude attended Westminster School with plans to go to Cambridge but was induced to join Oriel College, Oxford, where his elder brother Richard was a tutor. Details are unclear, but it appears he was there from 1828 until graduating in 1832, but retained his connections with the college until he received his MA in 1837. Despite having other employment, it is clear that he enjoyed a relaxed approach to life and that money was not a major problem.

In 1833, Froude was taken on as a pupil by the distinguished civil engineer H R Palmer, and among other projects was employed on survey work for the South Eastern Railway. This was in preparation for Parliamentary approval of new routes, and despite opposition from some quarters, the work was successful. Presumably through his railway connections, Froude was introduced to **I K Brunel** and in 1838 joined his staff as an assistant. He remained with Brunel for eight years and was well paid and highly regarded for his excellent work on the railways of the West Country. It appears that he may have left this work due to problems with his eyesight.

Froude married in 1839, and no doubt both he and his wife were pleased to move back to Dartington in 1846, ostensibly to look after his father who was not enjoying the best of health. For eleven years his lifestyle was adjusted to country ways, which allowed him time for study and intellectual pursuits. He was active as a Justice of the Peace, as a judge on mechanical matters at local agricultural shows and as a Commissioner for Dartmouth Harbour. At home he had established a well-equipped workshop and had started to make model ships, not for display purposes but for practical testing and experimentation on the River Dart. In later years he found himself and **Professor Macquorn Rankine** in total agreement as they strove to understand the complexities of ship motion through the interface of the two fluids, air and water.

During these 'quiet' years his wife Catherine was attracted to Roman Catholicism, and was received into that church in 1857 at the same time as Froude recommenced full time work. Froude was an unwavering Anglican, but he accepted the changes and both he and his sons became friendly with the man who had influenced his wife's thinking, the later Cardinal John Henry Newman.

The connections with Brunel were restored during the grim period when the great iron ship *Great Eastern* was being completed on the Isle of Dogs in East London. As the designer, Brunel approached Froude several times to discuss matters as diverse as the vexed matter of friction between the fixed and sliding ways required for the ship's launch, and also the need to evaluate the rolling period of the great ship. Froude approached the rolling problem in two ways; first the theory of rolling was thrashed out and the tedious calculations for ascertaining the ship's centre of gravity were completed. Secondly, an accurate model was tested in waves and Froude realised that to dampen the motion, raising the centre of gravity might be beneficial, a matter that naval architects and practical shipbuilding managers have struggled with ever since. All this was published in 1861 in the second-ever volume of the *Transactions* of the INA.

With the encouragement of **E J Reed** and others, Froude became more and more involved in research in which the Admiralty had interests. He carried out comparative tests on model hulls swung out on outriggers on either side of a steam launch, which might possibly be described as the start of his hull testing career. Froude, who had moved to a new house at Chelston Cross near Torquay, was convinced that a means could be established to predict hull resistance to movement through water by measuring the same for models. A masterly case was put to the Admiralty, and in 1870 their Lordships were pleased to announce that a testing tank was to be built and operated for two years by William Froude, at his own cost. They would also contribute the substantial sum of £2,000. Further discussion led to the agreement that the warships *Active* and *Greyhound* would be made available for full-scale tests in 1871. The tank was commissioned in 1871 and full scale and model tests of *Greyhound* in differing conditions of draft and trim were carried out. By 1874 these tests were published by the INA and for the first time ever the prediction of ship resistance and ultimately power and speed requirements could be ascertained with precision. This was the work that would make Froude world-famous, and he had just turned sixty-two!

The Torquay Tank, which was 85m (278ft) long, was equipped with a moving carriage pulled by a steam engine which in turn was controlled by a governor. The wax models were cast in a special mould and then cut to shape in a semi-automatic cutting machine and, most importantly, there was a printing machine which could produce long rolls of graph paper to pre-determined scales and to great accuracy. Propeller design blossomed as a result of hull resistance prediction, and model propeller-cutting machines were added to the ever-growing list of items on the tank establishment.

In 1878 William's wife Catherine died of tuberculosis. He was quite worn out with work and set off by ship for South Africa to recuperate. While there he contracted dysentery and died on 4 May 1879. He was buried at Simon's Town. It is possible that no other naval architect ever can claim to have so revolutionised ship design and operation. He has left an imperishable record. Many ship model tanks, including the Denny Tank in Dumbarton (now the oldest surviving tank) are places where his name is honoured. Like his son who followed he had become an FRS and had the Glasgow University LL.D.

SOURCES:

The Papers of William Froude MA LL.D FRS 1810–1879
Published by the Institution of Naval Architects, 1955

Abell, Professor Sir Westcott Stile
'William Froude: His Life and Work'
Devonshire Association for the Advancement of Science, Literature and Art
Vol 65 (1933).

Brown, David K
The Way of the Ship in the Midst of the Sea
Penzance, 2006

Robert Edmund Froude

1846–1924

RE FROUDE HAS been described as both a distinguished hydrodynamicist, and son of another distinguished hydrodynamicist. His vocation was in theoretical ship design with an especial interest in ship model tank testing. When aged just twenty-one, he joined his father **William Froude** and would continue to work in this field until his death nearly sixty years later.

Born at Dartington Parsonage in Devon, the home of his grandfather, Robert Froude was educated at a school near Exeter, then at Bradfield and finally at the Oratory School at Edgbaston, Birmingham where the Rev Dr John Henry Newman was one of his mentors and tutors. Newman, who later would be elevated to become a Cardinal in the Roman Catholic Church, had founded this college in 1847 on his return from studies in Rome.

In 1867, Robert began to assist his father in the testing of model ships on the River Dart. It is interesting to reflect that Robert Froude did not follow in the well-beaten family track to Oriel College, Oxford, and one is left pondering on his father's dry comment that he had to 'unlearn' all his mathematical skills on becoming a professional assistant to commercial engineers. Shortly after Robert joined the team, construction of the Torquay model test tank commenced at Chelston Cross and again shortly thereafter full-scale sea going experiments began with HMS *Greyhound* and HMS *Alert* – the results of which were published by the Institution of Naval Architects in 1874.

Following the death of William Froude in South Africa in 1879, Robert Froude was appointed Superintendent* of the Tank and from then on managed the affairs and also the expansion of hydrodynamic research. In 1883 he presented a paper to the INA on the subject of screw propeller efficiency, the fruit of five years of research and only his second paper to the Institution; he would present many more papers to the INA as well as the Royal Society of Edinburgh and other learned bodies.

The Torquay Tank operated from 1871 until 1885, when the lease on the land expired, and the building was taken down and the towing basin infilled and levelled. Another site had been obtained for a new tank at the Gunboat Yard in Haslar, and it was in full operation by 1887. The tank, which was the first of many subsequent developments on the site, was 121m (400ft) long, 6m (20ft) broad and had a water depth of 2.75m (9ft) – all fairly small by the standards of the twenty-first century. From the outset it was noticed that the resistance of models was considerably less than identical ones tried at Torquay; Robert Froude was anxious that all the model results whether from Torquay or Haslar should correlate and had a wax model of HMS *Iris* made as a 'standard'. Once the new tank had settled and the temperature had risen, results started to come into line and proper predictions could be made. The use of standard models was to become a world-wide practice and soon Haslar had reached the third *Iris* model, this time of a more permanent nature, manufactured from brass plate.

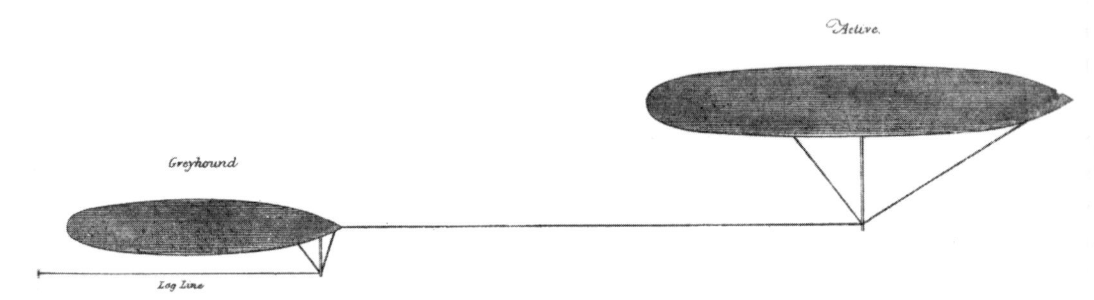

Drawing (possibly by Robert Froude) of HMS *Active* towing HMS *Greyhound* in the celebrated towing trials in the early 1870s. *(The Royal Institution of Naval Architects)*

Froude's work seamlessly followed on from that of his father, and he introduced 'Froude Constants' and other forms of analysis to systematise the tabulation of tank data. He was a most worthy Superintendent of the organisation which became known as the Admiralty Experiment Works, Haslar. (Note the word is not 'experimental'.) His recreations included the associated diversions of yachting, yacht designing and having oversight of the Rules of the then called International Yacht Racing Union. Froude, who was unmarried, retired in 1919 and moved to Cambridge. Like his father he was elected a Fellow of the Royal Society and was honoured with an LL.D from Glasgow University.

SOURCES:
Gawn, R W L
'The Admiralty Experiment Works, Haslar'
Transactions of the Institution of Naval Architects
Vol 97 (1955)

* Superintendent is the title that has been adopted for the senior professional engineer in ship model testing tanks, most often a person also holding the position of Director or of Chief Executive Officer of the Tank. It is normal for this person to be the Tank's nominated representative on the International Towing Tank Conference (ITTC).

Bruno Joannes Tideman

1834–1883

A WELL-KNOWN DUTCH naval architect and a specialist in hydrodynamics, then a growing field of research, B J Tideman was a remarkable man who accomplished a wide variety of tasks in the mere twenty-six years allotted to him before his untimely death in harness at the age of forty-eight. Reflecting on his career, only one word describes him adequately, and that word is 'polymath'.

Born in Amsterdam, he trained as a naval constructor at the Military Academy in Breda, to the south of Rotterdam, and then entered the full-time service of his country in 1857. During the following quarter of a century he would superintend new building contracts (mostly in the UK), advise on the setting-up of both merchant shipyards and naval dockyards, teach at the great naval architecture school of Delft as well as introducing experimental tank testing techniques to Holland. It is probable that his greatest contribution was towards the modernisation of the Dutch shipyards, which meant they could produce almost any kind of ship from about 1870 onwards. This alone would spare The Netherlands of the extreme cost and even greater inconvenience of building ironclads in the United Kingdom and elsewhere.

Tideman's first major task following his commissioning was oversight of the construction of the armoured coast-defence battleship *Prins Hendrik der Nederlanden* then laid down at Laird's shipyard in Birkenhead. During this two-year spell in the UK he spent time travelling and studying, much of it in Scotland where he was influenced greatly by **Professor Macquorn Rankine** of Glasgow University. This was of especial benefit to him as shortly after he was posted for a five-year teaching stint (in addition to his normal duties) at what was then the Polytechnic, but is now the University, of Delft.

On behalf of the government he acted as overseer for the first two Dutch cross-Channel ships to be constructed from scratch. This building contract was awarded to **John Elder** and Company of Glasgow and the hull form of one of the ships, the *Prinses Marie*, was selected for analysis by Tideman at the new open water test tank facility set up by himself in Amsterdam. Following on from his research work, Tideman proposed his own 'Coefficient of Friction' for hull model testing, and this remained in use in several countries until well after the Second World War.

This early expertise in model testing led to many similar contracts as the only other testing facility at the time was Froude's heavily-utilised tank at Torquay. The Amsterdam basin was commissioned to carry out many tasks by the Imperial Russian Navy and also for some years by some shipbuilders on the River Clyde, until the Denny Tank opened in Dumbarton in 1883. One task in particular was of note, the circular (or turbot-shaped) Imperial Yacht *Livadia* built by Elder's of Glasgow and launched in 1883. Her unique appearance was based on the work of **Admiral Andrei Popoff** who believed such forms would make steadier gun platforms, but in the case of this yacht a hull that would be comfortable for those prone to motion sickness, and in particular Empress Maria Alexandrovna, the wife of Tsar Alexander II. As large sums of money and – just as important – massive prestige was at stake, the builders, Elders of Govan, took the unusual precaution of building a further model, in this case quarter scale, and testing it in Loch Lomond. The *Livadia* passed all her tests with flying colours!

Despite these massive tasks, it is possible that Tideman's greatest contribution to The Netherlands was the impetus that he gave the shipbuilding industry, a stimulus which enabled them from 1870 onwards to design and build almost any kind of iron ship and then to engine it with reciprocating steam machinery. In 1873 he was appointed Director of the Engineers' Corps, the highest rank amongst the Constructors, giving access to almost all major engineering projects in the country, and bringing him into close contact with King William III, with whom he had a good relationship. The King requested Tideman to oversee the construction of the new shipyards at Vlissingen, resulting in the great Royal Schelde organisation, which set the standards for the vibrant Dutch shipbuilding industry. Tideman was ahead of his time in that he regarded naval architects, shipbuilders and marine engineers as fellow professionals serving together, and without the artificial divisions still apparent in the profession.

A few months before his death, he proposed the building of standard ships, described at the time as General Traders. This proposal received fairly scant support in the nineteenth century, but thirty years later when Britain and other countries were struggling under the exigencies of total war, this idea became a reality.

SOURCES:
Dirkzwager, J M
'Contribution of Dr Tideman (1834-1883) to the Development of Modern Shipbuilding'
500 Years of Nautical Science Symposium, National Maritime Museum, Greenwich, 1981

William George Armstrong (Lord Armstrong of Cragside)

1810–1900

WILLIAM ARMSTRONG, who was to become one of Britain's most powerful industrialists, came from a family with a professional background, and after leaving Bishop Auckland Grammar School, he served articles in a solicitor's office in Newcastle upon Tyne. At the beginning of the nineteenth century the city was regarded as one of the most overcrowded in Britain and further suffered from inadequate water supplies and poor sewage facilities. These unhappy conditions became apparent to Armstrong, as during the six years (1838–44) he worked as secretary to a company which later became the Newcastle and Gateshead Water Company. With his awareness of the privations of the area, coupled with a turn of mind that found legal work irksome, he strove to become more involved in scientific matters. His successful experimentation in hydraulics and later the development of small hydro-electric plants, moved one of his family to say that 'he had water on the brain'. Quite remarkably, his papers and publications were noticed, and in 1846 he was appointed a Fellow of the Royal Society.

In 1847, he severed his direct connections with the legal profession and set up an engineering company on the banks of the River Tyne at Elswick just to the west of Newcastle. Throughout his life he displayed the ability to work with successful partners, and his new enterprise, W G Armstrong and Company, was no exception. He and his fellow partners not only developed the principles of the hydraulic crane, but also produced the first of this new breed for Newcastle upon Tyne.

It was only in 1854 that W G Armstrong and Co made their first dividend payment – rather late in the day for a new company with several hundred on the staff, but this came through the exceptional amount of research and the high development costs in bringing forward new engineering systems. The onset of the Crimean War was to change the direction of the company, first with the design and construction of heavy ordnance and later with

The heavy breech-loading gun developed by Armstrong for the Royal Navy through the 1850s, being tested in 1862. *(Science and Society Picture Library)*

the production of warships of all sizes. Armstrong became aware of the deficiencies in current artillery and wholeheartedly researched and developed new guns for the British Army – and later for other nations as well. The production lines at Elswick soon were delivering 5-pounder and 12-pounder field guns, and thought was being given to the building of large-calibre guns for naval use. His expertise was recognised at high level and following the bestowal of a knighthood, he was appointed Engineer to the War Office in 1859. He held this post for only four years, tendering his resignation as he was aware of the deep-felt British dislike of senior figures enjoying the dual role of both industrialist and public servant.

In 1867, Armstrong approached a Tyneside shipbuilder, with a deal that he build warships, while Armstrong would supply guns. The two men had co-operated for years, but the long-term results of this proposal were nothing short of spectacular. The shipbuilder was **Charles Mitchell** (1820–95) who operated the Low Walker shipyard, east of Newcastle, where close on 500 hulls already had been built, including many for the Russians. Mitchell was an Aberdonian and throughout his life maintained close links with the ancient shipbuilding and university city where he had trained. In 1876, the swing bridge in Newcastle was opened and from then large warships could reach Elswick to receive their guns. The combined Walker/Elswick operation was studied in detail and the further decision was taken to move naval construction up-river, leaving Walker for specialised and merchant tonnage. In 1882, the companies merged formally forming Sir W G Armstrong, Mitchell and Co. and two years later Elswick began production, quickly to become one of the world's greatest warship builders. In 1885 they had two auspicious events, first **Philip Watts** (later to be Director of Naval Construction at the Admiralty) was appointed Naval Architect and General Manager, and secondly they launched Hull No 1, the Austro-Hungarian cruiser *Panther*, the first warship from Elswick, a place which was to continue building such ships for another twenty-odd years until moving their production to Walker-on-Tyne. Among the ships built were the Royal Navy's battleships *Victoria* and *Sans Pareil*. The former was to capsize with dreadful loss of life following a collision with HMS *Camperdown* during exercises in the Mediterranean in 1893. By 1895, Armstrong, Mitchell's had 13,000 employees at Elswick, which covered fifty acres and had at one time over twenty ships under construction, with in addition the workforce, land and production to be found further east along the Tyne. The Walker yard distinguished itself with pioneer tankers and latterly early icebreakers, including the *Ermack*.

Industrial relations within the company have to be described as primitive by today's standards, with several unhappy confrontations which could have been avoided with a less authoritarian approach by management. However, Armstrong Mitchell and Company did give regular employment and helped build up the shipbuilding and engineering infrastructure of Tyneside; they built workers' cottages and endowed many local schools and hospitals. This was fairly commonplace in nineteenth-century Britain; indeed a recent biographer described Armstrong in particular as 'neither a saint nor a sinner'! However, it must be recorded that William Armstrong and Charles Mitchell made many benefactions to Tyneside and elsewhere. It is probable that the most important from Armstrong was financial support in the setting-up of Armstrong College, now part of the University of Newcastle upon Tyne, and from Mitchell a generous gift towards the rebuilding of the ancient Marischall College of Aberdeen University.

In 1897, Armstrong's final conquest was the absorption of a Manchester armament manufacturer, Sir Joseph Whitworth and Company, a firm with a superb engineering record and an international reputation. At his death in 1900, Armstrong, now Lord Armstrong of Cragside, was proprietor of companies in the English north east employing well over 25,000 people. The later amalgamation with Vickers to form Vickers Armstrong was to come in the twentieth century, and is another story.

Armstrong had a long and happy marriage, but had no children as direct heirs: his wife predeceased him by seven years. In the latter years of his life he developed the massive house known as Cragside in Northumberland, now one of the jewels in the crown of the English National Trust.

SOURCES:
Dougan, David
The History of North East Shipbuilding
London, 1968
Smith, Ken
Emperor of Industry, Lord Armstrong of Cragside
Newcastle upon Tyne, 2005

Sir Andrew Noble

1831–1915

AN ARMY GUNNER WHO was to become a leading figure in the arms trade, throughout his life Andrew Noble was noted for dedicated hard work, and also for a fanatical interest in heavy ordnance. Commissioned into the Royal Artillery, he was marked out for higher responsibility, and soon was secretary to the British government committee investigating the rifled breech-loading field gun advocated by **Lord Armstrong**. Armstrong had just employed **George W Rendell**, and realising the potential growth rate of his new undertaking, quickly persuaded Noble to join him on the ordnance side. Noble took over as joint manager of the Ordnance Works with George Rendell in 1860, and he would remain on Tyneside for many years.

Two companies in Europe were deadly rivals in gun production, Armstrong's of Elswick, Newcastle upon Tyne, and Alfried Krupp in Germany. The armaments race ensured Elswick had plenty of work and as the years passed and Armstrong withdrew from the business, Noble exerted ever more control, and ensuring that Rendell and his family were bypassed for positions of power. Noble became chairman of Armstrong Whitworth and Company in 1900 and remained as such until his death in 1915. He also received a baronetcy. He is best remembered for the systematic experimentation and testing of guns, work that took Britain into the top rank of ordnance suppliers to the world.

SOURCES:
Scott, J D
Vickers: A History
London, 1962

Stanislas-Charles-Henri Dupuy de Lôme
1816–1885

DUPUY DE LÔME, a brilliant naval architect and strategic thinker, had the good fortune to rise to eminence during a period in the nineteenth century when the French were showing great innovation in warship construction. His influence can be gauged by the fact that shortly after his death, the French Navy saw fit to name a warship after him (a 20-knot armoured cruiser of 8,500 tons delivered in 1890). Such is a signal honour: it may have been accorded to only one other constructor, namely Admiral **Popoff** of the Russian Navy.

At the age of nineteen he entered the École Polytechnique, and for the following four years progressed up the tertiary academic ladder, although this time was interspersed with periods of practical training at the Lorient Dockyard in Brittany, a training system that was a precursor of what became known in Britain as the 'sandwich' system of education for engineers. In 1839 he was appointed an Under Engineer 3rd Class, and commenced his distinguished career in the French Navy, which led to becoming Directeur du Matériel (the most important position) a mere eighteen years later, an appointment he was to hold for many years. He was an eager traveller, and availed himself of the industrial atmosphere and technical experiences to be gained in countries like Britain where the use of iron in merchant ship construction was well ahead of the rest of the world.

The use of floating defence batteries had come to the notice of the naval authorities, especially after the heroic handling of these vessels by the Danes at the battle of Copenhagen in the early years of the century. Differing views on whether they should be (a) of timber, (b) of armour plate over timber, or (c) of complete iron construction, were unresolved in the 1850s at the time that explosive shells were taking over from solid shot. As Dupuy de Lôme was anxious that France have the most up-to-date equipment of this kind, he had to overcome resistance in various quarters, but managed to arrange that the ironclad floating batteries be authorised by Emperor Napoleon III for service in the Crimea. These became known as the Kinburn Batteries and their history is worthy of study. During this period, he was faced with the difficulty that ironworking facilities in the French dockyards were not equal to

The Dupuy de Lôme-designed ironclad *Gloire* of 1858. Her iron plating signalled the end for the unarmoured wooden ships of the line that had been the backbone of navies for 300 years. (From Souvenirs de Marine, *Paris* 1875)

those of Britain, and even the most imaginative plans were made difficult or sometimes impossible by lack of experience or skill.

From 1847 onwards, the French Navy commenced working with iron, although in almost all cases until well into the 1860s (and after the construction of the groundbreaking *Gloire*) they added armour plate to the outside of wooden hulls. In the long term this was to prove disastrous as the timber hulls were of inferior quality and the class lasted only about ten years. Dupuy de Lôme acknowledged that the full iron hulls of Britain's *Warrior* and *Black Prince*, delivered a couple of years later, were superior in every way. (History bears this out as HMS *Warrior* has survived into the twenty-first century.)

He believed that a few really excellent ships, preferably built of iron and propelled by steam, could overwhelm the vast might of the Royal Navy, which at that time was constructed almost entirely of timber. His oft-repeated words were '*Gloire* and her sisters (*vaisseaux à vapeur*) would be like lions in a field of lambs', the lambs he referred to were of course the British '*vaisseaux mixte*' (a mixed fleet of steam and sailing ships). His views modified as the navies developed, and he reckoned that as hull machinery in those days was high in the hull, it should be protected adequately by armour, and that the remainder of the hull be as light as possible. His objective was to achieve a 40 per cent reduction in hull weight to compensate for the armour.

He was interested in the introduction of the screw propeller in France, just a year or two behind the British *Rattler* and the American *Princeton*, and in the introduction of the steam compound engine to the French Navy around 1867, showing to all that he watched his competitors closely and was quick to adopt and adapt their successes. He became even more interested in propellers when in 1870 being caught up in the siege of Paris, he realised the potential of aviation. In common with other naval architects of that time and later, he looked into this new science and it is said he designed and built dirigibles airships, one of which was reported to have a gas capacity of 3,500 cubic metres. It was driven at 5.5 knots in still air conditions by a twin-bladed propeller with eight men labouring on a crank.

His interest in iron shipbuilding led to his offering advice to the companies operating passenger liners (*paquebots*) which were laying the foundations of the French merchant marine. Their continuing success and also that of the French shipbuilding industry owes much to this man as well as to several of his friends and contemporaries. In later years he accepted responsibility for a shipyard on the Mediterranean coast and also while still a fairly young man, was appointed a Councillor of State, and later a Parliamentary Deputy.

SOURCES:

Hamilton, C I
Anglo-French Naval Rivalry 1840–1870
Oxford, 1993

Hovgaard, William
Modern History of Warships
London, 1920

William Wain

1819–1882

A BRITISH ENGINEER WHO helped form one of Europe's greatest shipbuilding and engineering complexes, William Wain was born in Bolton, Lancashire, in March 1819. His father, an able and respected engineer, had little idea at the time that in less than one hundred years, the work of his son would make the surname Wain world-famous. The death of his father when he was twelve precluded any possibility of William continuing in full-time education, and he commenced an engineering apprenticeship first in Bolton and later in Wigan. His working skills and his organising ability were recognised, and by the time he was twenty, William Wain was a general foreman supervising 200 men in a Norwich engineering company. On the closure of this company, Wain found himself with money in his pocket and an urge to travel.

His first port of call was London. Within a short space of time he was introduced to Nicolai Tuxen, later to become Technical Director of the Danish Naval Dockyards, and he persuaded Wain in 1844 to accept a position as engineer on the *Geyser*, a naval vessel converted for the postal service. Four years later the *Geyser* was retrofitted as a warship and Wain found himself in the Royal Danish Navy 'by the back door'. In 1849 there was public disquiet in Denmark when Wain was appointed Chief Engineer in the navy, and even more when he rose to Assistant Director of Dockyards in 1862.

During the nineteenth century, Denmark went through a period of upheaval and adjustment. Constitutional changes were being forced through by the will of the people, education was being reformed and if that were not enough, the armed forces were fighting continuously against the Germans as Denmark tried to maintain sovereignty over the disputed region of Schleswig-Holstein. Further, the Royal Danish Navy had never forgiven Great Britain for the attacks on Copenhagen in 1801 and 1807. It was with this background that William Wain had to plan his life, but like many before and many since, Denmark captivated him and in the course of time he became a naturalised citizen.

With our modern views on public accountability, it is difficult to comprehend that in much of nineteenth-century Europe, senior civil servants were able to carry out private work in addition to their public commitments. Wain was no different, having designed some of the first effective floating docks whilst securing the intellectual property rights by patent. It was through these projects and also through naval contract work that Wain became known to the up-and-coming shipbuilders Baumgarten and Burmeister who had set up business in the centre of Copenhagen in 1843. It is of more than passing interest that until the very last years of ship repairing in Copenhagen (in the early 1990s) floating docks continued to be based at the shipyard.

In 1865 Burmeister, then sole partner, invited William Wain to join him. The latter accepted and the name of Burmeister and Wain (B&W) was promulgated. Wain retained his position with the Navy, but after severe public criticism regarding conflict of interest (which culminated in a debate in the Folketing or Danish Parliament), Wain resigned his defence appointments in 1868 to concentrate on building up the trade and goodwill of the shipyard and engineering practice. During the seven years between 1865 and 1872, B&W built and engined thirty ships, built seventy-five land engines, completed two railway locomotives and erected a replacement for the Knippels Bridge across Copenhagen Harbour. Despite obtaining work from all over Scandinavia and Russia, the company (possibly through being over-extended) ran into financial troubles forcing the partners to sell their assets to a new limited company which became known as A/S Burmeister & Wain in 1871. There has always been some mystery about this change to a limited company, but without question the organisation was strengthened and improved cash flow allowed a new shipyard to be developed at Refshale Island in Copenhagen during the 1870s. Known throughout Denmark and the world as B&W they traded as shipbuilders for a further 120 years and continue as engine manufacturers to this day.

Wain continued as the driving force of the new organisation. He received many honours, but his greatest moment must have come when he was sworn-in as a Privy Councillor to King Christian IX of Denmark. The saga with the navy was not over, as in 1870 they decided to continue drawing on his knowledge and appointed him Technical Consultant. He was twice married, first to an English lady and after her death to a Danish daughter of the manse. On his death in 1882, a plaque was raised in his honour in Holmens Kirke, Copenhagen, the resting place of the great seamen and admirals of Denmark and at the following AGM of the company he was described as 'a loveable personality and – a masterly genius'. The management of the Company was then entrusted again to someone from Britain, this time a Scot, David Halley from the shipyard of ***Robert Napier** in Glasgow. But that is another chapter in the story of B&W!

SOURCES:

Lehmann, Johannes
A Century of Burmeister & Wain
Copenhagen, 1948

William John Macquorn Rankine

1820–1872

MACQUORN RANKINE, A leading physicist and engineer of the nineteenth century, was to leave an imperishable mark on thermodynamics, naval architecture and the professional teaching of engineering. In a mere fifty-two years, not only did he produce over 150 papers and several textbooks of international standing but he also laid down the principles of thermodynamics. In addition to all of this, his greatest contribution to engineering was setting-out a syllabus of study for aspiring engineers. Rankine was a genial man with an outgoing personality, interested in music and with a gift for languages. It is said that while a professor, 'he disputed Greek derivatives with **Lord Kelvin** and corresponded with French scientists in French and in German with German'.

William John Macquorn Rankine, 1820–1872. *(Author)*

Rankine was born in Edinburgh, but as his parents had an Ayrshire background, his initial education was at Ayr Academy and later at the High School of Glasgow. After 1830 it seems that owing to ill-health his education was with private tutors in Edinburgh. During these years he received the gift of a copy of Newton's *Principia* in Latin. This he read and later wrote that in the year of 1834 he started to discipline his mind to be able to understand Newton's thinking. In 1836 he matriculated at Edinburgh University and studied natural philosophy, natural history and botany, all of great avail as whilst just sixteen years of age he was awarded a gold medal for an essay on the Undulatory Theory of Light. Rankine also indulged in private study of metaphysics, a discipline that must have helped him later in the abstruse field of thermodynamics.

His father, now superintendent of the Edinburgh and Dalkeith Railway, allowed his son (while still at university) to help him. Through this Rankine was introduced to John McNeil, a civil engineer with a successful practice in Ireland, and subsequently joined him, spending four productive years on harbour works and on the Dublin and Drogheda Railway. Quite on his own he made an especial study of metal fatigue, axle fracture and on the closely associated matter of setting out railway curves. His system, known as Rankine's Method, was in use for many years. During his time in Ireland he sent papers to the Institution of Civil Engineers and was the recipient of several prizes.

The years 1844 to 1855 saw him work on diverse projects including railway engineering, municipal water supply and telegraphic communications; increasingly he found himself advising on matters of design and construction in the shipbuilding industry. The largest civil engineering project in which he took part was the supply of fresh water from Loch Katrine and adjacent waters to the City of Glasgow. Proposed by Professor Lewis Gordon, this ambitious scheme met the requirements of a population which had grown from 110,000 in 1811 to 446,000 in 1861, and incidentally which continues to satisfy Greater Glasgow's ever-growing needs. Lewis Gordon, Glasgow University's first professor of engineering, had a substantial consultancy practice, much of it centred on London. Rankine was taken on as his personal assistant and spent part of 1853 and 1854 in London working on parliamentary cases. In 1855 he acted as deputy to Professor Gordon at the University, and when Gordon resigned to concentrate on consultancy, Rankine was poised to apply for the post. As ever there was opposition from within the senate, first because Rankine was an engineer and secondly being a Regius Chair, his appointment was by commission from Queen Victoria at a time when royal patronage was far from popular. Happily, in December 1855 the appointment was made and according to tradition within one week Rankine delivered his dissertation *De concordia inter scientiarum machinalium contemplationem et usum*.

Reflecting on Rankine's mere seventeen years of teaching, it is quite amazing to consider his achievements. In the field of theoretical heat engineering, collaborating with his friends Lord Kelvin and Professor Rudolf Clausius (1822–88), he was instrumental in describing Entropy and the Second Law of Thermodynamics; work that required patience, insight, mathematical genius and some say imagination! During this period of research his list of publications was prodigious, and included several key texts for different branches of engineering. He joined the Institution of Naval Architects in 1862 and presented papers to them every year but one for the rest of his life, and in one year he gave four papers. The naval architecture profession is honoured further with his monumental work *Shipbuilding: Theoretical and Practical* in which he was aided by **Isaac Watts**, **Frederick Barnes** and James R Napier, the son of **Robert Napier**. Much of which is written in this massive tome stands good to this day, and the volume is treasure trove to researchers in the history of ship design and construction. This authoritative textbook was complemented by four equally prestigious manuals respectively titled, *On the Steam Engine*, *On Applied Mechanics*, *On Civil Engineering* and *On Machinery and Mill Work*.

In 1859, and once he was a settled member of the University staff, he proposed the setting-up of a volunteer rifle unit, which is still extant and now is known as the Glasgow and Strathclyde Universities' OTC. He was in charge of A Company while Kelvin was responsible for B Company, making this a military unit with the unique distinction of having had two officers whose names are used for the scales of absolute temperature, °Rankine for the Fahrenheit based scale and °Kelvin for that based on Celsius. Shortly after his setting up of the OTC, he spent time persuading the authorities that engineering should be made a separate faculty and not part of Arts. At the time most men (and then it was only men) took an MA degree but after 1860 were allowed to supplement it with a Diploma in Engineering Science, which was awarded during the graduation ceremony. It took much time and required use of the Westminster Act on the Representation of the People, before the University succumbed and awarded the BSc in Engineering, quite possibly the first such degree in the world. However, full faculty status for the engineering department had to wait until well into the twentieth century.

In 1857, along with a group of notable engineers and some shipbuilders, the Institution of Engineers in Scotland was founded; by acclamation, Macquorn Rankine was appointed their first president. The organisation continues to this day and is now known as the Institution of Engineers and Shipbuilders (IESS) in Scotland, and the ongoing published transactions have well over 1,600 papers covering every aspect of engineering several of which were contributed by Rankine.

Rankine was at the height of his powers with, arguably, twenty-five years' work ahead of him when his health started to decline and then he died suddenly in 1872, it is believed now of undiagnosed diabetes. Another President of the IESS, the late Professor James Small in a paper given to the same Institution described Professor W J Macquorn Rankine in a worthy manner: 'Great as Rankine's achievements were as physicist and practising engineer it is yet possible that at the bar of history he will be judged greatest in his development of the education of the engineer and his elevation of the dignity of the engineer's studies.'

SOURCES:

Barnes, Napier, Watts and Rankine (also editor),
Shipbuilding Theoretical and Practical
London and Glasgow, 1866

Small, Professor James
'The Institution's First President William John Macquorn Rankine'
Transactions of the Institution of Engineers and Shipbuilders in Scotland
Vol 100 (1956–7)

Charles Mitchell

1820–1895

CHARLES MITCHELL WAS neither the first nor the last Aberdonian to make his mark in the vibrant shipyards of the Tyne in the nineteenth century. As a young man, his dedication, his engineering background, his formal education and above all his optimism led him to the North East where he formed a shipbuilding business which in the fullness of time became the renowned Swan Hunter organisation.

His schooling was first at Ledingham's Academy in the (aptly-named) Correction Wynd, and then at Aberdeen Grammar School. An apprenticeship followed in the engineering and iron-founding firm of William Simpson and Co., believed to be forerunners of Hall Russell and Co. of Footdee ('Fittie'). The exact details of Mitchell's tertiary education are difficult to ascertain, but it is clear that he matriculated as an undergraduate at Marischal College in the University of Aberdeen, although there is no record of graduation. In the four ancient universities of Scotland, this was not uncommon, as attendance at classes in the eighteenth and early part of the nineteenth centuries was regarded as sufficient proof of willingness and integrity. Indeed the great **Lord Kelvin** never took his first degree at Glasgow.

During his apprenticeship, Mitchell worked long hours in the factory and the drawing office, attended classes, studied, yet found time to make model ships. By the late 1830s, he found himself attracted to the shipbuilding industry, and when asked by Andrew Leslie (then foreman boilermaker at Bowman, Vernon and Co, shipbuilders in Aberdeen) to teach him mechanical drawing, Mitchell found himself in the company of a like-minded individual. This relationship must have been beneficial, as both men, later, were to head up shipyards on the Tyne. Incidentally, Bowman, Vernon had built Aberdeen's first iron ship *John Garrow*, which had the further distinction of being the first iron ship to enter the Tyne.

In 1842, on completion of his apprenticeship, he left Aberdeen and joined another Aberdonian named Coutts who had set up a shipyard on the River Tyne in 1840. Together they worked on iron colliers including the *QED*, which is reputed to be the first such ship with water ballast tanks, but after two years headed for London, only returning to the north-east in 1852 when he was ready to set up his own shipyard. It has been reported that he spent a short time at sea as Chief Engineer on the *QED*, for experience. In London Charles Mitchell worked for Maudslay, Sons and Field, then one of the world's finest yards, but possibly of greater importance, he rented rooms with a French-speaking family in order that he might be fluent in other languages. Holidays were spent on the Continent (something almost impossible in those days for most Scots), and Charles Mitchell, a gentleman in spirit, became an all-round engineer through his personal effort and integrity.

All people have to make decisions, and then work with them until success is achieved. Charles Mitchell's return to the North East was like this; good for him and his family, and of long-lasting benefit to the United Kingdom. Clearly monies must have been saved as he set up a new shipyard at Low Walker on the Tyne in 1852, and continued with it till his death in 1895. Between the years 1853 to 1882, the Low Walker yard produced 450 ships of ever-increasing tonnage and sophistication – that is one every three weeks for twenty-nine years! Within two years of re-settling on the Tyne, Charles met, fell in love and married Anne Walber, the eldest daughter of William Swan of West Farm. They set up home in the lands around Walker, which then had wildlife incongruously living close to hard-working coal staithes. In later years the couple moved to the up-and-coming suburb of Newcastle known as Jesmond and were to build the pretentious Jesmond Towers. Their son Charles William Mitchell did not follow in his father's footsteps, but became an artist of some renown, and indeed his portrait of his father can be seen in Aberdeen University.

The Russian connection was of great importance. In 1862, the shipbuilders on the Neva in St Petersburg decided on a complete reconstruction of their yards, which in time led to the setting up of the Admiralty Shipyards, in which Charles

Mitchell was to play a small but significant role. Following the obligatory due diligence, Charles left his son-in-law, Harry Frederick Swan in charge of the yard – what a challenge to a twenty-year-old former apprentice. In Walker, several armoured vessels were completed under an agreement whereby Mitchell completed the hulls and **Sir William Armstrong**'s company at Elswick, west of Newcastle supplied ordnance. This arrangement worked well and in 1882 the two companies combined to form Sir W G Armstrong, Mitchell and Co with works in Elswick, Low Walker as well as a small subsidiary in Italy. In all the new firm employed close on 15,000 men and in the closing years of the nineteenth century was to become a major supplier of warships to the world, being especially renowned for the 'Elswick Cruisers'.

Among the significant ships built at Walker were the pioneer cable-laying ships *Hooper* and *Faraday*, and shortly afterwards floating docks bound for Dutch service in Java, now Indonesia. Possibly the most important ship built at Walker was to be the *Gluckauf*, now regarded as the first oil tanker. However, by this time Charles Mitchell had taken a back seat in the operation and was involved in charitable developments in Tyneside and elsewhere. He funded the construction of St George's Church in Jesmond, and then after careful consideration made some quite significant gifts to Aberdeen University which responded by naming the tower in the magnificent Marischall College after him and then naming the graduation hall as the Mitchell Hall. Mitchell was awarded an LL.D. in 1893 and was to have received the Freedom of the City of Aberdeen, but died in August 1895 just prior to the ceremony.

In 1897, Sir W G Armstrong, Mitchell and Co merged with Sir Joseph Whitworth and Co and with no member of the Mitchell family being on the board, the name was omitted in the new appellation of Armstrong, Whitworth and Co Ltd.

SOURCES:
McGuire, D F
Charles Mitchell, 1820 1895, Victorian Shipbuilder
Newcastle upon Tyne, 1988

David Kirkaldy

1820–1897

ONE OF THE FIRST truly dedicated researchers in metallurgy, David Kirkaldy, a Dundonian by birth, had his early education in that city whilst living in fairly comfortable circumstances. On reaching the years of secondary education, he was sent to Merchiston Castle School near Edinburgh to prepare for matriculation at Edinburgh University. The school was in the grounds of the ancestral home of the Napiers of Merchiston, a family whose forbears included one of the greatest mathematicians of his age, **John Napier** (1550–1617), a former student of St Andrews and the creator of logarithms. Kirkaldy's delight at being allocated Napier's room for his study shows his early interest in scientific matters and his awareness of the intellectual tradition of his homeland.

In 1843, Kirkaldy moved to Glasgow and commenced an engineering apprenticeship under the engineer and shipbuilder **Robert Napier**. After four years on the shop floor, Kirkaldy entered the drawing office and within a few years was recognised as one of the finest ship draughtsmen to come from the Clyde. Not only could he record, understand and transmit technical detail on paper, but he had the ability to produce plans and even rough sketches which were a joy to behold. In 1855, Napiers built the wonderful iron paddle-steamer *Persia* for the company later to be known as the Cunard Line. The 'as fitted' plans of this ship, drawn in Kirkaldy's home in North Kelvinside, Glasgow, were to be awarded medals at the Paris Exhibition of that year and later to be exhibited at the Royal Academy in London. They are now recognised as being amongst the finest of their kind in the world, and fittingly are in the possession of the National Maritime Museum, Greenwich. In later years David Kirkaldy was to admit that his work on the *Persia*'s plans had been 'a greatly enjoyed indulgence'.

As the Napier Shipyard went from strength to strength, Kirkaldy rose through the ranks, reaching the ultimate position of Chief Draughtsman and Calculator. In the late 1850s, the shipyard was involved in quotations for advanced boilers and steam machinery and for early ironclads. As an aside, Robert Napier was the first major shipbuilder to break the monopoly of the Royal Dockyards and the shipyards of Southern England in building the Queen's Ships. This breakthrough followed recognition by the Admiralty that Napier was building for truly prestigious customers, including the Royal Danish Navy.

With the daunting task of building HMS *Black Prince* (the sister-ship of HMS *Warrior* now preserved in Portsmouth), the shipyard's technical arm was moving into top gear. Among the first requirements were accurate predictions on the strength and qualities of puddled iron, wrought iron and the relatively new alloy known as steel. For three years Kirkaldy worked on tensile and other test experiments, and in 1861 published his preliminary findings in the *Transactions of the Scottish Shipbuilders' Association* (now the Institution of Engineers and Shipbuilders in Scotland). Shortly after in 1862, his great work *Experiments on Wrought Iron and Steel* was published in London, bringing him international acclaim.

In 1861, Kirkaldy resigned from Robert Napier's, moved to London and for over two years worked on the setting-up of proper metallurgical testing facilities at The Grove in Southwark. The role of the independent testing engineer was becoming appreciated in engineering circles and soon the testing house was overwhelmed with work. Within eight years the laboratory had to be moved to larger premises at 99 Southwark Street, London, an address they were to remain at until 1974. He had to endure some bitter attacks on his professionalism, as those whose work had been shown to be sub-standard used the ages-old complaint that decisions had been made either in conditions of unnecessary commercial privacy or in conditions that were organised to be *sub judice*. Such complaints, whilst hurtful, did not deter him in any way. He used almost all of his personal resources to design and manufacture what was then the ultimate in tensile testing machines, a monster of 116 tons. This machine was built practically fault-free through his care and attention to detail; it was able to make a wide variety of tests with surprising delicacy and accuracy. During the move from The Grove to Southwark Street, it had to be dismantled and transported this relatively short distance.

The machine carried out some remarkable tasks, starting with the testing of materials used in the building of Blackfriars Bridge in London. Later it would be involved in the aftermath of one of Britain's greatest transport tragedies. On 28 December 1879, thirteen girders of the Tay Bridge fell into the River Tay, as the Burntisland to Dundee train crossed this wide estuary. All seventy-five passengers and crew were drowned and a full judicial enquiry was ordered. David Kirkaldy and his laboratory were instructed to examine the iron structure as well as the design of the ill-fated bridge. They did so and produced an illuminating and helpful report, making suggestions for improvements in tie links, riveting and material hardening. The business never looked back and by the early twentieth century, the Kirkaldy Testing House in south-east London was recognised in the structural engineering field as one of the leading arbiters for most metallurgical problems.

David Kirkaldy died in 1897, and his business was continued by his son William G Kirkaldy and ultimately by his grandson David W Kirkaldy until it closed in 1974.

SOURCES:
Kirkaldy, D
'Results of an Experimental Enquiry into the Tensile Strength and other Properties of Wrought Iron and Steel'
Transactions of the Scottish Shipbuilders Association
(1860–1)

Thomas B Seath

1820–1903

IN THE CENTRE OF GLASGOW, at the point which divides the tidal and the non-tidal River Clyde, is a centuries-old park known as the Glasgow Green. Nowadays the few miles up-river from the Green to Rutherglen have little of maritime interest beyond a few moored converted lifeboats and the regular passing of University and City rowing crews. It was here, however, that **James Watt** took his legendary stroll one Sunday in May 1765, and

In 1888 the *Lucy Ashton* was delivered by the small shipyard of T B Seath, and for the next sixty years served unceasingly in the passenger and mail service of the upper Clyde estuary. In 1950 she was purchased by the British Shipbuilding Research Association for the testing of skin friction co-efficients. Stripped of all appendages and superstructure, she was driven up and down the Gareloch measured mile by four Rolls Royce jet engines, and the results were compared with those deduced in several test tanks world-wide using extremely accurate geosims (Geometrically Similar Models) correct down to the original hull's 150mm hog. *(Author)*

it was near here that a remarkable maritime enterprise flourished in the late nineteenth century.

In 1853, Thomas Seath commenced iron shipbuilding at a yard in Partick near the western boundary of Glasgow and with access to deep water and good moorings, but within three years moved up-stream to the shallow stretches of the River above Glasgow Green. A couple of acres of ground was leased from Rutherglen Corporation and despite the unpromising nature of the area, over 300 ships were produced here in the following forty-seven years; one every seven working weeks. As the shallow twisting and non-tidal river made large-scale shipbuilding impractical, Seath concentrated on vessels less than 60m (196ft) in length and with minimal delivery draft. The massive nineteenth-century sales of ships for the overseas market, enabled him to break into the 'knock-down' or 'Meccano' market and here he developed an enviable expertise in small vessels for delivery in package form or sometimes as deck cargo to places as far afield as Burma and Australia.

'Tammie' Seath was born in Prestonpans, but shortly after the family moved to Glasgow, largely it is believed that their son could obtain good medical attention following a spinal injury which was to trouble him all his life. Seath's father was employed by a coastal shipping company, and Thomas grew up knowing much about the management and operation of small commercial vessels, and on leaving school he joined the crew of a Glasgow–Liverpool steamer. Despite his continuing health problems, he worked and studied to obtain the qualifications necessary for him to act as both master/pilot and engineer for small ships operating in the upper Clyde. In 1856, for his own account, and it believed at the Partick yard, he built a 33m (108ft) paddle steamer, the *Artizan*, which plied six times daily in each direction (a fifteen-minute journey) between Hutchesontown Bridge in Glasgow and Rutherglen Quay. It proved a great success and was replaced soon after by another the PS *Royal Burgh*, again owned and often commanded by Seath. The *Artizan* was a remarkable vessel operating with a draft of a mere 0.7m (27in) and with the main engine controls operated from the bridge – arguably a maritime first. In time the *Royal Burgh* was replaced by another paddle steamer, the *Royal Reefer*, but by then the shipbuilding side of the business kept him so busy that he was forced to forego his beloved river jaunts.

Later he designed and built the 'Cluthas'; small passenger steamers which operated on the main river near the city centre until made redundant at the turn of the century by Glasgow's tramways, then the largest network in the world. Almost all his ships were built of iron, a factor contributing to their longevity. Currently the two oldest are the *Esperance* of 1869 and the *Raven* of 1871, both on Lake Windermere and in their original condition, and on nearby Ullswater the slightly younger *Lady of the Lake* (1877) and *Raven* (1889) are both in operating condition. Two royal yachts were commissioned from T B Seath and Company in 1872, the *Fairy* for the King of Burma and the *Little Eastern* for the King of Siam.

Without question, their most famous hull was Ship No 258, the Clyde paddle steamer *Lucy Ashton*, built in 1888 for the North British Steam Packet, an arm of the North British Railway, later to become part of the LNER group. Throughout the Second World War the *Lucy Ashton* served year in and year out, round the clock, on passenger and mail services and on tendering troopships at the Tail of the Bank. By the late 1940s her condition was such that British Railways placed her on the disposal list. But instead of going to the breakers, she was purchased by the British Shipbuilding Research Association, and prepared for hull trials similar to those of HMS *Greyhound* of eighty years before. Stripped of machinery and all appendages except her rudder, she was fitted with four Rolls Royce Derwent jet engines and then, using ear-splitting jet propulsion, was subjected to carefully monitored resistance trials on the Gareloch. Six meticulously-manufactured geosim models were produced and the test results compared with the predictions of six ship model testing tanks throughout the world. The results, the first re-analyses of skin friction undertaken for many years were published in the 1951 and subsequent *RINA Transactions*. The first paper was presented by **Sir Maurice Denny**.

Around 1901, the yard found itself without orders and Seath's sons took the opportunity to look around for a more suitable building site, and sold the yard to William Chalmers and Company. Thomas, who was then aged over eighty, died shortly after and the sons decided then to change the emphasis of the business and concentrate on work as shipbuilding consultants and naval architects. Seath had an influence on shipbuilding far beyond that of many yards with greater output; and despite being one of the smallest of the (then) fifty or sixty shipyards on the Clyde, the company led in specialist and in knock-down tonnage and exported small vessels to all quarters of the globe. Thomas Seath had to contend with physical disability throughout his life, but is remembered as a genial man, with a ready wit, considerable literary and musical talent and an abundance of sheer enthusiasm.

SOURCES:
Bowen, Frank C
'The Rutherglen Yard'
Shipbuilding and Shipping News
(14 July 1949)
Denny, Sir Maurice E
'BSRA Resistance Experiments on the Lucy Ashton – Part 1 Full Scale Measurements'
Transactions of the Institution of Naval Architects
Vol 93 (1951)
Obituary for T B Seath
Transactions of the Institution of Engineers and Shipbuilders in Scotland
Vol 46 (1902–3)

Andrei Alexandrovitch Popoff
1821–1898

A RUSSIAN ADMIRAL with unconventional views on ship design, Andrei Popoff studied at the Russian Naval School and on graduation was commissioned into the Russian navy. His father A A Popoff (1788–1859) was an admiral and shipbuilder, and the son was to follow closely in his footsteps. His early career saw service in the Black Sea and Pacific fleets and ultimately command of the auxiliary cruiser *Meteor*. Having served the obligatory apprenticeship as a staff officer, he took command of the Pacific fleet, where for many years he was regarded as a harsh taskmaster making unreasonable demands, but with the ships acknowledged as smart. One contemporary commentator described him as a successful admiral and the vessels under his command as 'taut rather than happy'. His technical knowledge was good and he was one of a small group of admirals involved in the rethinking of policy within the Russian navy following the Crimean War. While in the Pacific he paid several well-publicised official visits to the USA, during

Admiral A A Popoff, 1821–1898, one of only two Russians to have become honorary members of the (Royal) Institution of Naval Architects. *(The Royal Institution of Naval Architects)*

one of which he sent Russian sailors ashore in San Francisco to assist in fighting a fire.

In 1856, a new role came with his appointment as superintendent for construction of steam-powered ships. He threw himself into this task with enthusiasm and started to travel in Europe, visiting shipyards and naval establishments. In Britain he became acquainted with **Sir Edward Reed**, later to become Director of Naval Construction and with **John Elder** and his successor Sir William Pearce, principal of John Elder's shipyard in Glasgow. These three men were to give him encouragement and support while he investigated some unconventional ship designs.

His first unusual vessel was the turret ship *Petr Veliki*, completed in 1876 with the fairly normal length-to-beam ratio of 5.5, but low freeboard and heavy machinery low down with resulting high metacentric height which gave her a most unpleasant motion in rough seas. Popoff noted that Reed had decreased the length-to-beam ratio of many of the ships of the Royal Navy and with the need for two or more defensive gunboats for the Black Sea and the Sea of Azov, he decided to take the matter to the extreme and build ships with low freeboard raked inboard, and completely round in plan view. There were a series of substantial arguments in favour of this including improved protection from shells, the probability of reduced ship motions and the decrease in the cost of armour (relative to ship length and capacity).

The new ships were designed to be ultra-steady gun platforms for coastal defence in shallow waters such as the Black Sea. The first, *Novgorod*, with a maximum 'diameter' of 31m (101ft 8in), was laid down in 1871 at St Petersburg, then 'knocked down' and delivered to the Nicolaiev yard on the Black Sea, re-assembled and then commissioned in 1874. The second was the slightly enlarged *Kiev* which was completed in 1877. The Russian Navy renamed the latter vessel *Vice Admiral Popoff*, and she and her sister have been known ever since as 'Popoffskas'. Her crew reported that the *Novgorod* behaved well and could operate in the shallow waters of the Sea of Azov, and indeed Sir Edward Reed agreed with this following a visit to the area. Steering proved more difficult, however, and at the Institution of Naval Architects in London, many members were sceptical about the claims for speed. Had these ships been accepted as slow, stable gun-platforms for use in shallow waters, then they might have been remembered as a success, and it is possible that other navies might have copied them.

One remarkable development was to follow: a contract for a new Russian Imperial Yacht was put out to tender, based on a modified 'Popoffska' design; rumour had it that Empress Maria Alexandrovna was prone to seasickness. The Elder shipyard at Fairfield in Govan, following large-scale research and experimentation, secured the work. They had instructed **Johannes Tidemann** of the Royal Netherlands Navy to carry out open water model propulsion tests in Amsterdam, which were replicated on a larger scale in Loch Lomond shortly after. The new ship was not circular, but described by William Pearce as being similar to a turbot, a beautifully-shaped flatfish. With the order came a penalty clause for a massive financial retention in the event of the ship failing to meet the stipulated speed. The ship was constructed with Lieutenant Goulaeff of the Russian Navy as owners' representative. She was named *Livadia*, after the Tsar's Black Sea residence in the Crimea, and was launched on 17 July 1880 by the Duchess of Hamilton. Her trials were an unqualified success with the ship meeting her minimum speed with ease, and then travelling under her own power from Greenock to the Black Sea. *En route* she had several distinguished passengers including Grand Duke Constantine, Sir Edward Reed and others. In frightful sea conditions and with waves up to 8m (26ft) in height in the Bay of Biscay, the *Livadia* rolled less than 2.5 degrees and pitched less than 4 degrees. However, on arrival at the Spanish port of Ferrol it was found that she had sustained severe slamming damage, then an only recently-recognised phenomenon. By the time *Livadia* arrived at Sevastopol, Empress Maria Alexandrovna was dead and shortly after that Tsar Alexander II was assassinated in St Petersburg. The *Livadia* was placed in reserve and her magnificent outfit and equipment allowed to perish. The ship remained a hulk well into the communist era, and has now disappeared. Popoff was promoted Admiral in 1891 and died in 1897.

SOURCES:

Goulaeff, E E
'Circular Ironclads'
Transactions of the Institution of Naval Architects
Vol 17 (1876).

———,
'The Russian Imperial Yacht
Livadia', *Transactions of the Institution of Naval Architects*
Vol 22 (1881).

Mitchell, Donald W
A History of Russian and Soviet Sea Power
London, 1974

Reed, Sir E J
'The Injuries sustained by the Livadia in the Bay of Biscay'
Transactions of the Institution of Naval Architects
Vol 22 (1881)

Sir Charles Mark Palmer

1822–1907

AN INDUSTRIALIST FROM the north-east of England, Charles Palmer founded the unique industrial complex of Palmers Shipbuilding and Iron Company at Jarrow on the Tyne, which encompassed every aspect of ship production, from the smelting of ore to the delivery of capital ships. At its peak it employed just over 10,000 men and in eighty-three years produced over 1,000 ships.

Born into a prosperous South Shields family, after leaving school Palmer spent some time in Marseilles learning French before joining a firm of coal merchants. The coal business was expanding in Britain and by 1847 he had become a partner, giving him a taste for commercial operations. In 1851, with his brother George, he made the first of the many thrusting developments that were to characterise his life, in this case the leasing of a former shipbuilding site at Jarrow, on the south bank of the Tyne 3 miles from the Shields and 7 miles from Newcastle. Despite no previous relevant experience, they resolved to set up as shipbuilders and from the outset all vessels were to be of iron (and later steel). The first launch was that of the tug *Northumberland*, one of the few ships slid into the water without the great ceremony that later was to be associated with this company.

Success in a new shipyard is dependent on the quality of supervision, and here Palmer was astute in appointing John McIntyre from Govan as manager and William Cleland, another Clydesider, as foreman. Their second ship was the single-screw steam collier *John Bowes*, one of the most innovative designs of the mid-nineteenth century, with her engines aft and with water ballast tanks designed by the yard manager. The *John Bowes* could lift 650 tons of coal and complete a round-trip to London in five days. This compared most favourably with the collier brigs which could carry at most 300 tons and which in good conditions might make the same round-trip in five or six weeks. The iron colliers cost around £10,000 against the £1,000 for a collier brig, so the brothers took a gamble when they set up the General Iron Screw Collier Company in

The historic photograph of the pioneer steam collier *John Bowes* **passing her birthplace, Palmers Shipyard, fifty-four years after her launch. Behind are the famous Jarrow shipyard gantries.** (*From Palmer's Handbook, 1909*)

1852. It paid off handsomely, however, at a time when the railways were targeting the coal traffic from the eastern coalfields to London.

Developments continued with Palmer setting up an engineering works from which the first new product, quite appropriately, was a single-cylinder steam engine for the collier *Jarrow*. In 1856, the shipyard delivered the floating armoured battery *Terror* to the Royal Navy, the first naval contract for an iron ship to come to the north-east of England. This was the beginning of a long and profitable builder/owner relationship between the Jarrow Company and the Senior Service, culminating in the order for the magnificent battlecruiser *Queen Mary* of 1911. This line of business ensured that Palmer's could venture into iron smelting and steel manufacture, and in the fullness of time develop armour plate rolling mills.

With the building of blast furnaces, the Jarrow site (now of over 100 acres and a ¾-mile river frontage) could claim to complete the cycle of changing iron ore into nothing short of complex steamships, warships, and steam engines. Palmer had ore brought to the site from Spain and North Africa in 3,000-ton deadweight freighters, and by 1900 the plant was producing almost a quarter of million tons of ferrous products per year.

This complete vertical integration included a plate glass company and a metals company. The shipyard, which was to remain in business until 1932, continued to develop with an early entry into the tanker business and the successful building of some high-class intermediate passenger and cargo liners, then in great demand for the mail routes of the British and other overseas empires. Niche markets were developed, one being the supply of riveted pre-fabricated parts to shipyards and construction sites. One of the most unusual aspects of the Jarrow yard was the (then) unique erection system, where two great gantries, one at the head of the berths and another at the river end, held in place a network of wires on which travelling lifting gear could reach any part of the ship. In keeping with all of this Palmers built the largest dry-dock in the north-east of England and developed a successful ship-repair business.

The infrastructure of the town of Jarrow changed beyond recognition in fifty years; the quiet rural area became a small industrial town, bringing with it all the drawbacks of heavy industry in close proximity to a population of 40,000. With the help of Palmer, the town had a Mechanics Institute and an excellent hospital, named after his first wife. However, the most remarkable feature was the founding in 1860 of a building society which enabled many of the workforce to buy their own homes. By the end of the century Jarrow could claim that it had a higher owner-occupancy rate than any similar-sized town in the UK.

Charles Mark Palmer was a man of his time. In the words of David Dougan '... one cannot win economic battles, any more than one can win military ones with an altruistic spirit . . .'. In 1893, the company faced bankruptcy. Despite having been one of the earliest limited companies, a series of complicated moves were required to remain trading, including the Palmer's resignation. He continued to sit as a Member of Parliament until his death in 1907.

Palmers continued operation until 1934 when the yard was purchased and 'sterilised' by National Shipbuilders Security Limited. The ship repair and dry-docking business, however, carried on until the 1970s under the name of Palmers Hebburn Ltd.

SOURCES:
Bowen, Frank C
'Shipbuilders of other Days – Palmers of Jarrow'
Shipbuilding and Shipping Record
(24 January 1952)
Dougan, David
The History of North East Shipbuilding
London, 1968
Some Account of the Works of Palmers Shipbuilding and Iron Company Limited
Fourth Edition (Newcastle upon Tyne, 1909)

William Pile

1823–1873

SUNDERLAND HAS A long and distinguished shipbuilding history. A shipbuilding site on the banks of the Wear was authorised in 1346, beginning one of the longest runs of continuous industry in Britain, which ended with the closure of the Pallion Shipyard in the late 1980s, following the decision of the Conservative government to transfer support to Japanese car manufacturers in the north-east of England.

Of all the many great shipbuilders of Sunderland, a name that stands head and shoulders above rest is that of William Pile Jr. Being a man of unbounded enthusiasm for ships and coming from a family with long-standing shipbuilding connections, Pile's quick and successful rise in the industry will come as no surprise. In his teens, he had served an apprenticeship (under his father William Pile Senior who had a small shipyard on the Wear), then moved to Lightfoot's yard in Monkwearmouth before returning to his father's new yard in Southwick as foreman. At the age of twenty, he set up his own yard in the North Sands and in the 1840s one of the legends of the north-east was born.

Pile's yard would have been little different from the many small, undercapitalised yards in Sunderland, and is unlikely to have had more than a score of men and boys on the register. However, in one respect it was different: its clientele came from many parts of Britain, from as far north as Fraserburgh and as 'deep south' as the London River, indicating Pile's willingness to be adventurous, to travel and to nurture a new breed of client. This may seem of little importance in today's world, but in the 1840s travel was uncertain and credit arrangements were even more difficult to obtain. The 1850s were to witness some fine craft coming from Pile's slipways, and all the time these ships were becoming bigger and the hulls becoming 'finer', emulating the fine shape and hollow bow of the fast sailing vessels from Aberdeen. Ships were built for the Baltic trade, for the Indian trade, the Australian trade and ultimately the very high-class South Australian emigrant trade. In 1852 the new yard had the good fortune to receive an order from John Hay of Sunderland for the *King Richard*, believed to be a ship (that is a full-rigged ship) and whose hull shape was based on that of the Sunderland coble. In a short time the ship had been sold to **Richard Green**, the shipbuilder at Blackwall on the Thames, and had been renamed *Roxburgh Castle*. This ship had the effect of introducing William Pile and Richard Hay (one of John's family) who became partners in 1860 and of persuading Green to order further vessels from Pile – a fantastic achievement, as Green had his own shipyard at Blackwall! Many ships were built for the Greens, and almost all with names associated with the South East of England, like *The Lord Warden*, *Walmer Castle* and *Dover Castle*.

In 1860 Pile and Hay went into partnership and the business was moved to a site recently vacated by J L Thompson. The new company was to exist for a mere six years, but during that period it built about sixty ships, introduced iron construction and commenced the construction of steam reciprocating engines. The growth was so remarkable that by 1865 the total labour force numbered 3,000 men. One of their most distinguished vessels was the

Launched into the River Wear by William Pile in 1864, the very fast composite-built clipper ship *Coral Nymph* had a short but distinguished career in the China tea trade. In 1867, she arrived back in Britain with an apprentice George Arthur, a young Shetlander, in command following various accidents during the voyage. The ship was lost the following year off the China coast. *(Chinese School ship portrait in private collection)*

composite-built fully-rigged South Australian emigrant ship *City of Adelaide* built for Devitt and Moore and (in the year 2009) still intact, but awaiting probable breaking-up. This ship, after a very full career, became HMS *Carrick*, a Royal Naval Volunteer Reserve (RNVR) accommodation ship on the Clyde and later, the ship of the RNVR (Scotland) Club. Currently it is in the hands of the Scottish Maritime Museum, Irvine. The first steamship built by them was the iron screw brig *Stettin* of 480 tons. In 1866, following the retirement of Richard Hay, the name of the firm reverted to William Pile and Company and work was to continue until Pile's death seven years later. 1868 saw a further expansion with the purchase of the Bridge Graving Dock, making the Pile organisation a real force to be reckoned with in Sunderland.

The first composite vessel was the barque *Sarah* launched in 1863. Altogether another eighteen such hulls were completed including the fast tea clipper *Coral Nymph* which is referred to elsewhere in this book. Pile seems to have had a fairly straightforward relationship with Lloyd's surveyors; he was known to defend his views in a robust manner, but equally was intent on building the highest quality of ship. An example of this occurred in 1850 when Lloyd's Register increased the topside plank thickness of wooden ships by a significant amount. Pile informed the Lloyd's visiting committee courteously that this would cost his business several hundred pounds a year (then a considerable sum) but he acknowledged that he would accept their ruling without further complaint. Several of his composite hulls were built under cover in order that they might qualify for the Lloyd's class 17A1, an endorsement that the hull with normal care should be serviceable for seventeen years. Few shipyards anywhere could claim to have such a level of experience in this unique form of construction.

In 1873 and at the early age of (around) fifty, William Pile died in London. He left a large and complex organisation, and it has been reported that difficulties arose in the settlement of both business and estate matters as close to twenty ships were under construction. One of Pile's employees, and also a former apprentice, George Hunter, formed a new company named Austin and Hunter. He took over two hulls, had them dismantled and moved to his new yard for completion. His success can be gauged by the fact that he became Sir George Hunter and his surname became enshrined in the title of Tyneside's great Swan Hunter shipyard. J L Thompson's shipyard acquired much of the work and plant of Pile and Co.

SOURCES:
Bowen, F C
'Pile of Sunderland'
Shipbuilding and Shipping Record
(January 1945)
Clarke, J F
Building Ships on the North East Coast
2 vols (Whitley Bay, 1997)

Bernard Waymouth

1824–1890

FOLLOWING STAFF reductions at Devonport Dockyard at the end of the Napoleonic Wars, Bernard Waymouth's father accepted an appointment at Pembroke Dock, and moved with his wife Eliza and eleven children to Milford Haven. Their third child, Bernard, who had been born in 1824, served a shipwright apprenticeship at the Dockyard. Around 1846 (for family reasons) Bernard moved to London and joined the staff of Money, Wigram and Sons which a few years earlier had taken over the western part of the former Blackwall Shipyard on the Thames, and was one of the companies in Britain then experimenting with iron ship construction. He remained there until he was twenty-nine years old and then made two changes, first by marrying the daughter of a naval officer and secondly, by joining the staff of Lloyd's Register as an assistant surveyor in London. With shipping and shipbuilding going through a technical near-revolution in the mid-nineteenth century, Waymouth had positioned himself to carry out the work that would bring him renown.

After work in various outports for Lloyd's, Waymouth was appointed London Senior Surveyor in 1858 and was charged with the task of preparing the Rules for Construction of Composite Ships, that is, vessels with iron keels, keelsons, frames, stringers and beams, but with timber hulls and decks. Around the late 1850s and the 1860s, composite ships were being built in Aberdeen, Glasgow, Greenock, London and Sunderland where their inherent strength was recognised. Possibly of greater importance was that this form of construction enabled vessels to be built longer than had been possible before. For this work, Waymouth had neither practical precedents nor theoretical research to guide him, and had to prepare the rules using pragmatism and empiricism. The final rulebook, beautifully illustrated by another outstanding naval architect Jack Cornish (1839–1928, and a vice president of the INA) was published in 1867. Composite shipbuilding lasted no more than twenty years, but the success of these specialist vessels (including the extant clipper ships *City of Adelaide* and *Cutty Sark*) is witness to the first of his triumphs.*

In 1825, George Thompson, an Aberdeen merchant, set up a shipping business known later as the Aberdeen White Star Line, and which in a period of 125 years was to have sixty sailing ships and close on twenty steamers, mostly serving on the London to Australia trade. Many of the ships were built at Walter Hood's Aberdeen shipyard, and one in particular, the composite full-rigged ship *Thermopylæ* was to become the fastest tea clipper of all time. For reasons that are obscure, Bernard Waymouth was allowed by Lloyd's Register to design *Thermopylæ*, and working together with these superb builders, produced a ship that could 'ghost along' at six knots in a near-calm but, more remarkably, that was to set the all-time record for a sailing ship of sixty days from London to Melbourne. The design of tea clippers was part art and part science, but the outcome had to be a sailing vessel capable of sustained high speed with bale capacity sufficient to carry enough high-value cargo in a single voyage (tea in this case) to pay all charges for one year. As tea is light, these ships rarely sailed on maximum drafts, and the loading in Shanghai or other Chinese port had to be closely supervised to ensure cargo was crammed into every conceivable space and then rammed down with mallets. With 1,000 tons of tea and 250 tons of ballast *Thermopylæ* would be brought to her marks for returning to Britain from China. It is accepted that the only competitor to the green-painted Aberdeen clipper was the Dumbarton-built *Cutty Sark* designed by **Hercules Linton** of Kincardineshire (1836–1900).

One might be forgiven for assuming that with the successful introduction of Lloyd's Composite Shipbuilding Rules and the design of what is arguably the greatest British sailing vessel of all time, Waymouth would be happy to rest on his laurels. Nothing could be further from the truth, as in the years that followed he was to make a singular contribution to both Lloyd's Register and shipping in general. The first was a complete revision of the Rules for Iron Ships which were formulated after proper scientific analysis, and were to be the model for many later publications. In 1870 he was appointed Principal Surveyor, a post he held for two years before becoming Secretary of the Classification Society until his death in 1890. Immediately after becoming Principal Surveyor, he made a tour of the Continent, resulting in the setting up of 'Non-exclusive Lloyd's Surveyorships' in major cities like Copenhagen, Genoa and Marseilles, appointments that became key to the long-term development of 'LR' in twentieth century Europe. In a similar manner, he acted for Lloyd's Register in 1885 when they fused with the Liverpool Registry, the first of many mergers. This in turn led, at Waymouth's suggestion, to the setting-up of Lloyd's Printing House, which produced the 1891 Register Book shortly after his death.

It is interesting to note that even after being appointed Secretary of Lloyd's Register, he found time (and persuaded his employers there was no conflict of interest) to design a sailing ship, this being the highly successful fully-rigged iron passenger and cargo ship *Melbourne*. She was built on the Thames in 1875 by **R & H Green**, the company which had taken over the eastern half of the Blackwall Shipyard. Twelve years after her launching she was purchased by the crack passenger shipping line of Devitt and Moore, renamed *Macquarrie* and put on the London to Sydney run.

SOURCES:
Annals of Lloyd's Register
London, 1934
Coates, Jane, and Coates, John
Bernard Waymouth and the change from Wood to Steel Ships
Newcomen Society, 1999–2000
Lubbock, Basil
The China Clippers
Glasgow, 1919

*HMS *Gannet*, a composite naval sloop built in 1876, can be viewed at the Chatham Historic Dockyard.

Hercules Linton
1836–1900

ONE OF THE ADMIRABLE traditions of shipbuilding is that the credit for a new ship is given not to individuals but collectively to the builders. Most naval architects have shared in the team pride as a 'new-building' leaves the yard for the sea. However, from time to time an individual ship is attributed publicly to her designer, and two notable examples come to mind, both ships with an imperishable name. The Clyde-built clipper ship *Cutty Sark* designed by Hercules Linton, and her most deadly rival, the Aberdeen built *Thermopylæ* which came from the drawing board of **Bernard Waymouth**.

Hercules Linton was born in Inverbervie, a small town 40km (25 miles) south of Aberdeen, then in the County of Kincardineshire. Schooling was at the nearby village of Arbuthnott, and later at Arbroath Academy. His father had trained as a shipwright, and was an independent ship surveyor and was friendly with the Hall family of Aberdeen, the

Small, fine-lined and with a sharp entry, *Cutty Sark* **was what has come to be defined as an extreme clipper, a specialist ship built for speed in the valuable China tea trade. This was at a time when the development of steam and the building of the Suez Canal sounded the death-knell of the fast sailing ship.** (© *National Maritime Museum, Greenwich, PO2414*)

proprietors of the shipyard of Alexander Hall and Company, which had been founded in 1790. The first concrete evidence of Hercules Linton's career is that on 1 January he was indentured to Alexander Hall and then served five years as an apprentice. Clearly his unusually late start did him little harm as he was 'fast-tracked' for promotion and rose to a position of some responsibility within the company. Hall's were a distinguished yard, having in 1840 built the *Scottish Maid*, the forerunners of the Aberdeen Clippers, and during the period Linton served there (from 1855 to c1863) he had wide experience working on their considerable output including several full-rigged ships like the *Robin Hood* and the *Friar Tuck* for the China tea trade.

A few years later he moved into the service of the Liverpool Underwriters' Registry as a surveyor, ultimately becoming an independent surveyor and working from time to time with Lloyd's Register. During this period, and while he resided in Glasgow, he became friendly with a much younger man, William Dundas Scott. They decided to enter shipbuilding as partners and after looking at various sites, settled on Dumbarton and rented a part of the Wood Yard of William Denny's shipyard. Linton's duties were to handle the design and construction, while Scott was to deal with office and engineering matters. The yard, which commenced operations on Whitsunday 1868, had ceased operations by January 1870, but despite this had built seven ships and nearly completed two others in that very short period and with a turnover of something close to £40,000. It is said that Scott's ineptitude was the main cause of the cash-flow problems that beset them from the beginning, as the quality of work was good. Incidentally their fourth contract was an early 'knock-down' hull for the Japanese, then a new and growing market.

Scott and Linton, the name of this short-lived shipyard, will be inscribed forever in the shipbuilding halls of fame, as they were the main constructors of the composite-built tea clipper *Cutty Sark*. The order was placed under quite punishing terms at a mere £17 per ton, for a composite hull formed of iron skeletal framework with timber hull sheathing and decks of timber of the highest quality. (Generally the Aberdeen yards had better rates, were in areas with lower labour costs, had completed several hundred large sailing ships, and had a great deal of experience under their belts.) Despite the novelty of the work all proceeded well, except that some costly additions were demanded during construction, and that nearing completion time, Scott and Linton had to borrow from creditors including Matthew Paul, marine engineer and Provost of Dumbarton. It is said that Paul and the Denny's made it difficult for the new shipyard to remain open, and in the end the company was declared bankrupt, the *Cutty Sark* was towed across to Denny's outfit quay and completed there at the end of November 1869. At the end of the whole sorry proceedings it became clear that the forced liquidation of Scott and Linton had been a mistake, as no-one gained anything from the action, and an up-and-coming shipyard had been obliterated.

Hercules Linton continued as a surveyor, working in Glasgow, Aberdeen and the British east coast. Life was quite difficult until he was discharged from the bankruptcy proceedings, but ultimately worked freelance for Gourlay's of Dundee and then T R Oswald of Pallion, Sunderland, a yard which was later to continue under a different guise as Oswald Mordaunt at Woolston, Southampton. Linton worked at Woolston from 1880 until 1884, during a period of quite innovative shipbuilding.

Hercules Linton's wife died in 1885, leaving him with nine surviving children. Ultimately he returned to the north-east coast of Scotland, settling in Inverbervie where he was a town councillor from 1895 until his death in May 1900. Outside ship design he was a respected Fellow of the Society of Antiquaries of Scotland, and contributed regularly at their meetings and in their Proceedings. Despite public duties and family affairs, the foreclosure of Scott and Linton was a desperate tragedy which hung over the rest of his life. On a happier note, in a memoir written by his daughter, she mentions that his last years were peaceful and he died as he would have wished on 15 May 1900, seated at the fireside reading *The Glasgow Herald*.

SOURCES:
Brettle, Robert E
The Cutty Sark: Her Designer and Builder Hercules Linton
Cambridge, 1969
Lubbock, Basil
The Log of the Cutty Sark
Glasgow, 1924

Wilhelm Bauer

1822–1875

ONE OF THE MOST inspired engineers of the mid-nineteenth century, Wilhelm Bauer left a legacy of bright and stimulating ideas and experiments which were all worthy of closer examination. Possibly his greatest claim to fame is that in 1850, when just twenty-eight years old, he produced a working submarine.

Bauer (the son of an NCO in a Bavarian regiment) was noted for his mechanical ability as well as a lifelong interest in maritime affairs. He learned the trade of a turner, but in May 1840, being unable to find work, followed his father into the army. He was posted to the war zone of Schleswig-Holstein, that part of the peninsula of Jutland which for years had been contested by Prussia and Denmark. Here Bauer had been amazed at the efficiency of the Royal Danish Navy and in the course of time felt that the only way to neutralise its ships would be by having vessels able to attack them from underwater. The politics of this part of the world were complicated, but it is sufficient to say that on peace being declared between Denmark and the future Germany, a further battle continued between Denmark and powers in Schleswig-Holstein that were looking for independence. Bauer threw in his lot with the latter and persuaded them that he could build a submarine.

With contributions from friends and from sources within the army a working model was constructed and then between 1850 and 1851 a full-sized boat was manufactured at Kiel. As ever, the construction had been compromised by cost-cutting, and on the first dive the boat *Brandtaucher*, as it had been named, took on too much ballast water and stuck on the bottom. With the hull leaking, Bauer calmed his two companions and they waited some hours till the pressure inside and outside the hull equalised and then using a shell door opening from the inside were able to make their escape in a rush of compressed air. Undoubtedly the first submarine escape!

Bauer then tried to interest the Austrians in his submarine designs, but to no avail, and then again the British where despite an introduction to Prince Albert, the Prince Consort, nothing was forthcoming. A short time after he travelled to Russia, where in 1855 under his direction a 15.8m (51ft 10in) submarine was built in St Petersburg. After being named *Le Diable Marin* (French was the language of the Russian Court), it was transported the 32km (20 miles) west to the naval base at Kronstadt and there went through a total of 144 trials, some of which had limited success, including the one when Bauer spent fours hours under water during the coronation of Tsar Alexander II. However, everything ended when the boat finally sank for good, fortunately without loss of life.

Bauer returned to Germany and produced many original ideas, most of which are beautifully drawn and recorded. In 1870 he drew up the plans of a helicopter-like flying machine called the *Deutscher Adler*. It was not dissimilar to the helicopter built and flown at the Denny Shipyard of Dumbarton shortly after 1905. In 1861 he was asked to raise the mailship *Ludwig* which had sunk in Lake Constance; for this successful operation he used two ships acting as camels, hundreds of empty barrels and two steam tugs. It was reported, however, that the costs of the recovery outweighed the receipts from the sale of the *Ludwig* and all the associated gear. As a postscript the former German submarine U-2540, which was built at Hamburg in 1945, has been restored and renamed *Wilhelm Bauer*. She is preserved afloat at Bremerhaven.

SOURCES:
Denny, Dumbarton 1844–1932
Wm Denny and Bros Ltd, 1932
Science and Technology in 19th Century Germany (Exhibition Handbook of Goethe-Institut, London, 1982)

Jakob Amsler-Laffon

1823–1912

THE BEAUTIFUL LAKES of Switzerland are host to fleets of elegant and well-operated excursion steamers; the country has a sizeable merchant marine operating worldwide and a great tradition of marine engineering. However, the success of Swiss naval architects is legendary, and in this field the contribution of Jakob Amsler was supreme. His mathematical research was nothing short of fundamental in the development of naval architecture, and until the 1970s, the family name was known in every ship design office throughout the world.

At the General Meeting of the Institution of Naval Architects in their old headquarters at Adelphi

A Polar Planimeter designed to calculate the area within an irregular shape, by tracing the outline of the shape and then noting the difference in the dial reading. This figure, when multiplied by a previously-calculated constant, gives the area within the shape. (*Author*)

Terrace, London, in 1884, seven papers – a remarkable number on ship stability – were presented. This upsurge in research was the inevitable reflection on the mounting ship losses of the time, culminating in the disastrous capsize of the ss *Daphne* after her launch into the Clyde in 1883. One of the papers at this historic gathering was presented by an Associate, Dr A Amsler from Switzerland, who described the Integrator designed by his father, an instrument which had eased and transformed the work of naval architects in preceding years, and which enabled extremely accurate stability information to be obtained. Using both integrators and planimeters, high-quality work was assured provided the ship plans were drawn to exacting standards. In the discussion following Dr Amsler's paper, Mr R E Froude, speaking on behalf of the Admiralty Experiment Tank at Torquay, said: 'We use almost nothing else for calculations of displacement, and hardly ever use the [Simpson's] rule at all ... we have found the planimeter calculation to be more correct than the rule ...'. Presumably there was pressure at Torquay to spend more time on resistance, propulsion and similar matters, and the planimeter, which saved time, had become their first choice for working on hull hydrostatics and stability.

The man who developed and marketed the planimeter was Jakob Amsler. Born into a farming family in Switzerland, he grew up in Stalden, a town on the banks of the River Rhone. Then as now, Swiss education was excellent, and Amsler qualified to enter the University of Jena to study divinity, but later on changing to another German university, that of Königsberg (now Kaliningrad), he developed a passion for mathematics and physics, and in the fullness of time returned to his native country with a science doctorate. After working for a year at the Geneva Observatory he moved to Zurich to teach and then moved again to the north of Switzerland and the Gymnasium at Schaffhausen where he had time to engage in mathematical research. It was here that he learned of the pioneering work of Poisson and others in the early years of the nineteenth century, and must have been shown the earliest-known planimeter which it is believed was invented in 1814. The planimeter is an instrument where a tracing arm, taken round the outline of an irregular plane shape, records the area within the boundary.

The year 1854 was of considerable importance, as it was then that Amsler took the matter further by inventing the polar planimeter, and it was also the year of his marriage to Elise Laffon, the daughter of a prominent scientist. It has been suggested that he adopted the name Amsler-Laffon to reap the benefit of this marital connection, but it is more likely to have been no more than a courtesy to his wife in a country with a tradition of using both surnames in marriage. This is borne out by the fact that his sons did not follow this tradition and reverted to the name Amsler. In the year of his marriage, he set up a workshop for precision mathematical instruments at Schaffhausen, and this became his main source of income. In the first thirty years of operation alone over 12,000 planimeters were produced and sold all over the world. Sales remained buoyant for years through careful marketing, high-quality construction and reasonable cost. In time his eldest son Dr Albert Amsler (1857–1940, and an associate of the INA) became involved and the father-and-son team produced some remarkable instruments including not just planimeters but also integrators and integraphs. Among the most advanced instruments were planimeters which were able to measure areas from maps produced in turn from unusual projections not necessarily giving true areas on their expanded profiles. The young Dr Amsler is known to have worked for a while in the Scientific Department of Denny's Dumbarton shipyard.

Jakob Amsler, a former candidate for the Church who was to find his true vocation in science, died after a long and productive life in 1912 at Schaffhausen, Switzerland. Nowadays planimeters are rarely used, but with the growing importance of collections of scientific memorabilia, the name Amsler is unlikely to be forgotten.

SOURCES:

Amsler, A
'On the Uses of J Amsler-Laffon's Integrator in Naval Architecture', *Transactions of the Institution of Naval Architects*
Vol 25 (1884)

Baxandall, D (revised by Pugh, Jane)
Calculating Machines and Instruments
Catalogue of the Science Museum, London, 1975

Robb, A M
Theory of Naval Architecture
London, 1952
In Chapter 2 of this wide ranging text book, clear descriptions with background theory are given on planimeters, integrators and other instruments.

Frederick Kynaston Barnes

1828–1908

FREDERICK BARNES WAS one of the first eight Dockyard employees to attend the Admiralty 'second' school of naval architecture at Portsmouth, an opportunity which he grasped with both hands, graduating with distinction.

Barnes was born in Pembroke in 1828, commenced training at Pembroke Dockyard sixteen years later and then in 1848 was selected as one of the eight men to study at Portsmouth under the Rev Joseph Woolley, formerly of Cambridge, and left in 1851 as a prizeman. He spent his whole career working for the Admiralty, rising steadily in rank and acclaim. In 1864 he was one of three Constructors reporting directly to **Sir Edward Reed** and from 1872 until 1886 when he retired he held the appointment of Surveyor of Dockyards, a post then changed to Director of Dockyards.

His great legacy to the Navy was the introduction of the systematic study of and the testing of ships using the Stability Experiment (better known as the Inclining Experiment). In 1853 he was asked to conduct inclining tests on a series of ships, starting with HMS *Perseverance* which had capsized at Woolwich. This laid down a formal and disciplined approach to the subject through which he became well acquainted with **George Atwood**'s 'transfer of wedges' theory. The calculations for this had been cumbersome, but after careful study, Barnes introduced a simplified method which was used by some naval architects up until the twentieth century. He was a regular contributor to learned journals and was one of the 'four' who contributed to Professor Rankine's illustrious tome on shipbuilding. In 1860 he was one of the signatories of the memorandum setting up the INA.

He was well-liked and with his fellow 'second' school contemporaries had considerable influence in the final establishment of the Royal School of Naval Architecture and Marine Engineering at South Kensington in 1864. He died at Llandridod Wells in 1908.

SOURCES:
Barnes, F K
Five papers (four on stability) published in the *Transactions of the Institution of Naval Architects*
Vols 1–7 (1860–6)
Rankine, W J M, Watts, I, Napier, J R, and Barnes F K
Shipbuilding, Theoretical and Practical
London, 1866

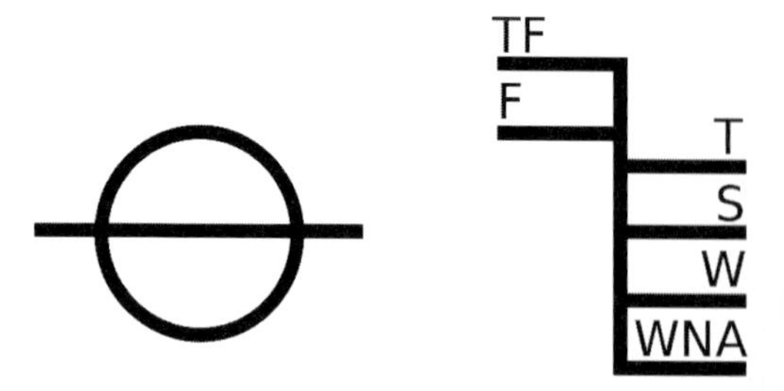

Modern load lines, often referred to as 'Plimsoll Marks' and found on all merchant ships, became compulsory thanks to the efforts of Samuel Plimsoll. The example here shows lines for tropical fresh water (TF), fresh water (F), tropical sea water (T), summer sea water (S), winter sea water (W), and winter North Atlantic water (WNA). *(Author)*

Samuel Plimsoll

1824–1898

IT IS REMARKABLE THAT Samuel Plimsoll (remembered as the 'Sailors' Friend'), and a man destined to leave his name stamped imperishably in the shipping and shipbuilding world, had little connection with the sea for the first forty years of his life. One of a large family, he was born in Bristol, spending his first four years there, followed by ten in Penrith. When he was fourteen, the family moved to Sheffield and a year later he obtained his first job with a local firm of solicitors, but after two years become a clerk to a brewery. With the death of his father, Samuel moved house again, where he had considerable responsibility for his five younger siblings, as by this time six older ones had flown the nest. The family were close knit and as active members of the Congregational Church practised kindness and showed social responsibility. While still a humble clerk and in his twenties, Samuel undertook two mammoth tasks. The first was acting as Honorary Secretary to the Sheffield committee for the 1851 Exhibition and organising the city's stand at the Crystal Palace. The second task, raising a relief fund for the widows and orphans of a colliery disaster, typified his concern for others.

In 1853, he moved to London and set up as a coal merchant, working from a room in the Coal Exchange in Lower Thames Street. Fortune did not smile on him for some years, and he experienced the pain and humiliation of bankruptcy, made even harder by suspension from his Church at that time. However, business was to improve, the suspension was rescinded and following his marriage he bought a large London house and there he and his wife cared for his mother and an invalid sister. By 1864 he was wealthy enough to purchase a large mansion near Sheffield, but sadly the following year he lost his only child shortly after birth. The young couple adopted their niece Nellie Plimsoll, then a baby.

Like many men of his time, the accumulation of wealth allowed him to indulge in political pursuits, and he aligned himself with the Liberals (Whigs) and the reformers. In the international field he espoused the cause of Garibaldi and both Samuel and his wife Eliza accompanied the great Italian leader during his triumphal visit to the Guildhall to receive the Freedom of the City of London. After one unsuccessful attempt, he was elected Member of Parliament for Derby in 1868, and then showed courage and mettle by proposing the legalisation of trade unions in his maiden speech. It is not recorded whether he was accorded the normal privilege of an uninterrupted hearing on such an important event in the life of an MP, but certain newspapers commented on his wasting the time of the members and the House! Throughout his parliamentary career Samuel Plimsoll voted thoughtfully, consistently and (with hindsight) in a fair manner on matters as wide-ranging as Ireland, the Church, trade and industrial reform.

Transport issues were brought to his attention, and it was in the 1870s that he became interested in the inadequacies of the British and international merchant fleets. This came about through meeting a Newcastle shipowner, James Hall, who in 1867 had published an article in *The Shipping World* on the unsatisfactory state of the shipping industry. The problems he outlined included lack of training for officers and crews, poor international navigational aids, ship designs that had little understanding of stability, poor supervision of ship construction/ condition and above all lack of supervision of loading. Hall recognised the importance of having an MP on his side, and Plimsoll quickly adopted the campaign to improve shipping standards as his personal crusade. He was moved by the plight of the widows, whose seafaring husbands had been lost on ships which were downright unseaworthy. These men had no right to legal representation, and refusal to sail the vessel brought an automatic prison sentence. To put this in perspective, losses of British ships (excluding fishing smacks) averaged close to 2,000 per annum in the mid-nineteenth century.

Efforts to pass a Merchant Shipping Bill around 1870 had failed in Westminster, and it was at this time Samuel Plimsoll petitioned for a Royal Commission to be appointed to investigate the seaworthiness of ships. A full ten years of campaigning followed during which time Samuel Plimsoll enjoyed both public support and also persecution from a small part of the shipowning community, including litigation despite having parliamentary privilege. In the Merchant Shipping Act of 1876, the 'Plimsoll Mark' was introduced, but with regulations that were totally inadequate and which could be avoided by devious owners. The mark was cut-in and painted on both sides of the ship at amidships, and indicated the maximum depth to which the ship could be loaded. Throughout his parliamentary career (which continued until 1880 when he 'gave' his seat to the Liberal Home Secretary) he was involved in continuing disputes and his successes were slow in coming. He was bolstered greatly by the London company of George Thomson (the Aberdeen Line) who named one of their superb clippers built by Hood's of Aberdeen after him, and by a shoe manufacturer who adopted the name Plimsoll for one of his products. It is probable that Samuel Plimsoll, a consummate politician and reformer, will be remembered at the gates of history as the man who brought the plight of 'Our Seamen' to public attention.

SOURCES:

Cope Cornford, L
The Sea Carriers: 1825–1925 The Aberdeen Line
London, 1925

Foster King, J
'Annual Load Line Surveys'
Transactions of the Institution of Engineers and Shipbuilders in Scotland
Vol 81 (1937–8)

Jones, Nicolette,
The Plimsoll Sensation: the great campaign to save lives at sea
Boston, Mass., 2005

Plimsoll, Samuel
Our Seamen: an appeal
London, 1873

John Elder

1824–1869

THE EARLY DEATH OF John Elder, the man who developed the compound steam engine, at the age of forty-five was described by **Professor Macquorn Rankine** as 'the greatest misfortune which the Institution of Engineers and Shipbuilders in Scotland has had to sustain since its foundation'.

Despite the next biography being that of John Elder's wife Isabella, it is felt that Elder made such a significant contribution to marine steam engineering his a short life, that he is deserving of the highest recognition. John Elder was born in Glasgow, educated at the High School of the City and then spent a fairly short period at Glasgow University attending classes in Civil Engineering. He served a five-year apprenticeship in **Robert Napier's** works under the immediate direction of his father David Elder, a renowned marine engineer. On completion of the five years, Elder was employed first as a patternmaker at Bolton-le-Moors and subsequently as a draughtsman on the Great Grimsby Docks. In 1849 he returned to Glasgow and was appointed Chief Draughtsman by Robert Napier – a position of immense responsibility at that time.

In the summer of 1852, a Glasgow firm of millwrights, Randolph Elliott and Company, decided to extend their business as marine engineers and invited John Elder to join as a partner. The company was to be known as Randolph Elder and Company for the next sixteen years, and on the retirement of the other partners became John Elder and shortly after that John Elder and Company. During those sixteen years several highly-important inventions were produced by the company and all were patented either in the name of John Elder or jointly in the names of Charles Randolph and John Elder, encompassing steam jacketing, epicyclical gearing, paddle floats, machinery balancing and circular warships.

Elder had been with the new company only two years when they built the first marine compound engine in the world and fitted it in the small coastal steamship *Brandon*. On trials in July 1854 her coal consumption was measured at 3¼lb per indicated horsepower, a considerable saving on the anticipated amount of around 4½lb per indicated horsepower for less sophisticated machinery. Overnight Elder and his colleague had a success story on their hands and the way was clear for more advanced designs such as three-cylinder compound machinery and ultimately a quarter-century later the steam triple-expansion engine.

Mrs Isabella Elder, 1828–1905. *(Author)*

In 1868 the company passed into the hands of Elder as sole partner. In sixteen years they had built 111 steam engines, 106 ships and three floating docks. The ship numbers may include sub-contracted hulls, then a common practice on the River Clyde. Among their greatest clients was the Pacific Steam Navigation Company whose long-haul operations in the Pacific were dependent on high thermal efficiency.

In the last year of his life, John Elder had close on 4,000 employees. As a director he was certainly of the best kind and one innovation was the setting-up of an accident and welfare fund into which he contributed an equal amount to that raised by the workforce. He died in London in September 1869, a few days before he was due to give his presidential address to the Institution of Engineers and Shipbuilders in Scotland.

Mrs Isabella Elder

1828–1905

IN 1901, ACADEMIC HISTORY was made when four ladies received the degree of Honorary Doctor of Laws from one of Europe's oldest universities. The occasion was Founders' Day at Glasgow on the 450th anniversary of the University, and the ladies were: Mrs Campbell of Tulichewan for having started higher education for women in Glasgow, the then undisputed Second City of Empire; Mrs Emily Davies, who had been instrumental in starting higher education for women in England and who had founded Girton College, Cambridge; Miss Agnes Weston (later Dame Agnes) a leader in seamen's welfare, for her work in founding 'Sailors' Rests' at Portsmouth, Devonport and other British naval bases; and Mrs John Elder, a lady of immense character, a philanthropist and who had held the chair of a shipbuilding company. These academic awards to ladies reflected the broadening of academic institutions and a desire to acknowledge those people who had initiated changes in society during the latter part of the nineteenth century.

Isabella Ure was born in Glasgow in 1828. The family was comfortably off, her father being a Writer or Procurator of the city. Her education was limited, with spells at private schools and the probable services of a governess for some years; indeed the lack of information on this topic indicates the complete lack of public interest in women's education in the nineteenth century. Through her father's connections on the River Clyde, Isabella met the young shipbuilder and engineer John Elder (1824–69) who had been educated at the Glasgow High School and later at the University. He was well regarded in the burgeoning shipbuilding industry where innovation was an everyday part of life. One of his especial interests was the introduction of multi-expansion steam cycles to reciprocating engines. Following the successful trials of the retrofitted steam coaster *Brandon* which had been built for the trade between Britain and Limerick in western Ireland. In 1854 the company took out patents on compound engines, and their marketing was so successful that by the time of John Elder's death fifteen years later, 'Elder Compounds' were to be found on every ocean of the world.

John and Isabella were married in 1857 and the following twelve years were blissfully happy. Isabella began to move in society where creativity and academic research were the norm. Personal friends included **Professor Macquorn Rankine** and the charismatic Reverend Norman MacLeod of the Barony Kirk, Glasgow (a building which is now part of the campus of Strathclyde University). She played no part in the affairs of the shipyard, but like any wife married to a shipbuilder developed a sense of how the industry was structured. Their marriage ended abruptly in 1869 with John's death while at the height of his powers and during his term as President of the Institution of Scottish Engineers. At that time he was sole proprietor of the Elder Shipyard in Govan, an organisation with about 4,000 employees. His widow had no option: she had to keep the shipyard going and despite her grief and despair ran it single-handedly until she was able to recruit a manager and other directors about a year later.

On 1 July 1870, the new firm of John Elder and Company was established under the management of John F Ure, civil engineer (brother of Isabella), J L K Jamieson, former chief draughtsman of the Govan Shipyard, and William Pearce (later Sir William), shipyard manager of **Robert Napier** and Co. It is a pleasure to record that this new shipyard was to become the illustrious Fairfield Company and continues today as the Govan Shipyard, having been from time to time part of British Shipbuilders, Kværner and BAE Systems. It is in this shipyard that Britain's latest Type 45 destroyers are being assembled.

While the experience of keeping a shipyard alive was draining, it did enable Isabella to have a deeper understanding of the society and way of life of the West of Scotland. Looking back over her years as a widow it is probable that the three matters that concerned her most were the higher education of engineers, the introduction of higher education for women, and the improvement of living conditions in the city of Glasgow. In all three she was to make a massive impact, using her great wealth efficiently and generously. At the University, her benefactions included the setting up of a second chair of Civil Engineering, and in 1883, the provision of the world's first Chair of Naval Architecture.

1883 was a dramatic year in shipbuilding. First there was the founding of the Royal Corps of Naval Constructors (RCNC) at Greenwich and then the establishment of the John Elder Chair of Naval Architecture at Glasgow University, both of these furthering the professional training of engineers in both the naval and merchant sectors. This was underlined that year by an event which forced the whole naval architecture profession to sit up and take notice. On Tuesday 3 July 1883, the steam coaster *Daphne* rolled over immediately after launching on the Clyde, with the loss of 124 lives. Mrs Elder was deeply affected by this tragedy, but must have felt relieved that her munificence in education was coming on stream at the right time. Looking back one might agree that naval architecture 'came of age' in 1883.

One of Mrs Elder's gifts was to have far-reaching results. She purchased buildings and ground in the Hillhead district of Glasgow which became Queen Margaret College, a ladies' university college named after Saint Margaret, the bluestocking Queen of Scotland. Shortly after it was absorbed into Glasgow University, and by 1894 had produced a lady graduate in medicine. On a further happy note, we are able to report that the two deadly rival but distinguished schools of naval architecture and marine engineering, Glasgow and Strathclyde, have merged and thanks to Isabella Elder produce both male and female graduates.

SOURCES:
Barnaby, K C
Some Ship Disasters and their Causes
London, 1968
'Engineering' London
The Fairfield Shipbuilding and Engineering Works
London, 1909
McAlpine, Joan
The Lady of Claremont House
Glendaruel, Argyll, 1997
Rankine, W J Macquorn
'Sketch of the Life of John Elder'
Transactions of the Institution of Engineers and Shipbuilders in Scotland
Vol 15 (1871–2)

Sir William Thomson (Lord Kelvin)

1824–1907

LORD KELVIN HAS BEEN described as one of the greatest intellects of the nineteenth century, a man who out-performed his fellow academics as well as the cream of practising engineers of 150 years ago. Through his research and fundamental knowledge, scientific work of the highest order emanated from his laboratories. It required his knowledge, but above all his courage, to turn the lacklustre career of the ill-fated mammoth steamship *Great Eastern* into a profitable venture with pioneering work in the laying of the transatlantic telegraph cable.

William Thomson was born in Belfast in 1824, one of seven children in a family of Scots descent. When his father, James Thomson, was appointed to the Chair of Mathematics at Glasgow University in 1832, the family moved to the city which was to remain William's home and inspiration until his death in 1907. Professor Thomson supervised the education of his children, and by the age of ten when he matriculated at the University, William Thomson was expert in Latin and Greek and fluent in French and German. He studied and lived at the dark and dingy buildings of the 'old College' until 1841 when the opportunity arose to go south to Peterhouse College, Cambridge. There is no record of his graduation at Glasgow, as it is believed that he sacrificed this to protect his status as an undergraduate at Cambridge. William Thomson's years at Cambridge were amongst the happiest of his life, with study, research and music, as well as an active social life. Peterhouse became his second academic home, and was a place to which he repaired regularly throughout his life as one of their most senior Fellows. His portrait hangs in the College to this day. In the now outmoded form of competition, he became Second Wrangler in 1845, won the first Smith Prize for Mathematics and on the athletic front the Colquhoun Silver Sculls. Following graduation, for a brief period he worked between Cambridge and Paris and naturally presented his papers in French.

Sir William Thomson (Lord Kelvin), 1824–1907 with his compass. *(Author)*

In 1846, at the tender age of twenty-two, he won the competition for the Glasgow Chair of Natural Philosophy and commenced a half-century of work, first at the Old College and later at Gilmorehill when the University moved west to a new campus. In keeping with the now-lapsed tradition of the Scottish Ancient Universities he presented a well-received inaugural paper in Latin – *De caloris distributione per terrae corpus* – signalling the start of a singular career in physics which enabled him to have close personal and professional friendships with the greatest scientists of the day including Joule, Clausius, Helmholtz, Faraday, **Froude** and the two brilliant professors of Civil Engineering at Glasgow, **Macquorn Rankine** and his successor **James Thomson,** none other than his own brother.

As early as 1848, he proposed a scale for absolute zero temperature, and commenced work on low-temperature physics. In the 1860s in collaboration with Professor Peter Guthrie Tait of Edinburgh, there was a publishing first with the *Treatise on Natural Philosophy*, which in turn led to an investigation into electrical effects and the problem of sending electrical impulses along copper cables. As a shareholder of the Atlantic Telegraph Company, he was instrumental in setting up the world's first laboratory for the testing of factory products, in this case undersea cables, and in turn was asked to be technical adviser for the laying of the Atlantic cable. Through no fault of the operators, the first cables laid by the *Agamemnon* and the *Niagara* were unsuccessful, and then the 'Great Iron Ship' *Great Eastern* was chartered to carry another set of cables and try again, an operation that was to be successfully completed in 1866. As soon as the new cables started to work, the first cables unexpectedly came to life, giving the Telegraph Company more than enough capacity for their immediate needs. For this wonderful piece of engineering science, William Thomson and three other colleagues were awarded knighthoods.

Sir William Thomson was a man of great discernment and culture, endowed with a fine sense of humour, but not regarded as the easiest of lecturers by the average student. One of the apocryphal stories of the University is that when Thomson was in London receiving the accolade, some of his classes were taken by a lecturer called Mr Day. One morning when the class assembled, emblazoned on the blackboard was 'John 9.4'. A shortened form of the Biblical text is: 'Work while the day is here for when the night comes no man can work.'

In the 1860s he purchased a beautiful schooner yacht the *Lalla Rookh* of 126 tons, humorously referred to as a ship of 128 x 10 (to the power 6) grammes! He used it both for pleasure and also as a test-bed for proposals on matters including depth sounding, the marine compass, tidal predictions and wave predictions and theory. Following the death of his first wife, he sailed the yacht to Madeira to win the hand of a Miss Blandy and make her Lady Thomson.

His interest in the marine compass came through an invitation to write an article about it in the journal *Good Words*, a task which turned into a monumental part of his life's work once he analysed the deficiencies of the compass of the time which oscillated wildly, suffered from serious inaccuracy while in use on warships firing their guns and so on. His proposals (which were criticised rudely by Sir George Airey, the Astronomer Royal at Greenwich, also an expert on compass deviation) were for a new design, which was adopted by the German and French navies and shortly after by the Admiralty in London. This enabled Thomson to partner with a Glasgow optician named James White, forming a company which after many changes continues to this day as Kelvin-Hughes. It is said that on one occasion when the Professor escorted the scientist Monsieur Joule round the factory in the west end of Glasgow, the Frenchman learned that the massive stock of piano-wire on the premises was for sounding. 'Sounding what note?' said Joule. Sir William replied 'The deep C'.

In 1892 Sir William Thomson was appointed a peer of the realm and took his title from Glasgow's second river which flows below the main university buildings in Gilmorehill. He was the first scientist to be so honoured. Other honours came thick and fast, but none more pleasing than his election as University Chancellor in 1904. On his death in 1907, it was decreed that his last resting-place would be in Westminster Abbey next to the tomb of Isaac Newton. His name now ranks along with two other men of his university – **Watt** and **Rankine**.

SOURCES:

Lord Kelvin authored a multitude of papers during his life, with nearly 700 listed in his biography, many of which were published by the Royal Societies of London and Edinburgh. Surprisingly, Lord Kelvin never produced a paper for the Institution of Naval Architects, although he presented four to the Institution of Engineers and Shipbuilders in Scotland.

Thompson, Sylvanus P
The Life of Lord Kelvin
2 vols (London, 1910)

The Barnaby Dynasty

Three generations of the Barnaby family served the profession of naval architecture on a continuous basis from the middle of the nineteenth century up until the 1960s. At one time, the Institution of Naval Architects had three Barnabys enrolled: Nathaniel the grandfather, Sydney his son and Kenneth the grandson. As far as is known this situation has never been repeated, and may remain unequalled for many years to come but as each of them gave remarkable and conspicuous service to the profession, all three are included here.

It is uncertain where the Barnaby family had their original home, but it is likely to have been in the London area as Nathaniel served for some time at the Naval Dockyard, Woolwich. His son Sydney served an apprenticeship at the remarkable engineering firm of John Penn of Greenwich, and after some interesting periods of training, was lured to the shipyards of the south coast. The grandson, Kenneth, was brought up in Hampshire and served an apprenticeship with Thornycroft of Southampton, a company to which he devoted many years of his life.

Nathaniel Barnaby (1829–1915)

Nathaniel Barnaby lived from 1829 to 1915, serving the Admiralty for almost his entire career. After working at Woolwich Dockyard as a draughtsman, he joined the staff of Sir Edward Reed, and at an early age was singled out for promotion. In 1872, while in his early forties, he was appointed Chief Constructor of the Navy, a position he held until 1885, and by which time it had been re-designated Director of Naval Construction (DNC) making him the first man to hold this distinguished post.

During his thirteen years at the helm, the Royal Navy took delivery of some interesting ships, whilst experimenting with steel, armour plating and different forms of bracketless construction, a forerunner of longitudinal framing. There was a mild flirtation with composite construction and several sloops (some later re-designated as corvettes) were built, one of which, HMS *Gannet* (Sheerness Dockyard 1878), has just been restored at the Chatham Historic Dockyard, Kent. During his tenure of office, a race developed between arms manufacturers and suppliers of armour plate, forcing the size of ships upwards and creating complexities with regard to weight and displacement. At a meeting in the Institution of Naval Architects, Barnaby made the classic remark: 'There could be no question that we could not allow foreign seamen to have guns afloat more powerful than our own, however ready we might have been to allow them to defend themselves with thicker armour.' The turret battleship *Colossus* launched at Portsmouth in 1882 was the Royal Navy's first capital ship built of steel.

Nathaniel Barnaby presented a remarkable number of papers to the Institution of Naval Architects, something like twelve in the twenty-nine years from 1863 and 1892. It is interesting to note that in his paper on armour in 1879, his appellation is 'N Barnaby' while in the following year for the paper on the *Nelson* class it had changed to 'Sir Nathaniel Barnaby'.

Sydney W Barnaby (d.1925)

Sydney W Barnaby grew up in an atmosphere permeated by shipbuilding and there is little wonder that he chose to serve an apprenticeship with the remarkable engineering and shipbuilding company John Penn of Greenwich. On completion of his time, he attended Victoria University, Manchester, and studied engineering, before joining the Pacific Steam Navigation Company as a junior engineer officer for several voyages. He then joined John I Thornycroft & Co and quickly gained the trust of John Thornycroft, who asked him to assist in propeller experiments at the Thornycroft private ship model testing tank at Bembridge, Isle of Wight.

In 1885, he published one of the world's first books on propellers, being based on a series of lectures he gave at the Royal Naval College, Greenwich. He became an established public figure giving the biennial James Watt lecture in Greenock in 1906 and a series of lectures at the Massachusetts Institute of Technology In 1910, he presented a paper on torpedo boat destroyers to the INA.

In time, Sydney was transferred from Chiswick to Southampton and appointed naval architect. Later he was known as a Technical Director at Thornycroft and was to lead the thinking of the company in the early years of the twentieth century when small, fast

HMS *Gannet*, a composite sloop built at Sheerness in 1878 during Sir Nathaniel Barnaby's period as Chief Constructor of the Navy. *Gannet* has been restored and is now part of the excellent three-ship display at Chatham Historic Dockyard, and forms part of the Core Collection of the UK's National Historic Fleet. (*Author*)

warships were becoming fashionable. During the First World War he was appointed chairman of the INA committee looking into the effects of mines and torpedoes. This committee made recommendations which were adopted before hostilities ceased. In 1924 Sydney handed over his post as naval architect of the company to his son Kenneth. He died a year later.

Kenneth C Barnaby (c1887–1968)

Kenneth C Barnaby started his apprenticeship with John I Thornycroft in 1904 and simultaneously studied engineering at the Central Technical College, South Kensington, gaining his BSc before going on to work with **Augustin-Normand** at Le Havre, John Brown of Clydebank, and Costiera of Rio de Janeiro.

In 1924, he was appointed naval architect of Thornycroft in succession to his father, and commenced over thirty years service in this position. During the Second World War, he was responsible for the design of specialised destroyers as well as for floating 'sea-dromes' to combat the U-boat threat. Sadly these were never built.

Despite a speech impediment, Kenneth Barnaby gave four papers to the INA. His most important contribution to the profession must be the quite remarkable number of published works of which pride of place must go the Centenary History of the Royal Institution of Naval Architects. This volume gives remarkable background information on the 'affairs' of the profession, but written in a light manner with much good humour. He retired in 1966, and accepted the post of honorary naval architect to his former employers, but sadly died within two years.

SOURCES:

Barnaby, Sir Nathaniel
Naval Development of the Century
London, 1904

Barnaby, K C
The Institution of Naval Architects 1860–1960
London, 1960

———,
Some Ship Disasters and Their Causes
London, 1968

Barnaby, Sydney W
Marine Propellers
London, 1885

Alexander Carnegie Kirk

1830–1892

THE MARINE ENGINEER who developed the triple-expansion engine in the 1880s, then the ultimate in steam technology, A C Kirk was born around 1830 at Barry in the rural county of Forfarshire (now known as Angus). By the time of his death sixty-two years later, he was acknowledged as one of the United Kingdom's most distinguished marine engineers, and the man largely responsible for the successful evolution of the nineteenth century long-distance steamship.

Following schooling at Arbroath, he attended Edinburgh University before making his way westwards to serve an apprenticeship at Robert Napier's up-and-coming Vulcan Foundry in Glasgow. On completion of his articled work, Kirk decided to move to the Thames, then the centre of shipbuilding and marine engineering in the country, and for some years was with Maudslay, Son and Fields, shipbuilders and engineers at Lambeth in South London, and later at Greenwich. He rose to the position of Chief Draughtsman, then one of most responsible jobs in the industry, but after some years was lured back to Scotland as engineer of a remarkable concern known as 'Paraffin' Young's Works, an industrial site destined to become renowned world-wide for developments in chemical engineering. Kirk must have felt drawn back to the River Clyde as in the mid-1860s he moved to the Cranstonhill Engine Works and then to John Elder's engine shops and later (as will be explained) as a partner of Robert Napier and Sons, following the founder's death.

While working at Fairfield for **John Elder** and Co, Kirk was instrumental in producing the first effective triple-expansion steam engine. This was a new engine produced for a retrofit to the SS *Propontis* in 1874. Unfortunately this engine never reached its

Right: The passenger and cargo steamship *Changsha*, launched by Scott's of Greenock in 1886, was typical of the vessels which could now cross the globe after the opening of the Suez Canal and through the introduction of multi-expansion steam machinery, pioneered by John Elder and Dr A C Kirk. (*John Swire & Sons*)

full potential as boiler design at the time could not match up to the then advanced theories of heat engines. Men like **Professor Macquorn Rankine** of Glasgow University understood entropy and his Second Law of Thermodynamics was unchallenged, while others lead by Kirk were mastering the complexities of designing and building triple-expansion engines taking advantage of higher temperatures and the full range of pressure through three successive drops. Despite the disappointment, the *Propontis* set matters going; the engineering profession recognised the possibilities of multi-expansion machinery and the engine (and boiler) builders responded to the challenge.

In 1876, the Clyde lost its greatest shipbuilder and engineer **Robert Napier**. The registered company Robert Napier and Sons was taken over by a group of well-qualified and enthusiastic engineers, including A C Kirk, who wished to see the company succeed for the altruistic reasons of loyalty and allegiance to the Napier name. The reconstituted company continued to build ships and engines until 1900 when incorporated into William Beardmore and Company.

In the late 1870s, the new partners were approached by the principals of arguably the most prestigious sailing fleet operating under the Red Ensign, namely the Aberdeen White Star Line which was managed by George Thompson of London. The ships of this line, all with green-painted hulls, included some of world's most celebrated clippers including the record-breaking full-rigged ship *Thermopylæ* which had been launched by Hood's of Aberdeen. Their management style was thought through carefully, with larger deck crews on the southbound trip, the total avoidance of the Suez Canal, and whilst always carrying first class passengers, alternated the use of their 'tween deck spaces between steerage passengers and cargo depending on current market conditions. Dr Kirk (as he was always known) persuaded them that they might benefit from the introduction of steamships operating through Suez, and from this came the order for the single-screw iron ship *Aberdeen*, which when delivered in 1881 was described as a masterpiece of naval architecture. Compared to similar ships on this run, the *Aberdeen* reduced coal consumption on the round-trip to Australia from London by 500 tons, while of course using sail on her three-masted barque rig at appropriate times. The machinery for *Aberdeen* was a three-cylinder triple-expansion set with steam supplied by two double-ended steel boilers, and with a host of new inventions including an innovative type of condenser. Engine-room crews had to be selected for their understanding of steam reciprocating machinery, and this reinforced the tradition of ships' engineers being signed on straight from the engine works. This pioneer ship operated on the Australian trades for twenty-five years before being sold to Turkey around 1906 and finally being disposed of in 1919. Possibly the only disappointment regarding her was she was built of iron and not steel, which at that time was being introduced by the **Denny** Shipyard some miles away in Dumbarton. This innovation would have reduced her lightweight and increased her cargo capacity by possibly 200–300 tons. However, her success was such that the triple-expansion steam freighter was now firmly on all shipowners' wish lists and Kirk had the satisfaction of seeing the Aberdeen Line move their allegiance westwards to Messrs Napier in Glasgow. Napier's capitalised on this situation, and soon were building machinery with higher thermal efficiency (up to 10 per cent) for the Admiralty and the Russian navy, and in late 1881 they delivered the *Parisian* for the Allan Line, the first steel-hulled vessel to cross the Atlantic.

Kirk gave two papers to the INA and another two plus a presidential address to the Institution of Engineers and Shipbuilders in Scotland. He was awarded an LL.D from Glasgow (which still awards the Kirk Medal in naval architecture) as well as a Fellowship of the Royal Society of Edinburgh. Among his publications are papers ranging from the punching of steel plates for riveted boiler construction through to methods of estimating the wetted surface of ship hulls.

SOURCES:

Cope Cornford, L
The Sea Carriers 1825-1925: The Aberdeen Line
London, 1925

Griffiths, Denis
Steam at Sea: Two Centuries of Steam-powered Ships
London, 1997

Mackrow's Naval Architect's Pocket Book

SENIOR DRAUGHTSMAN IN most of the older British shipyards were the 'doyens' of the drawing office and were recognisable by the embellishments at the end of their long drawing boards: they would have a polished wood instrument case (usually just under a metre long) in which would be assembled their personal drawing instruments of Stanley or Riefler manufacture, plus an enviable collection of trusted ship curves, mostly home-made copies of curves that some generations before were true Copenhagen Curves. These men would also have their small but important personal library, which might contain the Dorman Long Steel Handbook or the American Haswell's *Mechanics' and Engineers' Handbook* but their most valued possession would be Mackrow's *Naval Architect's and Shipbuilder's Pocket Book.*

There were two Mackrows, father and son, both distinguished naval architects who worked for the Thames Ironworks and Shipbuilding Company. This is a short description of their careers, and the editorial work of the son, Clement Mackrow, which made their name widely known in shipbuilding circles.

George Colby Mackrow (1830–1907)

George Mackrow was a Londoner, born in 1830 and upon reaching the age of fourteen began his apprenticeship with the Blackwall shipyard of Ditchburn and Mare in 1844. Two years later Ditchburn retired early and the yard became known as C J Mare and Co; the ground was extended at Bow Creek and the facilities introduced for large-scale construction of iron ships. Financial difficulties followed and in 1857 the company was restructured, becoming the Thames Ironworks & Shipbuilding Company. Clearly the training Mackrow received was excellent as he was retained throughout and in 1862 he was appointed Naval Architect, a position he would retain until into his seventies. In 1880 a new young director appeared, Arnold Hills – a man with advanced views on industrial relations, which took the 'Thames' along a new path, something which strengthened Mackrow's hand as the chief technical officer of the yard. In 1899, the shipyard merged with the engineers John Penn and Sons of Greenwich.

In the years up to 1907, the 'Thames' built close on 110 ships ranging in size from HMS *Warrior*, the first iron warship (still afloat in Portsmouth), to the famous paddle tug *Anglia*, which on account of her three funnels was known as 'Three Fingered Jack'. They built a series of small but popular paddle steamers for the London County Council river services as well as many warships for foreign governments. Towards the end of his life, at the behest of the Admiralty, Mackrow and the Ironworks were studying improved methods of coaling and bunkering ships and a patent had been registered for the Mackrow-Cameron system. Just before his death George Mackrow was elected to the Council of the INA, having presented two papers over the years and contributed at many of their meetings.

Clement Mackrow (1856–1912)

George Mackrow's son Clement was the author of *The Naval Architect's and Shipbuilder's Pocket Book*. He had followed his father into the profession of naval architecture, and is believed to have been employed all his working life with the Thames Ironworks. In the early editions of the *Pocket Book*, he is described as a 'Naval Draughtsman and Member of the Institution of Naval Architects'. At some stage in his life he was a lecturer at the Bow and Bromley Institute which appears to have held special classes – probably in the evenings for the employees of the Thames Ironworks and other nearby shipyards. He became Shipbuilding Manager of Thames Ironworks and around 1907 succeeded his father as Naval Architect.

Clement Mackrow was to have little time in the post as on 23 September 1912 he was hit by a train and killed at a level crossing at the Canning Town entrance to the Ironworks. The *Pocket Book*, which was first printed in 1879, ran to at least fifteen editions, with in addition several reprints. Following the death of Clement Mackrow the editorship was passed to Lloyd Woollard MA RCNC.

Lloyd Woollard (1882–1963)

Woollard started his working life in an architect's office in Hereford, but having met the Shipbuilding Manager of the Thames Ironworks, Clement Mackrow, he was persuaded to join the drawing office of that shipyard. In 1902 he was awarded the Martell Scholarship of the INA and entered the Royal Naval College, Greenwich, as a private student. Obtaining a first class professional certificate, with in addition an MA degree in mathematics from London University, he was appointed a member of the Royal Corps of Naval Constructors. His career in the Corps lasted forty-two years, and saw his involvement in some fascinating tasks in both World Wars. He was promoted Assistant Director of Naval Construction in 1936.

Around 1905 he assisted Sir Philip Watts with the section on 'Shipbuilding' in the *Encyclopædia Britannica* and worked on several similar literary tasks. From 1911 onwards he was an instructor at the RNC Greenwich. In 1912, on the death of Clement Mackrow, he became editor of *Mackrow's Pocket Book*, a post he was to hold for the rest of his life.

Sir Edward J Reed, 1830–1906.
(The Royal Institution of Naval Architects)

Sir Edward J Reed
1830–1906

AT THE AGE OF TWENTY-NINE, Edward Reed subscribed as one of the founding members of the Institution of Naval Architects and was appointed Secretary. This was the start of a life devoted to the development of ship design and to public service.

Reed was born at Sheerness, Kent and joined the Royal Dockyard as a shipwright apprentice. On completion of his training in 1849 he was invited to become a student at the 'Second' School of Naval Architecture at Portsmouth, which had only been open for a year. There he joined up with a select band of students and teachers headed by the Rev Dr Joseph Woolley and in three years was tutored on all the available information on the science of naval architecture. He and his fellow trainees must have appreciated the great privilege of being in one of the few places in the world where advanced theories were propounded and where practical learning took place under the guidance of John Fincham, the Master Shipwright of Portsmouth Dockyard. The next few years were less enjoyable, for as often happens with highly skilled young 'graduates' their first task is less than exciting; certainly this was the case with Reed who was sent back to Sheerness and appointed a draughtsman attached to the Dockyard mould-loft.

Reed faced up to these tasks with equanimity, but widened his interests and engaged in other matters, including writing novels and poetry and then accepting in 1853 the post of editor of *Mechanic's Magazine*. The following year he and a fellow former student submitted plans to the Admiralty for a steam-driven ironclad frigate, something nowadays one might think was high-handed but was then accepted by the powers that be. While the design was turned down, an avenue opened which enabled a further proposal to be accepted a few years later. In 1859 **John Scott Russell** called a meeting at which several distinguished naval architects attended and the groundwork was completed for the Institution of Naval Architects with the young

Edward Reed acting as honorary secretary. Scott Russell made arrangements for accommodation for the Institution and once the body had been promulgated, Edward Reed was formally appointed as the Institution's first secretary, a position he held from 1860 for about three years. Around 1862, Reed again used the chambers of the Institution as a platform to submit further proposals to the Admiralty for another, smaller ironclad ship. This time the submission was well received, the proposals were approved and Reed was asked to complete the design work and to oversee the retrofitting of three new wooden vessels (two sloops, *Research* and *Enterprise*, and one corvette, the *Favorite*) into protected ships with armoured waterlines and central citadels. With the assistance of a draughtsman, the work went well and all three ships were to serve Queen and country for a goodly number of years.

In 1863, Edward Reed was appointed the Chief Constructor of the Navy. He held the post for the next seven difficult years as the Royal Navy tried to come to grips with armour, structural design, mechanisation and the implementation of proper naval architecture practices in ship design. The problems associated with stability, then a far-from-exact science, came to haunt the Navy, and much to Reed's disapproval, the Admiralty ordered the turret ship *Captain* designed by Captain Cowper Phipps Coles (a man with no formal engineering qualifications) from Lairds of Birkenhead, a company which signally failed to check the stability. Reed warned the shipyard that they had an overweight ship, but little effort seems to have been made to rectify a design which had too little freeboard. On her third voyage in 1870, the *Captain* capsized with the loss of almost 500 men including her commanding officer and designer. By this time Reed had become disillusioned and had resigned from the public service. In his seven years as Chief Constructor, Reed had overseen the building of a very large number of ships and had encouraged the staff to develop their systems in line with current scientific thought. Stability was a particular issue, and freeboard a close second.

Reed was knighted and held many prestigious appointments including sitting at Westminster as a Liberal MP from 1874 to 1895 and from 1900 until 1905 when he withdrew from parliamentary life. Throughout his life he promoted education and in particular was a supporter of, and also a popular lecturer at, the Royal School of Naval Architecture, South Kensington and thereafter the Royal Naval College, Greenwich. He died in London in 1906

One of Reed's most important tasks was that of the Government Commissioner handling the inquiry into the loss of the ss *Daphne* following her launch in Glasgow on 3 July 1883. A total of 124 people lost their lives and within a few days the Lord Advocate for Scotland had appointed Reed to carry out an investigation with the assistance of the Sheriff Principal of Glasgow. His job commenced after the salving of the vessel and recovery and identification of the dead. After the ship had been cleaned and inclined, a public enquiry took place to which shipbuilders from Scotland, England and France came forward and offered information on past launching experiences. Clearly none had carried out full stability enquiries prior to launching, but none withheld information. Reed had his masterly report ready for presentation at Westminster six weeks to the day from the accident, and as the late Kenneth Barnaby wrote in his 1968 work on ship disasters: 'The inquiry was completed in only a month, which emphasises the great advantage of having a technical matter investigated by a technical authority and not by a legal gentleman dependent on a panel of "assessors" for his understanding of the case.' This report is recommended reading for all naval architects, and should be mandatory for those pursuing a career in shipyard management.

SOURCES:

Barnaby, K C
Some Ship Disasters and their Consequences
London, 1968

Reed, Sir Edward J
Report on the 'Daphne' Disaster
London, 1883

———,
A Treatise on the Stability of Ships
London, 1885

Sir Edward J Harland

1831–1895

ON CHRISTMAS EVE 1895, Edward Harland, founder of the great Harland and Wolff shipyard, died peacefully at his home in Co Leitrim, Ireland, and despite it being a time of serious industrial unrest in Belfast, his passing was mourned by members of all sections of the community. In a mere sixty-four years, he had learned not only a trade, but had educated himself as a shipbuilder and had gone on to found one of the mightiest shipbuilding organisations in the world.

Edward Harland was born in Scarborough, the sixth of eight children. His father, a medical practitioner, had planned that two sons should follow in his footsteps, one to study medicine and the other to train as a lawyer at Edinburgh University. Edward had spent, or mis-spent, a fair amount of time in his early school years visiting workshops and small shipyards on the Yorkshire coast, but all this was to change when at the age of twelve he was sent to Edinburgh Academy to prepare for the University. Once again his interests in mechanical matters came to the fore and while there he persuaded his medical undergraduate brother to arrange that he attend classes in mathematics. Three years later, his father (who had considerable mechanical aptitude himself) accepted the inevitable, and instead of studying law, it was arranged that he be indentured for five years as an engineering apprentice to a family friend George Stephenson, the locomotive builder of Newcastle.

The five years in Newcastle were highly productive, and Edward used every opportunity for advancing his skills and knowledge. He enjoyed the experience despite the long hours, averaging over sixty per week. In 1850 and during his fourth year he submitted a model lifeboat for the competition sponsored by the Duke of Northumberland. As one of several hundred entries, this model did not even gain a 'mention', but it must have been fairly original, being designed for operation by sixteen men driving a single shaft, presumably akin to the Fleming hand gear so often seen in the lifeboats of early twentieth-century passenger liners. In 1851 after a short period as a journeyman with Stephenson's he left and spent some time travelling and in absorbing the delights of the 1851 Exhibition in the Crystal Palace.

The shipyards on the Clyde beckoned and Edward Harland joined Messrs J & G Thomson (later renamed John Brown and Company) and before long was appointed chief draughtsman, for which there was no change in remuneration except that his 'take-home' wage was redefined as a salary! On the recommendation of George Stephenson, he was invited back to Newcastle to become a manager in the small shipyard owned by Thomas Toward, but for various reasons Harland never settled in this job and shortly after started looking around for other employment. At the end of 1854 he was appointed manager of the Queen's Island shipyard of Thomas Hickson and Company, Belfast, and the remainder of his life was to be devoted to shipbuilding in Northern Ireland.

Hickson's had suffered from poor-quality workmanship as well as time and cost over-runs, and this was addressed by Harland. By the standards of today, his methods were unpleasant and inflammatory, but they were successful in uniting the yard and also enabling Edward Harland to become outright owner within just a few years. Thomas Toward of Newcastle died at the same time and several of his senior employees accepted Harland's invitation to come across to Belfast, again strengthening the organisation.

Harland came to know a gentleman resident in Liverpool by the name of G C Schwabe; indeed they were distantly related. Schwabe had a nephew Gustav Wolff who was well qualified as an engineer having served an apprenticeship with Joseph Whitworth in Manchester, which he had then backed up by shipbuilding experience on the Mersey. He and Harland were introduced and felt able to work with one another, culminating in Wolff becoming Harland's 'private assistant' and handling all routine administration and shipyard organisational problems. In 1862, and when Edward Harland was only thirty years of age, Wolff was assumed as a partner and the name Harland and Wolff adopted, which today remains as one of the longest running titles in the whole industry. In the following thirty-three years, close on 300 ships were completed, the largest reaching over 10,000 gross tons, a matter which encouraged the new partners to invest in an engine-building facility which came on stream shortly after 1880. Previous to that most of their hulls had been towed to the Clyde for machinery installation.

In 1884, the business yielded profits which were greater than the partners' capital holdings, and at this moment, Edward Harland and Gustav Wolff chose to withdraw from the routine management of the company, to work in other businesses and in politics, but to offer their help to Harland and Wolff in the form of long-term loans to both the shipyard and to prospective owners. At this time W J Pirrie (later to become Lord Pirrie), was a member of the board and on his rise to the chair gave great encouragement to the two original partners; there were first, changes of company trading names, as a precaution enabling Harland and Wolff to move east across the Irish Sea in the event of major political changes in Ireland, and secondly to allow Edward Harland (now knighted) to remain a Member of Parliament without facing charges of unethical behaviour in respect of government contracts awarded to the shipyard in Belfast.

Harland and Wolff are remembered for pioneering ships with unusually high length to beam (L/B) ratios and as Edward Harland had great faith in sailing ships they also built a long line of hard working ships, barques and four-masted barques. While possibly not at the cutting edge of ship design in the 1880s and 1890s, the Queen's Island yard produced remarkable and long-lasting vessels. Harland, knighted and laden with honours, died in 1895, while his fellow partner G W Wolff would outlive him by a further eighteen years.

SOURCES:
McCluskie, Tom
Harland and Wolff: Designs from the Shipbuilding Empire
London, 1998
Moss, Michael, and Hume, John R
Shipbuilders to the World: 125 Years of Harland and Wolff, Belfast 1861–1986
Belfast, 1986
Parker, T John
'Harland and Wolff: Towards 125 Years of Shipbuilding'
in Walker, F M, and Slaven, A (eds), *European Shipbuilding – one hundred years of change*
Greenwich, 1983

James Howden

1832–1913

A FORTHRIGHT, POSSIBLY OVER-OPINIONATED mechanical engineer, James Howden was a remarkable nineteenth-century engineer who left a legacy of industrial improvement. Despite lack of formal education, he displayed engineering originality and the ability to build up and sustain a great industrial concern. It is difficult to assess the personal qualities of a person so far removed in time and lifestyle from us today, yet from papers and publications, one is able to build up the picture of a man, professionally direct and confident, and running his business with dedication and enthusiasm. In private life, Howden did not look for recognition, quietly serving the Church, working for charities and sitting on the bench as a Justice of the Peace.

James Howden was born at Prestonpans on the Firth of Forth, just east of Edinburgh. When about fifteen, he set off alone for Glasgow, travelling on one of the many day canal passage boats working between the two cities. He obtained an apprenticeship at the light engineering works of James Gray, and before completing his 'time' had been appointed chief draughtsman. His draughting skills secured him an appointment as a teacher of drawing at one of the government schools of art, which gave him valuable direct contact with an influential group of young men. Over the next few years he worked for various companies and then on his own account; one of his first successes was the design of a rivet manufacturing machine for which he sold the patent rights to a Birmingham company. This early success drew his attention to heavy engineering and in particular to the design and manufacture of boilers, and also gave him the capital to set up his own business. He had a few months with an acknowledged expert on ship propellers but this, however, was one of the less successful aspects of his future activities.

In 1859 he received the order which was to set him on his way. Henderson Brothers, the proprietors of the Anchor Line, placed the design of the compound engines and water tube boilers for the *Ailsa*

Craig with him, machinery that was ahead of its time with a working pressure of 100lbs (6.5 bar). In 1862, he set up the organisation which became known as James Howden and Co with their first machinery shop in Scotland Street, Glasgow. Business was good and within a short time they were the manufacturers of engines and boilers for many well-known steamship companies, necessitating a move to larger premises in the same location a mere nine years later.

An unusual feature of mid-nineteenth century shipbuilding was the appointment of marine engine builders as prime contractors for new shipbuilding contracts, and engine builders in turn subcontracted the hull, outfit and rigging to established shipyards nearby. This was especially prevalent on the Clyde for some years, a system developed by **Robert Napier** and Company as early as 1840 with the contract for the first four Cunarders (hence the use of Napier's funnel colours on the Cunard Line ships as at that time, Clyde engine manufacturers supplied the smokestack). Howden had several contracts of this nature, a risky undertaking as the failure of a shipyard in the days before the Limited Liability Acts could prejudice every organisation in the chain of supply.

Howden's engines became known for high-quality construction, but even more for their high thermal efficiency. He carried out experiments aimed at reducing energy losses caused by poor coal combustion and in turn the heat loss from the exhaust direct to the atmosphere. This led to his ideas for using exhaust gas to heat the air on its way into furnace combustion chambers, a method that became known as the Howden Hot-Air Forced Draught System, and which was the key element in making Howden's a world leader in marine engineering. This system was complex and throughout the 1880s there were costly experimentation with applications becoming more efficient every year. On the delivery of the White Star liners *Teutonic* and *Majestic* in 1890, it could be proved conclusively that their coal consumption (of 320 tons per day) could be reduced by more than 3 per cent with hot air draught.

James Howden was one of the founder-members of the Institution of Engineers in Scotland in 1857, and indeed, he was the longest surviving member at his death fifty-six years later. He was also a member of the Institution of Naval Architects and of the Civil Engineers, writing at least five papers each for the IESS and the INA. It was here that he made controversial remarks and on more than one occasion produced papers that were somewhat less than successful, particularly on subjects not in the mainstream of his work – such as propellers and torpedo-boat construction. However, his papers on forced draught were of immense importance, and it was through the ensuing debates that the conflicting views of naval engineers and merchant operators emerged and were reconciled. While the naval men required high evaporative rates in relation to the weight of a boiler, Howden advocated long-term overall efficiency for commercial shipping operation on long ocean routes. Many of the discussions in the two sets of Transactions are amusing for their forthright quality, and the late **K C Barnaby** (author of the INA Centenary volume) remarked, tongue in cheek, on '... the Howden tradition of vigour of statement'.

In the latter years of the nineteenth century, Howden's entered the market for forced lubrication engines, with the high and stable speeds required by the electricity-generating companies, and again in the early 1900s with the new technology presented by the Howden-Zoelly impulse steam turbine. James Howden withdrew from the business about the same time and by 1907, the firm had become a private limited company. Howden died in his eighty-second year, greatly mourned as one of the founding engineers of the nineteenth century.

SOURCES:
Griffiths, Denis
Steam at Sea
London, 1997

Colin Archer
1832–1921

COLIN ARCHER, NORWAY'S greatest ship designer, was born in 1832, in the small town of Larvick, just south of Oslo in the Telemark region. In Derry's *History of Modern Norway*, his parents are described as 'Scottish immigrants who kept an open house at Larvick for their British relations'.

At the age of seventeen, young Colin was recruited into the workforce of the small wooden shipyard belonging to Michael Treschow and worked there for about eighteen months. Little is recorded of this yard, but one thing is certain, the training in wood shipbuilding would have been top class. To this day the small boatyards of Norway – and of Denmark – have retained their name for quality and individuality. Archer's older brothers had emigrated to Australia and in 1850 he followed them, but visiting California, Panama, Hawaii and other places *en route*, nothing short of remarkable for a young (teenage) nineteenth-century trainee shipwright. He joined his brothers in New South Wales and worked on a sheep farm from 1853 until 1861 when he felt obliged to return to Norway.

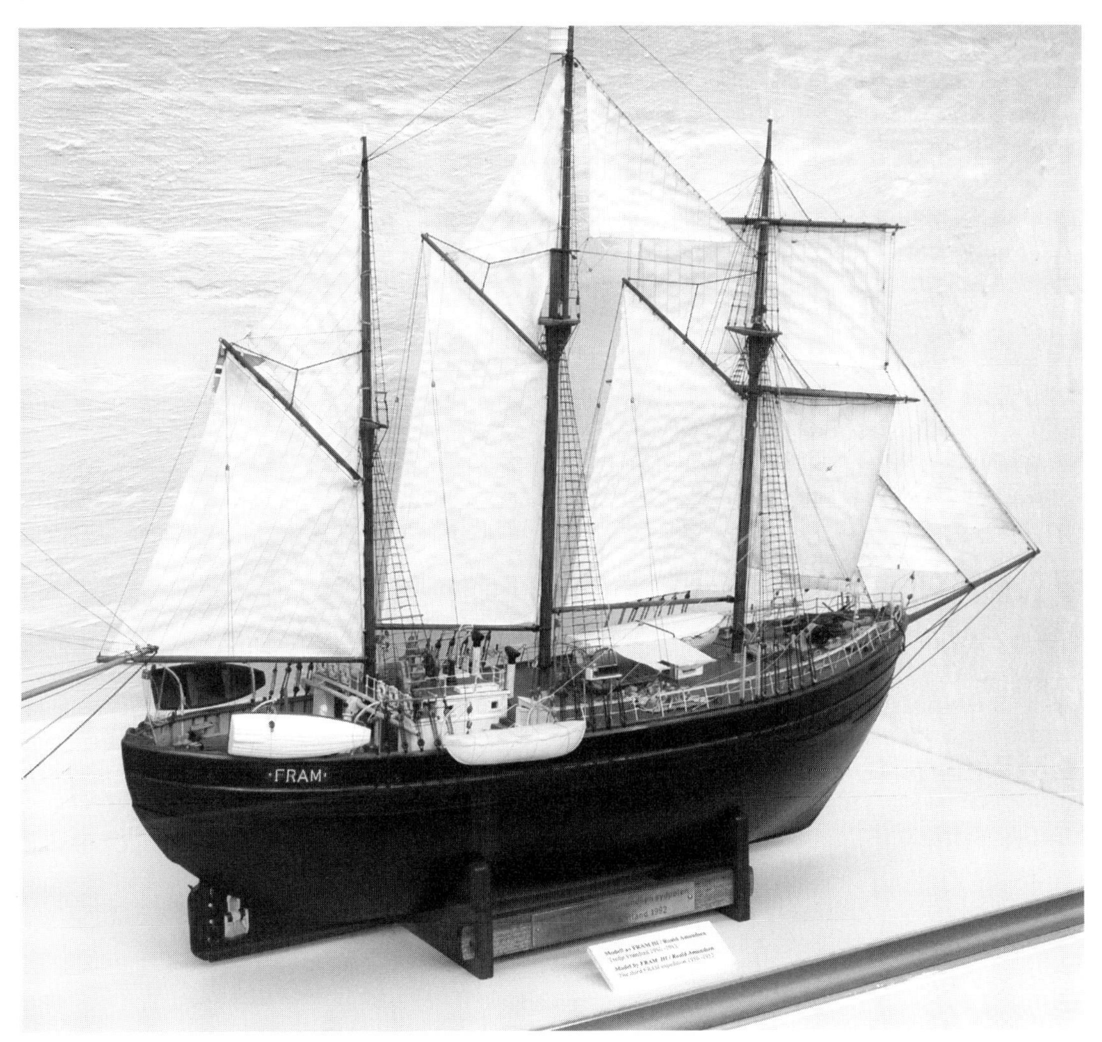

A model of the Archer-designed exploration ship *Fram*, in the Bydøy Museum, Oslo, Norway. (Author)

The following year his father died. After some time for reflection (and leisure), Colin decided to settle at the family home in Larvick, and of much greater importance set his mind to study naval architecture as well as ship and boat building. As the years passed he became a pioneer of innovative small craft design. Three years later he set up a shipyard in a fjord near his family home and started building some remarkable vessels. As the ships became bigger, the building berths were re-aligned, enabling almost every one of his ships to be built within a short walking distance of his home. One or two large ships, such as the polar exploration ship *Fram*, had to be built further afield.

In 1868 he married Karen Sophie Wiborg, and for her he built a new house, 'Lilleoden', which included an office for his design work and research. In 1879 Archer was elected a member of the Institution of Naval Architects having presented his first paper in 1878 and then in 1881 he gave another. The first was 'The Wave Principle applied to the Longitudinal Disposition of Immersed Volume' and it followed close in the train of thought first promulgated by **John Scott Russell**. Scott Russell was pleased with this recognition, but disagreed with Archer's interpretation. As is now known, neither theory stood the test of time.

Archer's work with small ships and his enthusiasm for boat-building led to his second paper entitled 'Shipbuilding a Thousand Years Ago'. This analytical approach enabled him to assess the requirements for improved safety in the timber-built part of the Norwegian coastal fleets. The hallmarks of his design were improved watertight integrity with completely enclosed decking, a matter on which he agreed with Captain John Washington RN following his 1849 investigation into losses of British fishing vessels. Inevitably as a 'disciple' of the wave form of ship design, Archer produced the most beautiful hull forms, most of which include the Norwegian or canoe shaped stern, now known as the 'Double Ender'.

In 1892 he designed and oversaw construction of the first ship in the world specifically built for polar exploration, the three-masted barque *Fram*. Her hull form was influenced by the whaling traditions of Norway and Britain which enabled ships to withstand long periods trapped in ice; the sections were well rounded, the hull was more than 75cm (2ft 6in) thick, and her propeller and rudder could be lifted into special cavities within the hull. Despite being prone to rolling, the *Fram* made some lengthy journeys and holds records for travelling further south or north than any other surface vessel. The record trips were for the intrepid explorers Fritjof Nansen on his 1893 attempt on the North Pole and for Roald Amundsen on his 1911 expedition to the South Pole. The *Fram* is now preserved in her own dry-dock at Bydøy, Oslo.

Colin Archer's most significant work was in the 1890s with the forming of the Norwegian Lifesaving Society. He designed their off-shore rescue boats or '*redningsbåter*', and to this day their influence on lifeboat design in northern Europe is noticeable. One of the vessels designed and built at Larvik in 1905 was a very lovely yawl-rigged yacht, which on completion was delivered by a professional crew to the owner and his new wife then living in the south of England; the owner was Erskine Childers and the yacht was the legendary *Asgard*.*

Colin Archer became active in community affairs in his later years. He retired in 1911 with two especial honours – the Cross of St Olaf and the medal of the Royal Geographical Society of London.

SOURCES:

Leather, John
Colin Archer and the Seaworthy Double Ender
Camden, Maine, 1979

*This yacht was designed and built as a wedding present for Erskine Childers and his American wife Molly. Erskine, who was British, had been brought up in Ireland and became a clerk to the House of Commons. He led an interesting life and wrote *The Riddle of the Sands*, a great story of yachting and a warning about German military expansion in the 1900s. In 1914 the *Asgard* was used for gun-running to Ireland, but Childers served as a Lieutenant Commander in the Royal Naval Air Service during the First World War. In the 1920s he joined the Anti-Treaty forces, was the victim of a set-up and was executed by the Irish in Dublin in 1922. His son Erskine Hamilton Childers (1905–74), became the fourth President of Ireland and the *Asgard* has been preserved by the National Museum of Ireland.

George Wightwick Rendel
1833–1902

GEORGE RENDEL AND his brother Alexander, both engineers, were sons of James Meadows Rendel FRS (1799–1856), who began his career as a surveyor employed by Thomas Telford, before branching out on his own and forming a dock design and engineering partnership that would became world-famous. The older brother Alexander continued in this practice and for much of his life was associated with India.

The younger brother, George, finished his formal education at Harrow School and then becoming a pupil of his father. At a very early stage, he was sent to India, becoming involved in the massive public works authorised there in the mid-nineteenth century. Some years later, the Newcastle industrialist **William G Armstrong** invited the young Rendel to enter his works at Elswick-on-Tyne and continue his learning. The Armstrongs, being childless, offered their protégé food and lodging at their Jesmond home during his early years on Tyneside. In 1859, the year in which Armstrong was knighted, Rendel was appointed manager, and shortly after made a partner of Armstrong's Elswick Ordnance Company which was sited on the north bank of the Tyne just west of Newcastle. A year later he was joined by a former Royal Artillery officer **Captain Andrew Noble**, and for the next twenty years they worked (presumably harmoniously) on the development of heavy ordnance. Noble was a physicist, while Rendel attended to the structural, hydraulic and administrative aspects of gun design and to the even more complex problem of gun testing. For a while gun-testing was carried out on the sands near Whitley Bay, but as this did not endear the gun manufacturers to the local residents, other means had to be found. Rendel struck on the idea of testing on barges at sea, and from this came the idea of light gunboats – ships designed for swift attacks using small calibre rapid-firing guns where the chance of hitting the target probably surpassed that of the large guns of cruisers and capital ships.

In the early 1860s, Armstrongs decided to commence shipbuilding and came to an arrangement with **Charles Mitchell**, the proprietor of the Low Walker Shipyard, the outcome being Armstrong, Mitchell and Company which was incorporated in 1862. Ironclads were built at Elswick while merchant and other tonnage including pioneer ice-breakers, came from Low Walker. Rendel, who had expressed misgivings at commencing shipbuilding west of Newcastle, found himself in the driving seat, and is remembered for being the 'designer' of several heavy-gun monitors, as well as the new class of armoured cruisers, which became known as 'Elswick Cruisers'. His misgivings were misplaced, for Elswick went from strength to strength and at one time in 1896 twenty warships were under construction simultaneously. The bridges in Newcastle were modified to ensure the great warships could pass through on their way to the sea, or up-river when being delivered for the mounting of their guns.

Arguably the most famous product of the yard was the Chilean armoured cruiser *Esmeralda* of 1884. She could steam at 18 knots, was devoid of cumbrous rigging and sails, and had a continuous armoured deck running from bow to stern just above the waterline. She transformed thinking on cruisers and this in turn was instrumental in the success of the Armstrong companies. (**Philip Watts**, a later Director of Naval Construction gave a clear exposition on Elswick Cruisers at Newcastle which subsequently was published as a paper in the 1899 Transactions of the INA.) Elswick had remarkable managers at different times in their history, and these included two future Directors of Naval Construction, Sir William White and Sir Philip Watts.

In 1882, Parliament established a new post, that of Professional Civil Lord to the Admiralty, a non-Parliamentary appointment the incumbent of which was charged with the task of assisting the Controller of the Navy. Rendel was offered this post and for three years was involved in the forward planning of fleet procurement. In 1885, with a change of government, the post was abolished and Rendel, who was not enjoying the best of health, made a new life for himself in Italy, living near Naples. He suggested to Armstrong that a branch of their Company be established there, and in 1887 the Pozzuoli works were set up, with his friend Admiral the Count Albini and himself joint managing directors. This plant remained part of the Armstrong Group until the setting-up of Vickers-Armstrongs Ltd in 1926.

George Rendel joined the Institution in 1879 and when he died in 1902, was a Vice President. His bust stands in the entry hall of the RINA offices in Upper Belgrave Street.

SOURCES:
Marshall, Ian
Cruisers and La Guerre de Course
Mystic Seaport Museum, Conn., 2007
Watts, Philip
'Elswick Cruisers'
Transactions of the Institution of Naval Architects
Vol 41 (1899)

Joseph Russell
1834–1917

BORN IN BLACKHEATH, London, Joseph Russell, the first shipbuilder to introduce mass and batch production, was the son of a solicitor who later became a Baptist minister. His early formal education was at Mill Hill School and then for a short period in his early teens, he attended Kings College London. When aged sixteen, he made his way to the Clyde and there commenced an apprenticeship with the new and little-known shipyard of J W Hoby in the east yard at Renfrew: it is understood the proprietor was a distant relative of the Russell family. In 1854 the business collapsed, but was taken over by its creditors and Joseph Russell was able to complete his apprenticeship in the following year. On reaching his majority he was given a fairly substantial sum of money from the family and, even better, appointed works manager. Possibly through his background the site became known as the London Works, a name that was to remain until the late twentieth century as the long-established company of William Simons (later Simons-Lobnitz) purchased the East Yard in 1860 and continued using the name. The next four years at Renfrew must have been more than exciting for a young man, having the full responsibility for a small shipbuilding facility and simultaneously courting and marrying a local girl. His marriage seems to have been happy; his wife was to outlive him by four years and they had three sons and four daughters.

In 1859 he moved to the Ardrossan Dockyard where in a period of six years over thirty small vessels were produced. In 1866, commercial matters became more evident when he was invited by Laurence Hill to manage his shipyard in Port Glasgow. Hill was a well-travelled and experienced academic who had worked with Professor Lewis Gordon of Glasgow University in the setting-up of the Loch Katrine reservoir, a public utility which placed Glasgow ahead of most cities for all time and which granted Glasgow the (almost) singular privilege of supplying feed water to Royal Navy ships 'direct from the tap'. In the three years that Russell worked there, twenty-nine hulls were completed. Russell left in 1869, ostensibly to be with his father who was ill and to take charge to family business in London, but it is believed the real reason for his moving south was a series of disagreements with his employer.

In 1873 he moved back to Scotland and set up in Port Glasgow as Russell and Company. In the next eighteen years, while principal, he enabled this new shipyard to become known and respected throughout the maritime world. Initially in partnership with Anderson Rodger, then joined later by William Todd Lithgow, the yard went from strength to strength, new shipyards in the area were acquired and the number of building berths increased to an astonishing number, possibly as many as twenty. In the nineteenth century and well before the days of prefabrication, the number of building slips was a real measure of a shipyard's production capability. To induce business the partners used a series of encouragements including building 'on spec' and part investment in the new ships under construction. While never in the lead technically like Denny of Dumbarton, they nevertheless, kept abreast or ahead of current technologies.

In 1878 a near-disaster occurred with the collapse of the City of Glasgow Bank. The economic devastation this caused in Scotland and in many other countries was serious. Russell, who had a

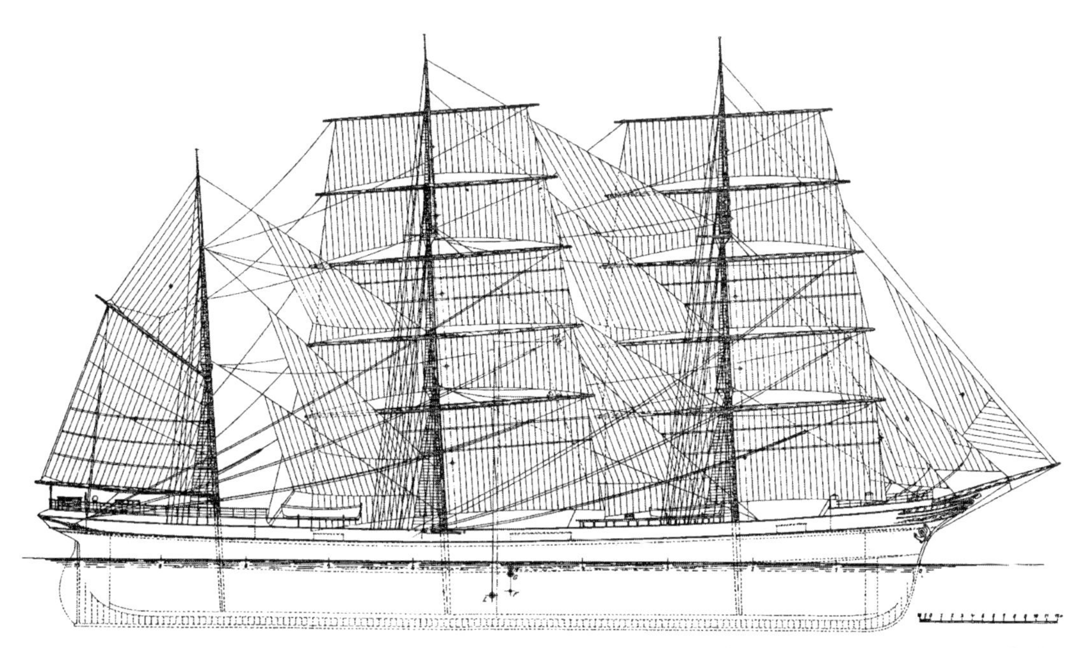

Joseph Russell's Port Glasgow shipyard won the international blue ribband of shipbuilding several times with their policy of standardisation and a small number of products. Their most successful designs until the First World War were three- and four-masted barques. (From *Middendorf's* Bemastung und Takelung der Schiffe)

very modest holding, found he had to meet liabilities that were twenty-eight times greater than the face value of his original stock. With great difficulty his liabilities were met and the shipyard survived. It is history now, but the collapse of this bank is regarded as one of the most serious financial collapses in nineteenth-century British history, and one in which all the directors ended up in prison.

Russell and Company was to become the largest privately-owned shipbuilding company in the world, and competed vigorously in the annual shipbuilding stakes of the Clyde, the United Kingdom and the world. Their reward came in 1890, when the world's greatest output (the Blue Riband of shipbuilding) of thirty-four ships (twenty-six sailing ships and eight steamers totalling 70,000 gross tons) was produced in Port Glasgow, possibly no surprise as then the commercial sailing fleet registered in Glasgow was itself the largest in the world. While under Joseph Russell's control, the shipyards concentrated on large three-, four- and five-masted sailing bulk carriers. A few steamships were constructed but in all cases the machinery was purchased from other sources. They built to high standards, subject to standardisation of parts wherever possible and in many cases hull lines were used over and over again; it is said that one set of scrieve boards was used over forty times.

In 1891, Russell retired and the business was dissolved, with Lithgow taking up the larger shipbuilding units and turning the production over to steamships. Anderson Rodger took over the Bay Shipyard and continued building sailing ships into the twentieth century, incidentally, one of which, the three-masted barque *Glenlee*, has now been restored and is open to the public in central Glasgow. Joseph Russell had an active retirement, but assisted William Lithgow on sundry professional matters, and following his early death, advised his sons Henry and James on the running of the shipyard then renamed **Lithgows** Limited.

Russell was active in many ventures, the Church and local education being two examples. He was a key participant in the merger of the United

Presbyterian Church and the Free Church of Scotland in 1900 which was the precursor of the 1929 final merger of the Church of Scotland. His full retirement came in 1913 and he died four years later.

SOURCES:
Blake, George
The Constant Star
London, 1945
An excellent historic novel on Port Glasgow shipbuilding.
Bowen, Frank C
'Joseph Russell'
Shipbuilding and Shipping Record
13 September 1945
Moss, Michael
'Joseph Russell' in
Dictionary of Scottish Business Biography
Vol 1 (Aberdeen, 1986)

Alfred Thayer Mahan

1840–1914

Captain A H Mahan USN, 1840–1914. *(Author)*

ALFRED MAHAN IS REMEMBERED for two roles; first that of a professional seaman officer in the United States Navy, and second as one of the greatest of the nineteenth-century naval historians, whose work influenced strategic planners, politicians and naval architects all over the world.

His father Dennis Hart Mahan (1802–71) after joining the US Corps of Engineers, was sent to West Point then a very new college but developing fast under the inspired leadership of Col. Sylvanus Thayer. Within a short period, Dennis Mahan had been commissioned and then appointed an acting Assistant Professor of Mathematics. Following some time for study in France, he returned and was appointed Professor of Engineering. In 1820 his first son Alfred was born, and reflecting the mutual esteem and regard of the two devoutly religious families, Alfred's middle name was Thayer.

At the age of fifteen, and on his own initiative, Alfred joined the US Navy as an acting Midshipman and on 30 September 1856 enrolled as a student at the Naval Academy, Annapolis. In 1857 he made his first cruise aboard USS *Plymouth*. His three years at Annapolis were overshadowed by the growing rift between the northern and southern states of the Union, and gradually he began to be separated from friends as they drifted south, some to die in the forthcoming conflict. At the outbreak of war all correspondence between the former student friends was to cease. In 1859 Mahan completed his course and joined the sailing frigate *Congress* on her way to the Brazil station. While on this station, he started to analyse the incidents of the war such as the success and otherwise of the blockade runners, and by the time he had been promoted Lieutenant aboard USS *Pocahontas*, he had honed his skills in assessing the effectiveness of naval strategies.

Between 1864 and 1875, he had several exciting sea-going appointments. While Executive Officer of the *Iroquois*, he took ill in Nagasaki, was sent ashore and then combining recovery and leave he was able to visit India, France and the UK, where he inspected the ill-fated HMS *Captain*. In 1872 he married, and after six months leave, was promoted to Commander and given command of the USS *Wasp* on the River Plate, an appointment giving him the power of the United States' representative in the area, and experience in the protection of American interests overseas. During this period, he was regularly writing for journals and corresponding with friends made during his world trip. In 1875 he was appointed to the Boston Navy Yard and within a very short time declared his horror at corruption in the yard administration. This annoyed many in the establishment and within months he was on 'furlough pay' – the equivalent of the much-disliked 'half pay' for officers in the Royal Navy.

In 1876 his life's work began as a lecturer and later professor at the US Navy's War College. Similar to the teaching of naval architecture in the nineteenth-century Royal Navy, the American War College was a pawn in the political system and was not to receive significant backing for many years. However, Mahan can take much credit for the growth of this establishment through his lecturing and above all his writing, including his 1883 contribution to the history of the Civil War, *The Gulf and Inland Waters*. His time there was broken by short seagoing appointments, but he returned regularly to the College, each time with greater authority and ultimately enjoying the friendship of Theodore Roosevelt (who became Assistant Secretary to the Navy in 1897 and President in 1901 following the assassination of President McKinley).

This was a period of intense naval rivalry, with Britain having the largest fleet in the world by a considerable margin. British policy was based on the principle of a 'two-power fleet', meaning that the Royal Navy was intended to be larger than the two next largest battle fleets combined. In 1889 the United Kingdom had forty-five battleships in service or building, while the French and Italian fleets had thirty-seven between them. In that year the total number of battleships serving (or under construction) in France, Italy, Russia, Germany and Austria amounted to sixty-four. In his works, Mahan maintained that the factors to be considered (some quite nebulous) when analysing the sea power of a potential enemy included: geographical position; physical conformation of the country; extent of territory; size of population; character of the people; and form and stability of the government

Mahan's name was established by a multitude of writings, the best known being *The Influence of Sea Power upon History* (1892) which asserted the points listed above. He was aware of Nelson's personal faults, but despite them admired him as a seaman and commander, producing his acclaimed work *The Life of Nelson* in 1897. Following his retirement in 1896 he found himself serving on overseas missions and on advisory work for the US government. He became known to most members of the British Royal Family as well as to the Kaiser who insisted that copies of Mahan's books be placed aboard all his warships. Mahan's view was that command of the seas could come only through strength, ability and willingness to act offensively, and this had enormous influence on the German ruler. Certainly few people had analysed sea power in a critical manner before, and Mahan's work laid the basis of war studies as well as influencing the thinking of those responsible for fundamental warship design. He did not live to witness the First World War, dying in 1914, by then with an unique set of honours – doctorates from Oxford, Cambridge, Harvard and Yale. He declined the honorary appointment of Captain in the Royal Navy, and despite having been made an Admiral of the United States Navy on his retirement, continued to be known as Captain Mahan.

While not a naval architect, his influence on the profession was greater than either historians or engineers have appreciated, and through his introductory studies many schools set up courses in naval ship design, like those in the early twentieth century headed by Professor William Hovgaard at the Massachusetts Institute of Technology.

SOURCES:

Mahan, A T
The Influence of Sea Power upon History 1660–1783
1890

Puleston, W D
Mahan
London, 1939

John Philip Holland

1841–1914

FOR A MAN WHO is remembered rightly as the father of the modern submarine, John Holland had an unusual start in life. His father was a minor official in the Coastguard and the family lived at Liscannor, a small village in Co Clare on the west coast of Ireland. His education initially was at the local school, but later at the Christian Brothers school in nearby Limerick. Clearly two matters left their mark on him, first the poverty and desolation of the Potato Famine (which reached its nadir in 1847) and secondly, on a more positive note, the bustling harbour scenes of one of Ireland's busier small coasting ports. These were desperate years for many parts of Europe; not least Ireland from whose shores around four million people emigrated, bound mostly for Quebec and New York. The Christian Brothers were hard-pressed keeping their schools manned with competent teachers and following an appeal, Holland joined the order. He never took his final vows, but encouraged by his interest in matters maritime and mechanical, worked for some years as an unusual and stimulating teacher and lay-brother in the community. It is said that he entertained his pupils by building and demonstrating a model duck that could dive underwater.

The two (and entwined) passions in his life were Irish independence and the development of undersea vessels. Around 1872, he emigrated to the United States settling in New Jersey where he continued for some time as a teacher. He had been studying all known sources of information on underwater craft while simultaneously designing a submarine, the plan of which was offered to the US Navy in 1875, but was rejected as a crank idea from a non-seafaring civilian. Financial assistance came in an unexpected manner from the Fenians (the Irish Republican Brotherhood) who envisaged this as a weapon to be used against the British.

The first boat built was a mere 4.3m (14ft) and driven by a steam engine. While on 'sea trials' in 1878 on the Passaic River it had to be abandoned suddenly and was to remain on the bottom there until it was recovered in the 1920s. Five years later the real precursor of the submarine was built and tested in New York Harbour – it was 10m (32ft 9in) long and displaced 19 tons – and was taken to the then-unprecedented depth of 20m (65ft). This craft embodied most of the principles of modern submarines including weight compensation, and can be seen to this day at Paterson in New Jersey. It has the intriguing name *Fenian Ram* but despite being seized by the Fenians shortly after construction never saw action.

Several further constructions were carried out, some successful and others fairly disastrous, and during this period Holland set up a shipbuilding enterprise known as the J P Holland Torpedo Boat Company. With the help of friends well-placed in the Navy, the new company received an order for a boat named *Plunger* for the then astronomic price of $150,000. Through general mismanagement and heavy-handed navy interference the contract was unsuccessful and Holland was almost on his uppers with little more than $5,000 left in the bank. With great initiative and faith he proceeded alone with one further vessel named *Holland* which was launched at Elizabeth, Connecticut in 1898. This new boat had a configuration akin to a cigar, a shape that would be used by many more times in the early twentieth century; she was 16.5m (54ft) in length, 3m (9ft 10in) in diameter, displaced 75 tons and having electric motors and batteries as well as internal combustion machinery, was able to run submerged for considerable distances. She so endeared herself to the authorities that, following successful trials, she was purchased outright by the US Navy in 1900, thereby marked the foundation of the US Submarine Service. There was no looking back. Six more boats were ordered by the Americans, and shortly thereafter further contracts were placed by the Russians and their bitter opponents, the Japanese.

The most surprising development of all was the signing of a licensing agreement allowing Vickers, Son & Maxim of Barrow-in-Furness to build submarines to the Holland design for the Royal Navy. The choice of shipyard was not inappropriate as Barrow already had experience of this kind of work

John P Holland, 1841–1914, photographed in the conning tower of one of his submersibles. *(Author)*

with Nordenfeldt boats in the 1880s. However, three key factors were responsible for this breakthrough. Firstly, Holland's political views must have mellowed, secondly, it is clear that he was persuaded by his colleagues on the board of the wisdom of working with what then was the world's largest navy, and thirdly Lord Rothschild, who assisted in brokering the deal, had visions of Vickers and an American submarine builder working in close co-operation.

Largely owing to Holland's ineptitude in business matters, relations between himself and his fellow board members were not happy, and following unsuccessful attempts to promote him to a non-executive chairmanship, they parted company in the early 1900s. The old company was restructured and renamed the Electric Boat Company and for many decades concentrated on building American submarines, and as often as not working in close harmony with Vickers of Barrow.

In the last ten years of his life, John Holland advised foreign governments on submarine design, he invented a submarine rescue respirator and it is recorded he dabbled with experiments in flying. He is remembered as a great pioneer, and arguably as the man who is the father of submarine operations. His memory is honoured in a unique manner, with three of his early hulls restored as memorials, two in the United States and HMS *Holland 1* now at Gosport in the UK.

SOURCES:

Harrison, A N
The Development of H.M. Submarines from Holland No 1 (1901) to Porpoise (1930)
MOD Ship Department (BR 3043)
Bath, 1979

Morris Richard K
John P Holland 1841–1914, Inventor of the Modern Submarine
Annapolis, Md, 1966

Scott, J D
Vickers: a History
London, 1962

Part 4
The World Wars
1900–1950

Annus Mirabilis

The shipbuilding returns of 1913 gave great comfort to the shipbuilders and marine engine builders of Britain, and as they had produced over half the world's ships, the country could claim rightfully to be shipbuilders to the world. England and Wales, headed by the shipyards of the three great rivers of the Tyne, the Tees and the Wear, produced 29 per cent of the world's tonnage, and Scotland could claim 17 per cent with the River Clyde in addition having delivered more than one ship for every day of the year including the world's largest ship, the new liner *Aquitania*, later known as 'The Ship Beautiful'.

Every aspect of maritime technology was available within the British Isles. The steam turbine had been proved as an outstanding success, the cutting of marine gears was a growing business and there were high expectations for the marine diesel engine. British companies were equal to any American or European competitors in the manufacture of steel, armour plate, forgings and big guns. Sadly the big guns would be required the following year as the world plunged into total war.

Marine engineering

Of the many engineering innovations of this half century, four stand out, namely the steam turbine, the diesel engine, the perfecting of marine gearing and the introduction of oil as fuel.

In 1901, the Clyde excursion steamer *King Edward*, a product of the **Denny** shipyard, had proved the efficacy of steam turbines for marine use, and she was followed immediately by others. By 1906, the **Parsons** Company were in receipt of a public accolade, when orders for the turbines for some of the most prestigious ships came their way. The ships were HMS *Dreadnought*, the first of a new type of all-big-gun battleship being built at Portsmouth Dockyard, and for the Cunard Line the Atlantic record-breakers *Lusitania* and *Mauretania*, then being built on the Clyde and the Tyne respectively. The steam turbine would become the choice of almost all passenger ship owners for the next thirty years, and indeed they continued being fitted until the 1960s.

Modern planning has much to learn from HMS *Dreadnought*, the ship that changed naval strategic planning overnight. The building time of this ship was 366 days – possibly unrepresentative of naval construction, but proving where there is a will, there is a way. (*Author*)

One of the problems with turbines is the vast difference between their optimum speed with that of economical and efficient propellers. Parsons experimented with a cargo ship, the SS *Vespasian* and despite the astronomical costs involved, it was established that geared turbines were the way forward. Further savings were introduced with the introduction of oil firing in place of the dirty and inefficient use of coal. This introduced cleanliness and efficiency into bunkering, ending the nightmare scenario of coaling ship, the process of first moving hundreds of tons of coal into the bunkers and secondly the trimming of this unpleasant and quite dangerous cargo. During the nineteenth century, when a passenger liner was bunkered in the tropics, it was the day on which most passengers chose to be ashore.

In 1911, the East Asiatic Company took delivery of the twin diesel-engined intermediate liner *Selandia* from Burmeister & Wain of Copenhagen. After long and protracted negotiations with **Rudolf Diesel**, the ship builders as an act of faith laid down the *Selandia*, and simultaneously Barclay Curle of Glasgow commenced work on her less well-known sister-ship *Jutlandia*. Despite many teething problems, the diesel ships were a success and the Danes found themselves in the van of diesel ship production. The determination of a large group of people led to the East Asiatic's diesel fleet, which can claim to be the forerunner of the vast bulk of ships now operating on all the oceans of the world.

Several major companies commenced building diesel engines, which as the years passed became known under their own names, such as Doxford of Sunderland, Sulzer Brothers of Winterthur in Switzerland and others. The vast bulk of marine engineers tended to build new machinery under licence from people like B&W, Sulzer or Doxford as they had the expertise and had invested heavily in design and research.

The Panama Canal and world trade routes

In 1914, after fourteen years of work, the **Lobnitz**-built 20-ton floating crane *Alexandre Lavalley* had the honour of being the first ship through the Panama Canal. This remarkable waterway changed the economics of shipowning and currently is in the throes of further expansion which will enable it to handle almost all the ships of the world.

The opening of the Kiel Canal (in 1898) was a major step forward for the Baltic trade. This canal remained fairly free of damage during the two World Wars and currently is the busiest canal in the world with nearly 200 ships traversing the 99km (62-mile) link every day.

The great maritime disasters

While the early years of the twentieth century witnessed exponential technological development and ever increasing growth in trade and tonnage, a number of major ship disasters during this era, both in war and in peacetime, were reminders that, at sea and despite all the advances, ships and their passengers remained vulnerable. The loss of the *Titanic*, in particular, seemed unimaginable at the time, so much confidence in her technological prowess having been invested in her.

Norge: In June 1904 this Danish steamship, *en route* from Copenhagen to New York, ran ashore on Rockall. Of the 700 emigrants and 80 crew aboard, only 129 were saved.

Titanic: This triple-screw Atlantic liner on her maiden voyage from Southampton to New York collided with an iceberg on 14 April 1912. The ship sank in about three hours with the loss of 1,490 passengers and crew. Only 711 persons were saved. The formal investigation found the loss of the ship was due to excessive speed. It was signed by the judge Lord Mersey and four assessors including

Professor Sir J H Biles. Lack of lifeboat space was a matter deliberated on at the following Safety at Sea Conferences, and new regulations were introduced. Incidentally, helm orders in those days were from the days of sail, an anomaly which was rectified in the 1920s.

Empress of Ireland: This particularly tragic event which place on the St Lawrence in May 1914. The Canadian Pacific liner *Empress of Ireland*, outward bound from Montreal, sustained damage when the Norwegian freighter *Storstadt* rammed her starboard side at amidships. It was a foggy night, and most passengers and all children aboard were in bed. The ship heeled over and sank very quickly and of the full complement of 1,477 only 465 survived, very few being children. The gathering war clouds of 1914 rather obscured the *Empress* disaster from public awareness.

Lusitania: This crack Atlantic liner operated by the Cunard Line was torpedoed by a German submarine off the Old Head of Kinsale, Ireland on 7 May 1915. 1,198 persons were drowned and only 761 were saved. This incident had massive repercussions and almost brought the USA into the war with Germany in 1915.

The *Imo* and *Mont Blanc* collision: On 6 December 1917 the French steamer *Mont Blanc* collided with the steamer *Imo* at the narrow entrance to Halifax Harbour, Nova Scotia. The *Mont Blanc* was carrying several thousands of tons of high explosive for the war effort and the *Imo*, which was in ballast had been chartered by the Belgian Relief Commission The resulting explosion killed 1,500 people with another 2,000 missing. More than 3,000 houses were destroyed.

Owing to the massive loss of life in this accident, the official enquiry had difficulty in ascertaining the facts. It is believed that the officer of the watch on one ship used the steam whistle to signal his intention to alter course to starboard and tried to give the mandatory single short blast. Unfortunately the whistle (possibly choked with condensate) did not sound and the officer tried a second time with success. It is understood that nothing was heard on the bridge of the other ship, but the officer in charge clearly saw two separate puffs of steam from the whistle and wrongly assumed the oncoming ship was turning to port.

A subsequent rule amendment issued by the British Board of Trade required that ships not only be equipped with whistles, but that the whistles be efficient.

War and standardised shipbuilding

With the coming of war in 1914 came the loss of tonnage and the need for quick ship replacement led to the expansion of the shipbuilding industries in both North America and the United Kingdom, with the two countries co-operating closely. In general it was agreed that the United States would concentrate on merchant ships

TSS *Sarpedon*, built and engined by Cammell Laird of Birkenhead in 1923 for the Blue Funnel Line of Liverpool, typifies the high quality passenger and cargo tonnage of the inter-war years. *(Author)*

while the United Kingdom and Canada would build a higher percentage of warships. The entry on **Henry Kaiser** gives an indication of the massive contribution of the American shipyards to the war effort – especially in the Second World War.

In Britain the setting-up of the Standard Shipbuilding Company is typical of the First World War and is described in the biography of **Sir James Caird**.

Concrete shipbuilding

Concrete as a shipbuilding material has been experimented with for over 150 years. The first example was a rowing boat built in France in 1849, and over the years larger ships appeared culminating in the 182-ton deadweight motor coaster *Namsenfjord* from Norway in 1917. With the material shortages brought on by the Great War, many shipbuilders gave serious consideration to this new system, as it had been estimated that hull steel requirements would be about 20 per cent of that required for a conventional hull. **Sir Maurice Denny** of Dumbarton and Walter Pollock of Faversham in Kent not only had such hulls designed, but also published detailed information in the *Transactions of the INA*. This form of building was based on concrete being poured into shuttering which encased pre-fitted steel reinforcing rods. Several small shipyards for concrete construction were set up in Britain and America at the end of the war, but with the flattened economy, they had little support and all had closed by the mid-1920s.

Welding

Considerable effort was expended by several shipyards in the 1920s and 1930s in the introduction of welding, and details are given in the biography of **Oscar Kjellberg**. In some ways Britain was held back in the 1930s by the difficulties besetting an industry with large numbers of steelworkers unemployed. Matters were not eased with the drive to build ships during the war, and when increased tonnage returns out-pointed the need for technical improvements. The United States yards under **Henry Kaiser** and others had the advantage of training the bulk of their labour force from scratch.

National Shipbuilders Security Limited

The setting up of National Shipbuilders Security (NSS) Ltd was one of the more controversial acts of the 1930s. At the depth of the depression all shipyards were struggling to find work and freight rates for shipping were falling. The idea, which had the support of the Bank of England, was that all shipyards would pay a small levy on their turnover to NSS Ltd. This company in turn would use their capital to buy up inefficient shipyards and hopefully reduce surplus capacity and the associated competition. The building slips purchased were to be in legal terms 'sterilised', taking them out of the building arena.

Altogether something like thirty-eight yards were affected, either completely or partly and 216 building berths closed. The size of yard ranged from the massive Beardmore site on the Clyde to the much smaller company of Earle's of Hull. At the outbreak of war some building sites were re-opened, but physical changes and legal restraints made this difficult.

The armadas of the Second World War

Few achievements can be as great as the work of the multifarious commercial companies which supplied the materiel for the D-Day landings on five sectors of the Normandy coast on 6 June 1944. This great undertaking, which involved 6,000 ships and tens of thousands of men, was commanded by Admiral Sir Bertram Ramsay, the former Admiral at Dover who had cut his teeth on massive naval operations with the evacuation of 366,000 men from Dunkirk in the dark days of 1940, and had gone on to command the great landings in the Mediterranean.

The unusual maritime projects involved at D-Day included specialist landing craft of many sizes, the Mulberry Harbours built to form safe landing jetties on the open beaches and PLUTO, the pipeline(s) under the ocean laid to transport fuel to the armies in France.

Liberty ships

The United States Maritime Commission arranged that over 5,000 ships were built during the years 1940 to 1945. Of these more than 2,700 were Liberty ships, or, officially, Emergency Cargo Vessels; each was able to carry about 10,500 tons of cargo. The hulls were based on British designs modified for North American shipbuilding practice, and they were built at eighteen different sites in the United States. The triple expansion steam machinery (also of original British design) came from seventeen US and three Canadian engine builders with water tube rather than Scotch boilers. Despite the ships being welded throughout, it is pleasing to report that not one ship was lost at sea through welding failure. The Liberties, the T2s and the faster C3s were part of America's major contributions to the winning of the Second World War.

KEY DATES

1901 First turbine passenger steamer *King Edward* built at Dumbarton. White Star liner *Celtic* built at Belfast, at 21,000 gr. tons the world's largest ship. First radio signal sent across the Atlantic.

1904 Danish liner *Norge* grounds off Rockall, then sinks with loss of 627 lives.

1905 Battle of Tsushima between the Russian and Japanese fleets. Roald Amundsen on auxiliary cutter *Gjøa* is first to navigate the North-West Passage.

1906 Enrico Forlanini designs world's first hydrofoil, tested on Lake Maggiore, Italy. Launch of HMS *Dreadnought*, built in 366 days at Portsmouth Dockyard.

1908 SS *Paul Paix* built at Middlesbrough to Isherwood system (classed with LR and BC).

1910 C A Parsons presents paper to INA on Geared Turbine Marine Machinery.

1911 World's first diesel liner MS *Selandia* delivered at Copenhagen.

1912 Sinking of the *Titanic* with the loss of 1,490 lives.

1913 *Annus Mirabilis* for British and especially Clyde shipbuilding. International conference on Safety of Life at Sea convened in London. Royal Navy commences trials of aircraft-carrying ships.

1914 *Empress of Ireland* and *Storstad* collision in the St Lawrence with loss of 1,012 lives. Outbreak of the First World War. Panama Canal opened.

1915	Cunard liner *Lusitania* torpedoed off Ireland with loss of 1,201 lives.
1916	Battle of Jutland.
1917	Sinking of the steam-driven submarine *K 13* during trials in the Gareloch. United States of America declares war on Germany. Setting-up of the United States Shipping Board Emergency Fleet Corporation. Halifax Disaster – explosion killing several thousand following ship collision. Sea-going motor coaster *Namsenfjord* built of concrete by N K Fougner in Norway.
1918	Launch of world's first all-welded hull, Barge *Ac1320*, at Richborough, Kent. End of First World War.
1919	German High Seas Fleet scuttled at Scapa Flow, Orkney.
1920	All-welded ship *Fullagar* built at Birkenhead and the tug *ESAB IV* at Gothenburg.
1922	Washington Naval Conference.
1924	Completion of Britain's first purpose-built aircraft carrier HMS *Hermes*.
1926	World's first high-pressure turbine passenger steamer *King George V* built at Dumbarton.
1928	Patent registered by Robert MacGregor for a steel hatch cover.
1929	National Shipbuilders Security Ltd set up to 'sterilise' non-competitive British shipyards. Severe world-wide economic depression. *Agnita*, the world's first liquefied petroleum gas (LPG) tanker, built at Newcastle for Shell.
1934	Liner *Queen Mary* launched at Clydebank.
1935	J M McNeill's paper in *Transactions of INA* on the 'Launch of the *Queen Mary*'.
1938	German forces occupy Austria and then invade Czechoslovakia.
1939	Germany invades Poland. Britain and France declare war on Germany (3 Sep). Liner *Athenia en route* Glasgow-Montreal is torpedoed (3 Sep) with loss of 128 lives.
1940	Germany invades Belgium, The Netherlands, Denmark and Norway. Withdrawal of British and Allied forces from Dunkirk. 366,162 servicemen evacuated. America starts planning for the emergency shipbuilding programme.
1941	Japanese attack Pearl Harbor and invade Malaya and Indonesia. America, Britain and The Netherlands at war with Japan. United States of America declares war on Germany. Collision between RMS *Queen Mary* and HMS *Curacoa* – generated by 'ship interaction'.
1943	Sundry landing craft designed and built in Britain, Canada and the USA.
1944	D-Day: the Allied invasion of Europe using an armada of 6,000 ships.
1945	Victory in both Europe and the Far East.
1947	Merger of two classification societies; Lloyd's Register and the British Corporation.
1948	First gas turbine craft in Royal Navy – *MGB 2009*.
1949	The now internationally-accepted container first proposed.

Sir Alfred Fernandez Yarrow

1842–1932

SUCCESS CAME TO Alfred Yarrow because first he was a good engineer and shipbuilder, and second he had a well-rounded personality and was a realist. When he judged the time was right (between 1906 and 1908) he moved his entire Thames shipyard – lock, stock and barrel – to a new site on the western boundary of Glasgow. His final argument was: 'It is evident that shipbuilding on the Thames is a waning industry, and if we imagine we are cleverer than other people in overcoming adverse conditions, we make a mistake; we must move when we can to some district where shipbuilding is growing and thriving.' This brave and successful decision marks out a man of character.

Sir Alfred Yarrow, 1842–1932.
(The Royal Institution of Naval Architects)

Alfred Yarrow was born and grew up in London in a devoted family. Following a good education, Alfred was offered through a fortuitous introduction an apprenticeship with Ravenhill, the marine engineers based at Stepney on the north bank of the Thames opposite Rotherhithe. Unusually for an appointment of this nature, the family did not pay a premium to the engineers. The next five years were full of activity which included founding a society for young engineers and setting up the first overhead electric telegraph line in London from his home to that of a friend. As he reached the end of his time, Yarrow's father was declared bankrupt, and as Ravenhill's directors displayed little sympathy, Alfred, having already designed (and patented) a steam carriage followed by some steam agricultural equipment, decided to set up on his own.

From 1865 until 1875 while partners with a friend of his named Hedley, he operated a small business which started with minor ship repairs and by 1868 had moved up to building small powered boats and ships. In less than ten years 150 steam launches* were constructed on the Isle of Dogs, with almost all the plans having been drawn up by Alfred Yarrow himself, working late into the night. The relationship between Hedley and Yarrow deteriorated and they parted company when Hedley tried to purchase land adjacent to the Isle of Dogs site without Yarrow's knowledge; Yarrow outbid Hedley, obtained the land and dissolved the partnership, ending up with sole occupancy of an enlarged shipbuilding site. The parting, which freed Yarrow from many constraints, is seen as the start of his great shipbuilding concern. Further expansion came with the purchase of The Folly public house on neighbouring land which became the company office – and the yard became known as the Folly Shipyard at Poplar.

In 1874, the company received an order for a small craft for work on Lake Nyasa, 400m (1,312ft) above sea level; the *Ilala*, a mere 16m (52ft 6in) long was built to be taken to pieces for porterage across country. Each part weighed no more than 25kg (55lbs) and with the addition of wheels became a cart. Her work was in the suppression of the slave trade and she had been ordered as a memorial to Dr David Livingstone. This was the start of Yarrow's African lake and river work that continued until the early 1960s. Many new developments came about, including the

Yarrow hinged flap which allowed ships to operate with tunnels under the hull allowing propellers of greater diameter than the ship's draft.

Of even greater importance was the business generated by building small fast craft for the Royal Navy and the navies of other powers. In 1871 a spar torpedo was fitted to a high-speed launch, beginning the development of modern torpedo warfare. The subsequent torpedo boat destroyers evolved into the destroyer which has been a recognisable ship type since the 1900s.

There was intense rivalry between companies like Thornycroft, then on the Thames, and French operators like **Normand** at Le Havre: This rivalry did not stop the companies keeping their doors open to one another, however. Possibly the most exciting vessel from Yarrow prior to the turn of the century was the *Sokol* built for the Russians in 1894. She was a mere 57m (187ft) long, had four funnels, twin screws and was reputed to be the first steam vessel to make over 30 knots, although a similar claim was made at the same time by Augustin-Normand for their vessel *Forban*. Most unusually for the time her structure incorporated high-tensile steel and even some aluminium.

Three other developments have to be mentioned: Alfred Yarrow was closely associated with the Whitehead torpedo and latterly all his destroyers were equipped to carry this revolutionary weapon. Vibration on ships has always given shipbuilders headaches, and is something most wish to try to ignore (even to this day); not so Alfred who attacked the problem head-on and allied himself to Mr Tweedy of Newcastle and to Professor Schlick of Hamburg. They attacked the problem at source by trying to nullify the excitation generated in the machinery. Their product was the Yarrow-Schlick-Tweedy system. Thirdly he started the manufacture of boilers, something which Yarrows continued right into the 1950s.

In 1905 it became apparent that some destroyers were not achieving their contract speeds during sea trials. Ships tested at the deep water of Skelmorlie on the Clyde had higher speeds than those tested in the shallow waters of the Thames. This was known as 'Shallow Water Effect' and forced Yarrows to move their sea trials area from Maplin Sands to the English Channel off Dover.

The rundown of steel shipbuilding on the Thames in the early twentieth century has generated some excellent academic studies, and indeed one might say that the jury is out still on this matter. However, it was plain to everyone at the end of the nineteenth century that costs in the London area had risen dramatically, there was a shortage of skilled labour and competition from elsewhere, notably the Rivers Clyde, Tyne and Wear, were eroding London's once-dominant position. Alfred Yarrow considered this carefully and then made the brave decision to move to another part of the United Kingdom. When his plans became known, the company was courted by many towns in Northern England and Scotland; Dundee is said to have been a front-runner, but the final choice was Glasgow, then the second city of the Empire. Throughout the move, which took place during the years 1906 until 1908, both the Folly Shipyard and the Scotstoun Shipyard were in full operation. Trainloads of plant, material and office records regularly left Poplar for delivery to the new yard which had excellent rail facilities offered by the competing Caledonian and North British Railway Companies. Yarrow's first Clyde-built ship, a destroyer for the Royal Navy, was launched on 14 July 1908.

In 1875 Alfred Yarrow had married a Miss Franklin and they had three sons and three daughters. In 1913 Alfred retired to his old home in Greenwich and his son Harold took over the company in Glasgow. Later another son, Norman, became head of their operations in Vancouver, British Columbia. The First World War brought Alfred out of retirement and his efforts and his charitable gifts were immense, for which he was rewarded with a baronetcy. He threw himself behind several shipbuilding initiatives, and was a tower of strength in the Scotstoun shipyard, where among other things he set up a department manufacturing artificial limbs for disabled soldiers. His own personal tragedy was the loss of his youngest son Eric, an officer in the Argyll and Sutherland Highlanders, in May 1915. Having lost his wife he remarried in 1922, to a Miss Barnes, the lady who had written his biography earlier and which he allowed to be published only in 1924. Honours included election to FRS in 1922 and a Glasgow LLD in 1924.

His most important benefactions included funding of the Yarrow Tank at the National Physical Laboratories as well as several homes and schools for the less advantaged. He was a man of integrity and of quiet generosity.

SOURCES:
Arnold, A J
Iron Shipbuilding on the Thames 1832–1915
Aldershot, 2000
Banbury, Philip
Shipbuilders of the Thames and Medway
Newton Abbot, 1971
Barnes, Eleanor C
Alfred Yarrow: His Life and his Work
London, 1924
Borthwick, Alastair
Yarrow and Company Limited: 1865–1977
Glasgow, 1977
Yarrow, Harold (student)
'Experiments on the Effect of Depth of Water on Speed'
Transactions of the Institution of Naval Architects
Vol 47 (1905)

* Some authorities say that 350 steam launches were built by Yarrow and Hedley.

Sir William White, 1845–1913.
(The Royal Institution of Naval Architects)

Sir William Henry White
1845–1913

ON THE FRONT PAGE of his *Manual of Naval Architecture*, William White was privileged to have the following endorsement: 'The Lords Commissioners of the Admiralty have been pleased to authorise the issue of this book to the Ships of the Royal Navy.' This high compliment placed White in the absolute top rank of nineteenth-century naval architects.

William White, the youngest of five children, was educated at Devonport and when aged about fourteen passed the entrance examination to the Dockyard and started a seven-year apprenticeship in July 1859; his first wage is recorded as three shillings per week. His competence and ability were recognised and in 1864, on the opening of the Royal School of Naval Architecture at South Kensington, White found himself in London at what is called by some the 'Third School', graduating top of his class in a particularly distinguished year. His first appointment came that year as a draughtsman in the Admiralty constructive department, and shortly after he was appointed personal assistant to **Edward Reed**, then Chief Constructor of the Navy. Promotion was steady and by 1881 he had risen to the rank of Chief Constructor and was also a part-time lecturer. During this period he produced two important printed works. The first was the *Manual of Naval Architecture* published in 1877, which ran to many editions and was translated into several languages. The second was an internal document discussing the need for formal recruitment techniques and for what is now known as 'staff development' of those working in the constructive department. The latter report was a key document in the setting-up of the Royal Corps of Naval Constructors in 1883.

From 1883 until 1885, White had his one and only experience of commercial work, having been recruited as director in charge of warship building at the Tyneside shipyard of Sir W G Armstrong,

Mitchell and Company. While based at Elswick, he gained wide experience in design, costing, ship construction and shipyard administration in an atmosphere untrammelled by the traditions and customs of the Royal Navy. However, in 1885, changes were underway in naval administration. Lord George Hamilton had become First Lord of the Admiralty and re-armament was planned. Pressure was exerted on **Lord Armstrong** to release William White from his five-year contract and he returned to public service as Director of Naval Construction. In return, the Navy released **Philip Watts** to fill White's place on Tyneside.

From 1885 until his retirement in 1902, White had ultimate responsibility for the design and construction of well over 200 ships, of which forty-three were battleships.* While none were be as revolutionary as the *Dreadnought* of 1906, he did have the satisfaction of seeing a steady rise in size, speed, displacement and armament, and he presided over the rebuilding of a fleet where many ships of one class were introduced, like the seven ships of the *Royal Sovereign* class and the eight of the *King Edward VII* class. Work of this nature required continuous oversight of the performance of the Royal Dockyards, then the largest industrial concern in the country, and the separation of the tasks of shipbuilding, ship repair and the more mundane tasks of service of the operating fleet. White was intimately involved in the design of new classes and could speak with authority when challenged on detail. The late David K Brown pointed out that he had one foible, that of inserting longitudinal bulkheads in machinery spaces, a feature which detracted from stability when the ship was damaged.

In 1902, Sir William's health began to deteriorate and it was more than likely that this had been brought about by his continuous hard work coupled with the stability problems associated with the new Royal Yacht *Victoria and Albert*. He resigned from the Navy after seventeen years of dedicated service, and then enjoyed some rest and recuperation before looking around for jobs that were fulfilling but less demanding. He was appointed to the main board of the Newcastle shipbuilder Swan, Hunter and Wigham Richardson during the construction of the transatlantic liner *Mauretania* for the Cunard Line, and similarly served as a director of the Parsons Marine Turbine Company, then one of the rising stars in the British marine engineering world.

White was a fine and articulate speaker** and was involved in scientific societies and institutions. Several universities (in Scotland, England and the United States) awarded him doctorates and he was a fellow of the Royal Societies of both London and Edinburgh. It has been said he was slow to recognise the efforts of others, and despite his earlier essay on staff development, had made little effort in planning his own replacement at the Admiralty. His death while working was sudden, something which one can be thankful for, but it was announced by *The Shipping World* with the most dated but amusingly lugubrious words: 'He was at his desk in Victoria Street, London when the messenger with merciful swiftness came to announce the end of mortal striving.'

SOURCES:
Brown, D K
A Century of Naval Construction: The History of the Royal Corps of Naval Constructors
London, 1983
White, W H
A Manual of Naval Architecture
London, 1877

* In the obituary for Sir William White in the 1912–13 *Transactions of the Institution of Engineers and Shipbuilders in Scotland*, it is quoted: 'During his term of office, he was responsible for the design and construction of 43 battleships, 26 armoured cruisers, 21 first class, 48 second class and 33 third class protected cruisers, and 74 smaller vessels, exclusive of destroyers.'
** Sir William White presented thirteen papers to the Institution of Naval Architects between 1871 and 1907.

Carl Gustaf Patrik de Laval
1845–1913

ONE OF GUSTAF DE LAVAL'S truly remarkable achievements is that in the early 1880s he invented a reaction turbine that produced a shaft speed of 42,000 revolutions per minute. It is known that he was born in the Dalarna District of Sweden, just to the north-west of Stockholm, and that from 1863 until 1866 he studied at the Stockholm Institute of Technology, graduating in mechanical engineering, before going on to Uppsala University, Sweden's oldest academic institution. There in 1872 he was awarded a doctorate in chemistry, and then started work at a steel manufacturing plant.

From the beginning of his career he seems to have been interested in rotary machines, as in 1878 he invented a centrifugal cream separator, and then followed this up with a machine designed to manufacture glass bottles using the same principles. Some years later (around 1887) he started the manufacture of centrifuges and similar machines with a new company known as AB* Separator, that later became better known as Alpha-Laval AB.

The turbine story is one of fast and exciting development. Starting with just the concept of an impulse turbine in 1882, de Laval had a small turbine operating five years later and as development proceeded he found himself working with ever-higher speeds which then were a new phenomenon in engineering. He invented and patented double helical reduction gearing, for over critical shafts and a host of new problems including that of strength of materials for machines where massive centrifugal forces were employed. The high shaft speeds were the result of de Laval's turbine being single-stage with steam being directed at the turbine blades. (Parsons turbines, being multi-stage, ran more efficiently and were slower.)

In 1890 a new company was formed for turbine development known as Ångturbinfabrik and three years later adopted the well-known name of AB de Laval Ångturbin, a company which developed reversible turbines for marine use. This was the peak of de Laval's career, and from 1888 till 1902 he served as a Member of Parliament. Sadly financial difficulties crowded upon him at the turn of the century and several of his companies went into bankruptcy. Further difficulties arose in that he had acquired the rights for the use of water at the famous Trollhätten waterfalls with a view to setting up a hydroelectric power station; all this came to nothing when the Swedish government nationalised water rights. Having contributed so much during his life it is tragic to report that when his life ended, he was penniless.

SOURCES:
Biles, J H
The Steam Turbine as applied to Marine Purposes
London, 1906
Jung, Ingvar
The Marine Turbine
Monograph No 50 (3 parts)
The National Maritime Museum, Greenwich, 1982

* AB is a contraction for the Swedish word Aktiebolaget or 'Limited Company'.
Other well-known engineers with a hand in early turbine development include; William de Roi Emmet, an American 1859–1929.
George Westinghouse, an American 1845–1914.
John H MacAlpine, British 1859–1927.
Charles Gordon Curtis, an American 1860–1953.
Heinrich Zoelly, Swiss 1862–1937.
August Rateau, French 1863–1930.

Sir Philip Watts
1846–1926

IT IS MORE THAN LIKELY that Philip Watts met John Fincham (the Master Shipwright of Portsmouth Dockyard until 1844) as Watts' father was a senior construction officer at the Dockyard and assisted Fincham in the production of *A History of Naval Architecture* (1851) and other technical texts. Such a background must have influenced the young man who not only was to live through, but also contribute greatly to, a period of immense change in the design and construction of warships.

Philip Watts served a shipwright apprenticeship at the Royal Dockyard quickly becoming proficient with the tools of the trade. He was enrolled in the Dockyard School and learned the principles of lofting, the methods of efficient timber construction as well as various hydrostatic calculations. His performance earmarked him for further studies and at the age of twenty he was selected for the Royal School of Naval Architecture at South Kensington, then in its second year. On completing the course successfully some four years later, he was appointed an Admiralty Overseer and for a short period worked on both design and superintending tasks at various dockyards. This must have been stretching technically, as old forms of construction remained in place while the new technologies were frowned on by the traditionalists in the naval service.

Watts' skills must have been obvious again as he was asked to report to Torquay and work under **William Froude,** then producing arguably the most influential work on naval architecture of all time. The two years there were followed by a series of jobs at Pembroke, Chatham and the Admiralty, then situated in central London. At the Admiralty he was entrusted with the task of setting up a Calculating Section charged with introducing efficient and accurate calculation methods into ship design, a science in its infancy as one comes to realises on reading the early transactions of the Civil Engineers, the Naval Architects and other learned societies. During this period he invented water stabilising tanks to reduce ship rolling having been allowed sea time for research on HMS *Devastation*, *Inflexible* and *Thunderer*. In the early 1880s he was appointed Constructor in charge of Chatham Dockyard where he remained until 1885 when at the age of 39, he accepted the civilian appointment of Naval Architect and General Manager of the Elswick Shipyard of **Sir W G Armstrong** of Newcastle upon Tyne.

The next seventeen years were instrumental in making the name of Elswick world famous for warships, and in particular for cruisers. These were built for many countries in South America, for Japan, Italy and elsewhere. The contracts completed on the Tyne included the battleship HMS *Victoria* which required considerable planning to move down-river and through the Tyne bridges. This same ship was lost in the Mediterranean in 1893 in her well-documented collision with HMS *Camperdown*.

In 1902, **Sir William White** retired and Philip Watts was invited to return to the Admiralty and succeed him as Director of Naval Construction. The pace of naval shipbuilding was increasing in the early years of the twentieth century, and it is certain that no person in the office of DNC, before or since has had so many ships under construction during his tenure of office. At the battle of Jutland most of the capital ships built under his control were engaged, numbering twenty-nine Dreadnought battleships and battlecruisers. His greatest achievement was the realisation of the Dreadnought programme. Before the programme was authorised a committee of some of the most influential engineers, politicians and seamen in the country had reviewed the plans and authorised them, underlining Watts' objectives of excellent manoeuvrability, greater protection from shellfire and higher speeds. The use of steam turbines was sanctioned, a greater breakthrough than is now appreciated as the Admiralty had had unfortunate experiences with two earlier turbine vessels, although the problems were not associated directly with the turbines.

Following his retirement in 1912, he was retained by the Admiralty for some years as a consultant, but then returned to his old company, now renamed Armstrong, Whitworth as a director. He was knighted and elected a Fellow of the Royal Society. On the formation of the Society for Nautical Research in 1910, he was elected a vice president, leading to his chairmanship of the technical committee supervising the restoration of HMS *Victory* at Portsmouth, a project that continues to this day.

Philip Watts was a man who had the good fortune to be offered superb training, followed by in-depth experience of naval architecture and shipbuilding before being asked to take responsibility at the highest level. His success was the result of a sharp intellect, wide understanding of the profession, excellent contacts which were developed and were maintained – and above all, enthusiasm and courage.

SOURCES:

Fincham, John
A History of Naval Architecture
London, 1851

Hovgaard, William
Modern History of Warships
London, 1920

Massie, Robert K
Dreadnought
New York, 1991

Murphy, Hugh, and Oddy, Derek J
The Mirror of the Seas: A Centenary History of the Society for Nautical Research
London, 2010

Watts, Philip
'Warship Building (1860–1910)
Transactions of the Institution of Naval Architects
Vol 53 (1911)

———,
'Ships of the Royal Navy on August 14, 1914',
Transactions of the Institution of Naval Architects
Vol 61 (1919)

Nathaniel G Herreshoff

1848–1938

ONE OF THE GREATEST American yacht designers and builders, Nat Herreshoff started work and studies at the age of sixteen and continued in active employment for a remarkable seventy-one years. On his death three years after retiring, the massive collection of ship plans in which he had been involved was catalogued. The register accounted for over 18,000 drawings, or more than one for every working day of his life. While this massive quantity of work is nothing short of amazing, it is overshadowed by the quality of his designs and inventions – including the plans for five successful defenders of the America's Cup.

Herreshoff was the seventh of nine children born to a respected New England boatbuilding family. Life was not easy for the parents as three of their sons and one daughter were blind from their early years, and all the children had to be brought up during the inflationary and unsettling times of the American Civil War. All this imposed heavy obligations on the aspiring young naval architect, as he had to help his blind siblings, but in later years he remarked on this as a positive influence, and how their highly-attuned sense of touch enabled him to develop a 'second sense' for the shape of good sea-keeping hulls by the use of half-block models. For the whole of his life, models were important and he could express initial thoughts better in three dimensions than on paper. Drawing work began at age sixteen, and a year later he travelled to Cambridge to pursue a three-year course in mechanical engineering at the Massachusetts Institute of Technology. (At that time naval architecture was not a graduating subject at MIT.)

During his early years he sailed in the Mediterranean and then through the waterways of The Netherlands on the small open sloop *Riviera* with his blind brother Lewis. This must have been a great personal undertaking for the two young men, both of whom were experienced sailors, helped happily by Lewis' linguistic skills. In 1878, when about thirty years old, Nat Herreshoff (in partnership with another brother John), formed the Herreshoff

Reliance **was regarded as the ultimate evolution of the 90ft waterline yachts that raced for the America's Cup after 1943, and Herreshof crammed the vessel with innovations, including twin wheels, a hollow rudder into which water could be pumped to assist with steering, and winches installed and manned below decks.** *(August Loelffler, © The Mariner's Museum)*

Manufacturing Company based in Gloucester, Rhode Island, which incorporated the original family boatbuilding business, Herreshoff and Stone. This new company was to produce hundreds of vessels ranging from small dinghies to steam yachts and from small naval craft to commercial fishing vessels large enough to operate on Narragansett Bay. General engineering and the construction of small high-speed steam engines and boilers ensured there was a wide range of products, enabling Nat and his brother to fulfil their in-built need for experimentation and development, and Nat to work as a naval architect.

Nat's inventions included a novel form of longitudinal framing for ships, hollow steel spars for sailing vessels, lightweight fasteners for timber, specially cross-cut sails and a design of flat stern for fast steam vessels to prevent squatting at speed. He designed lightweight high-speed steam plants suitable for the first US Navy torpedo boats, again a product of the company. Within a short time, the company had established such a good name, that in 1878 a 15-ton vessel built on speculation was purchased by the Royal Navy, and ultimately commissioned as a Second Class Torpedo Boat (named *TB63*). This was one of the few recorded instances of the Royal Navy purchasing a warship from a foreign supplier during the nineteenth century. *TB63* was unusual in having a wooden bottom with steel sides, but even more revolutionary was her coil boiler designed to raise steam quickly and her propeller placed well forward and at some distance below the keel.

The shipyard and associated plant grew until the labour force numbered well over 300 and might have prospered for years, but a series of misfortunes around the time of the First World War were to change things. First Nat was unwell for some years with rheumatism, then his brother John died in 1915 and his trustees wished to liquidate their holdings in the Herreshoff Manufacturing Company. These were sold easily and at great profit, but at the end of the war demand for luxury yachts fell away for a year or two. The new shareholders were not patient and over the years this great business wasted away. With hindsight, wrong decisions were made as luxury yacht building was to become buoyant in North America in the inter-war years, with costs in normal circumstances being ascribed as:

Labour	40 per cent
Material	30 per cent
Overheads	30 per cent

Fortunately the high morale of the workforce together with the intervention of outside investors kept much of the plant in operation until the Second World War, although by the mid-1930s the glory days had passed. Undoubtedly the new investors' greatest asset was the Herreshoff name and associated goodwill.

The most remarkable aspect of Herreshoff's career was his connection from 1885 until 1937 with no less than eleven consecutive defenders of the America's Cup. The first three, *Puritan*, *Mayflower* and *Volunteer*, were designed by his close friend Edward Burgess and the final three, *Enterprise*, *Rainbow* and *Ranger*, came from the drawing board of W Starling Burgess, the son of Edward. However, from 1893 until 1920 the five successive and successful defenders all came from the drawing board of Nathaniel Herreshoff; *Vigilant*, *Defender*, *Columbia* (twice raced) *Reliance* and *Resolute* – a number equalling the output of challenging yachts (plus the King's *Britannia*) from the design office of his friend and rival G L Watson of Glasgow.

Like most shipping people from New England, 'Captain Nat' as he was nicknamed, was warm and personable: he maintained friendly relationships with his British competitors, men like Charles Nicholson, **William Fife** and **George Lennox Watson** and he enjoyed the company of fellow professionals. Probably the greatest accolade he received was to become an honorary member of the New York Yacht Club, an appointment shared with Sir Thomas Lipton but reserved normally for heads of state. Few men will match him as an all-round engineer and ship designer. The Herreshoff Marine Museum is situated at the former site of the Herreshoff Manufacturing Company at Bristol, Rhode Island. Here one can find the celebrated Hall of Yachting Fame.

SOURCES:
Chapelle, Howard I
The History of American Sailing Ships
New York, 1935
Herreshoff, L Francis
Capt Nat Herreshoff – the Wizard of Bristol
New York, 1953

Frank Prior Purvis

1850–1940

A LONDONER BY BIRTH, Frank Purvis was destined to have a well-rounded professional career as a naval architect, working in many parts of Britain and ultimately in Japan. His early education was at the Blackheath School from where he went on to became a student at the Royal School of Naval Architecture in South Kensington, which moved to the Royal Naval College, Greenwich, in 1873. By the completion of his course in 1871, he had spent some time in the Royal Dockyards at Deptford and Chatham, and had rounded this off with a short spell at **Robert Napier's** Govan Shipyard on the Clyde.

In 1871 he joined the personal staff of **Sir Edward Reed**. Reed had earlier resigned from his post as Chief Constructor for the Navy, and was carrying out commercial work, albeit for defence contracts. For some time Purvis assisted him as a Superintendent during the construction of the German ironclads *Deutschland* and *Kaiser* at the Samuda Brothers shipyard on the Thames. Possibly restless, or unable to find his true place in the profession, after a short period he left to become a professional assistant to **William Froude** at the historic ship testing tank, Torquay. The next six years, working with one of the greatest naval architects of all time, were to help forge his future career.

In 1879, he moved to Scotland and there had a series of interesting and responsible jobs, first assisting Sir William Pearce, principal of the Fairfield Shipyard at Govan, then one of the largest shipbuilding firms in the country. Thereafter followed a short spell supervising the construction of docks on the Continent; again experience which was to help him in his next project, once again on the Clyde.

In the early 1880s, he was invited to join the staff of **William Denny** and Brothers in Dumbarton. At that time the Denny yard was becoming one of the leading shipyards in the world (if not the actual leader) in terms of scientific development and staff training, and it was to maintain this position until after the Second World War. Purvis was given the task of overseeing the building of a new ship model testing tank, and had the honour of supervising the first model experiment in 1883. This was a task dear to the heart of the third William Denny (1847–87) who had recognised the benefits model testing could bring to a yard building high-speed passenger ships and cross-Channel ferries. Purvis was to remain as head of the Scientific Department, as it was called (rather quaintly), at the Leven Shipyard until 1889, and at a time when they built the Belgian government's cross-Channel paddle steamer *Princesse Henriette* of 1888, which was built with cast-iron performance guarantees, and which was to establish Denny's for all time as top-quality shipbuilders and designers.

In 1889, he was induced to move to Port Glasgow as one of three new partners in the shipyard of Blackwood and Gordon, a long-established shipbuilder which had fallen on hard times. By 1892, and after the death of Mr Blackwood, the yard was in the hands of the new partners and was on the road to recovery, when other difficulties arose, with re-financing and the change of name to the Clyde Shipbuilding and Engineering Company in 1900 ensured it stayed in operation until 1927 when like many other yards it was wound up owing to the Depression.

Shortly after the Port Glasgow shipyard's change of name, Purvis left, having received an invitation from the Imperial University at Tokyo to become their Professor of Naval Architecture. In 1902, Frank Purvis he took over from the first incumbent of the chair, Professor Percy Hillhouse, who was returning to the UK to become naval architect of the Fairfield Shipbuilding Company at Govan. Purvis was to remain in Japan for sixteen years, years of fundamental importance to the development of Japanese shipbuilding. Relations between Britain and Japan were excellent during this period, and on his final return home, Purvis brought back the Order of the Rising Sun and other awards including an honorary engineering doctorate. Frank Purvis lived in retirement in Sussex until his death in 1940. He contributed two papers to the Institution of Naval Architects, the last one in 1925 when aged seventy-five, and another four to the Institution of Engineers and Shipbuilders in Scotland in Glasgow.

SOURCES:

Bruce, A B
The Life of William Denny, Shipbuilder
London, 1889

Purvis, F P
'Japan's Contribution to Naval Architecture',
Transactions of the Institution of Naval Architects
Vol 67 (1925)

Woollard, L
'The Centenary of the Royal Dockyard Schools',
Transactions of the Institution of Naval Architects
Vol 85 (1943)

George Lennox Watson
1851–1904

ONE OF THE WORLD'S outstanding yacht designers, George Lennox Watson was born in Glasgow in 1851, and died in the same city fifty-three years later. It is hard to imagine anyone equalling his output of ship designs, of which over 500 are known, and all produced within the short span of the thirty-one years that he enjoyed running his own naval architecture business. The early death of his father, who had a medical practice, resulted in the family having two homes, his mother taking up residence in London and young Watson remaining north of the border to complete his education at the High School of Glasgow.

At the age of sixteen he entered the great Govan shipyard of **Robert Napier and Co**, then controlled by William (later Sir William) Pearce, where he served three years in office and workshops. Possibly through influence beyond that available to most apprentices and students, he transferred to the much smaller shipyard of A & J Inglis across the River Clyde at Pointhouse. In the latter half of the nineteenth century, this yard was developing a reputation for scientific ship design, and under the watchful eye of one of the directors, Dr John Inglis, Watson carried out groundbreaking work on hull strength and power estimation. His desire to work on yachts became evident at this time, and as Dr Inglis was a sailing enthusiast, Watson received every encouragement to develop this interest. While at Inglis he designed and built an unconventional 9-tonne shallow draught yacht with a deep keel, a hull form which was to become popular in the following century.

In 1873, still in his early twenties, G L Watson set up his own business which from the outset attracted attention and gave the young naval architect the opportunity to attempt unusual and interesting projects. He designed, and then with the help of friends built, the 5-tonne yacht *Vril* in the Meadowside shipyard of D & W Henderson. *Vril* is reputed to be the first yacht to have an integral lead keel cast into the hull structure. At first sight the choice of yard seemed strange, but it must have been known to Watson as it directly faced the Inglis shipyard across the River Kelvin and they had a fine reputation particularly in the iron trades. The relationship with Watson was to deepen over the years, leading to the construction of the King's yacht some time later.

By 1879, Watson had broken into the luxury yacht market. Following a 10 tonne-yacht for the Paisley thread manufacturer James Coats, he was awarded the design for the 90-tonne cutter *Vanduara* for Coats' commercial arch-rival Mr John Clark, also of Paisley. From then he was awarded many big

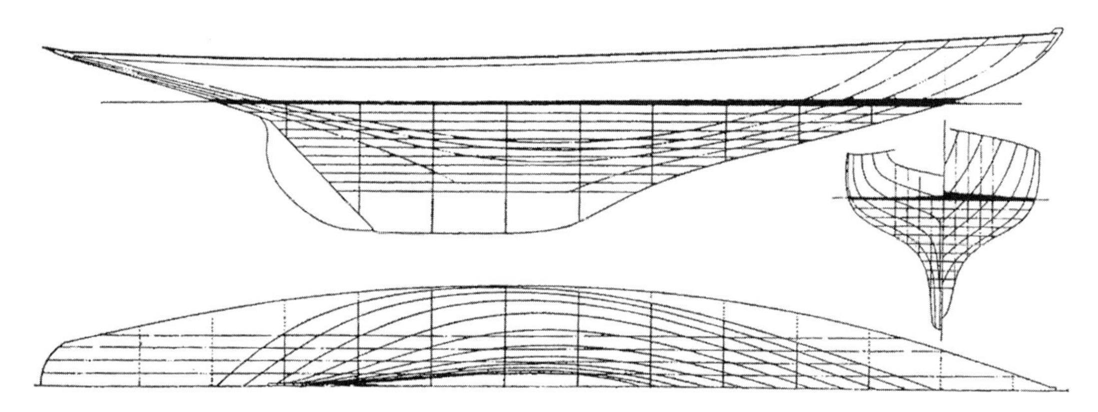

Of all Watson's designs *Britannia* was his most successful and perhaps his most graceful, as these lines and body plan reveal. Her spoon bow was a radical development in an era when the clipper bow still predominated, and in her long career she remained competitive and won 231 races. A replica of her was launched in Russia in June 2009.

yacht designs culminating in four America's Cup challengers; *Thistle*, *Valkyrie II*, *Valkyrie III* and *Shamrock II*. As a member of the Royal Clyde Yacht Club, which had organised several challenges, this must have given him enormous pleasure.

At this stage his company extended its portfolio and commenced the design of the great steam yachts so much in demand in the late nineteenth century. In these contracts, it was usual for the naval architect to handle all the work, which included of course the invitation to tender, the invigilation of responses, the placing of orders, and the supervision of construction at the selected shipyard. Realising the breadth of work involved, Watson had the wisdom and foresight to gather a team of talented people able to keep the company in the forefront of the fierce competition from the integrated design offices and production facilities of Camper and Nicholsons of Gosport, the Fife's of Fairlie and the Leith yard of Ramage and Ferguson. It is arguable that his finest steam yacht was the twin-screw *Lysistrata*, delivered by Denny of Dumbarton in 1901 on completion of her sea trials at which she attained nearly 19 knots with a hull displacement of 2,600 tons. While possibly not his most elegant ship (his hands had been tied by the American owner James Gordon Bennett), she must rank as one the most advanced in technical terms.

Then, as today, big yachts attracted complex dealings and clearly Watson had learned his way around as the greatest challenge was about to come. In the early 1890s, the Prince of Wales (later King Edward VII) asked him to design the ultimate large racing yacht. The result was *Britannia*, arguably Watson's greatest design. Construction took place at the shipyard of D & W Henderson sited in Glasgow at the confluence of the Rivers Clyde and Kelvin, and on 20 April 1893, she was launched with minimal ceremony. This yacht was to carry all before her for forty-three years, and, following the death of King George V, was scuttled in June 1936.

In 1886 the Royal National Lifeboat Institution (RNLI) suffered a calamitous loss, when two of three self-righting boats were lost with a total of twenty-seven men trying to rescue the crew of a German barque. The whole controversial issue of self-righting and non-self-righting lifeboats came to the fore, resulting in the Committee of the RNLI deciding on appointing a consulting naval architect. George Watson was appointed and remained adviser to the Institution until his death, and it was in his honour that the Watson type was so named. On his death in November 1904, one of his assistants, **J R Barnett** not only took over control of the naval architecture business, but was retained in the position of Naval Architect to the RNLI. He continued in both posts until 1947 and also had a lifeboat type named after him. After sixty years with Watson, the RNLI decided to have its own 'in-house' services, and responsibility for ship design was given to **Richard Oakley** at the head office, then situated in London. He too had a vessel named after him – the Oakley self-righting lifeboat.

Watson was a member of the Institution of Naval Architects but took little part in its formal affairs. His successor Barnett was to write two papers for the IESIS and four for the Institution of Naval Architects, mostly on lifesaving matters.

SOURCES:
Evans, Clayton
Rescue at Sea
London, 2003
Irving, John
The Kings' Britannia
London, 1936
Watson, G L
'Progress in Yachting and Yacht Building'
Lectures on Naval Architecture etc and Catalogue
The 1881 Glasgow Exhibition

Sir Charles Algernon Parsons

1854–1931

CHARLES PARSONS' LIFE story is so exciting and so wide ranging, that few people tire of hearing of his exploits or marvelling at his wide range of interests. He was the sixth and youngest son of the Earl of Rosse, a family with roots in Ireland going back to the sixteenth century and which maintained Birr Castle in Co. Offaly. His father was a noted astronomer, who had his children educated by private tutors whilst allowing them freedom to enjoy not only field sports but also to work in the castle's well-equipped observatory, workshops and

Viper, the first British turbine destroyer. Parsons guaranteed 31 knots but at the end of August 1900 she reached a mean speed of 36.8 knots, making her the fastest ship afloat. High fuel consumption made stoking a crippling task, but the Navy Board recognised the turbine as the engine of the future and persevered with its development. (From British Destroyers: From Earliest Days to the Second World War, *Barnsley* 2009)

laboratories. All the family enjoyed regular trips to the Continent and it was here that Charles first displayed his ability for languages.

In 1871 he entered Trinity College Dublin, and there spent two busy years mastering the classics and mathematics demanded in what was then an unimaginative curriculum. However, it was at Trinity that his ability in mathematics became apparent, and this was the 'passport' which enabled him to cross the Irish Sea to St John's College, Cambridge, for years that were more enjoyable and profitable. His distinctions in rowing were matched by being eleventh wrangler in mathematics in 1877.

In line with all well-educated graduates aspiring to work in the engineering profession, Parsons had to serve an apprenticeship, and he joined **Sir William Armstrong's** Elswick Works at Newcastle upon Tyne. Presumably a premium would be paid for this privilege, but irrespective of that Parsons held Armstrong in high esteem, something which was reciprocated, presumably as their lifestyles were similar. He moved on and a couple of years followed working alongside Sir James Kitson on research and experimental work for torpedoes, but as this seemed to be making little headway, in 1884 he accepted a partnership in the well-known engineers Clarke Chapman in the north-east of England. This was a well-deserved appointment, but available only to candidates with the financial power to buy into the company and then to underwrite their investments – which in this case amounted to many thousands of pounds.

Initially Parsons chose to work on the development of electrical power for ships' deck equipment, something which drew his attention to the real enigma of the Victorian engineering world, the incompatibility of speeds between prime movers and service machines. The optimum speed for a prime mover, like the steam reciprocating engine, was unsuitable for driving electrical dynamos; in a nutshell prime movers needed higher basic speeds, whilst other machinery either had to slow down, or work through very efficient forms of gearing, something which was not then available. As the idea of a rotary steam engine had been in Parsons' mind since his student days, he considered machines capable of 5,000 rpm and upwards, something unheard of for engines with three cylinders in the same vertical plane. However after long and protracted trials, his decision that the way forward was the axial flow steam turbine: conceptual designs were prepared and in the 1880s patents were taken out for this as well as for DC generators with speeds up to 18,000 rpm.

It is not surprising that Parsons, with private means and a clear vision of the way ahead, chose to leave Clarke Chapman and form his own company, which was set up in 1889 as C A Parsons and Co Ltd. In leaving his previous partners he lost control of his patents, but they were bought back later. Works were set up at Heaton and in 1894 another company was formed; the Marine Steam Company Ltd which was concerned with the operation of one of the world's most famous ships, the steam yacht *Turbinia*. Initially a radial flow turbine was employed on a single shaft, but after a long series of tests, the final configuration was three axial flow turbines serving triple shafts each with three propellers. During final trials in 1896–7 she achieved the remarkable speed of 34 knots, and at the Spithead Royal Fleet Review of 1897, Parsons showed off his invention to the world.

Consequently, the Admiralty ordered two turbine destroyers, the *Viper*, built on the Tyne by Hawthorn Leslie, and the *Cobra*, built on the same river by Armstrong Whitworth. These vessels confirmed the place of the turbine, and although both ships were lost shortly after, in neither case was the machinery the cause. The Admiralty moved over to this new form of propulsion and had turbines fitted in the new battleship *Dreadnought* which was launched in 1906. The merchant service was equally prompt in converting, with the Clyde steamer *King Edward* from **Denny** in 1901 followed by a string of liners, culminating in the Atlantic fliers *Lusitania* and *Mauretania* from John Brown, Clydebank and Swan Hunter of Tyneside respectively in 1907. The problem of incompatible speeds still haunted turbine design and in 1909 Parsons purchase the 4,000-ton steam tramp *Vespasian*, installed turbines aboard her and then fitted complex gearing which reduced the turbine speed of 1,700 rpm to a mere 74 rpm on the propeller shaft. He had 'closed the cycle' and (apart from first cost) turbines were now an efficient power source for almost all types of ship. The final triumph was the building in 1926 by Denny of Dumbarton of the twin-screw passenger and mail steamer *King George V* for service on the Clyde. This ship, with turbines from the Parsons company, made history in being the first high-pressure steam turbine ship, as steam was supplied by **Yarrow** boilers at 37 bar.

Charles Parsons continued with research into gear cutting and developed a gear cutting creep system in 1912. One of his earliest interests, probably emanating from his father's love of astronomy, was optics. With his ever-increasing financial resources, he was able to purchase two companies involved in optical work. Charles Parsons was married; his wife complained in jocular manner all her life at the many family outings she had had to attend in inclement weather to see models of ships, including the *Turbinia*, show their paces on duck-ponds and rivers all over England and Ireland. They had one daughter and one son, who was killed in the First World War.

Charles Parsons was not always an easy man to work with, but everyone spoke of his fairness and integrity. He had a clutch of honours and doctorates, but his most precious award was that of the Order of Merit granted by King George V in 1927. Parsons was the first engineer to receive this singular honour.

SOURCES:
Biles, J H
The Steam Turbine as applied to marine purposes
London, 1906
Clarke, J F
An Almost Unknown Great Man; Charles Parsons and the significance of the patents of 1884
Newcastle upon Tyne Polytechnic, 1984
de Courcy Ireland, J E
'Charles Algernon Parsons'
The Mariner's Mirror
Vol 41 (1955)

Sir John Harvard Biles

1854–1933

ONE OF THE MOST distinguished and approachable teachers of naval architecture, John Biles was one of the few naval architects who may claim to have influenced aspects ranging as widely as design to professional education and from hydrodynamics to strategic planning.

Born in Portsmouth in 1854, he had the twin benefits of a family with Dockyard associations, and an environment that allowed him to nurture his love of ships and the sea. Having an aptitude for the mechanical sciences it will come as no surprise that he entered Portsmouth Dockyard, and during his years there as an apprentice spent much time working on HMS *Devastation*, a then-revolutionary turret battleship. These were exciting days for the Royal Navy, which had discarded timber construction and sail power, was contemplating ship model testing and was experimenting with new types of ordnance and marine engineering.

In 1872 Biles came top of the list for candidates to the Royal School of Naval Architecture and Marine Engineering and after working for a year at South Kensington, he moved with them to the Royal Naval College, Greenwich, where he finished his studies in 1875. The following five years were packed with useful experience; a short time at Pembroke Dockyard, followed by work as an Admiralty

Sir John Harvard Biles, 1854–1933.
(The Royal Institution of Naval Architects)

overseer at an ironworks at Landore near Swansea which enabled him to come to terms with the fast-changing iron and steel industry. In 1877 he joined the staff of the Admiralty and through this came into contact with **William Froude**, and became acquainted with his pioneering work.

In 1880 he left government service and joined the Clydebank shipyard of Messrs J & G Thomson which was beginning to make their mark as builders of large passenger liners for ocean service. During the next nine or ten years the Clydebank yard (later to become John Brown and Company) produced some remarkably fine vessels including the pioneering twin-screw liners *City of New York* and *City of Paris* for the Inman Line, each with a length to beam ratio of 8.3. While acting as naval architect for Thomson's, Biles was called to give evidence at the enquiry (chaired by **Sir Edward Reed**) into the loss of the SS *Daphne* in Glasgow in 1883. Here he reported fully on the stability problems that they had encountered the previous year during the launching of the SS *Hammonia*, a high-sided cargo vessel.

Around 1890 Biles was working in Southampton, but the following year he returned to Scotland upon being offered the Chair of Naval Architecture at Glasgow University. Glasgow which rightfully claims to be the oldest school of engineering in the English-speaking world, also has the distinction of having the senior chair of naval architecture in the world. The first incumbent was Francis Elgar, who trained at the Royal School of Naval Architecture, but who left after just three years to become the Director of HM Dockyards. His successor, appointed in 1886, was Philip Jenkins, who had worked with William Froude and with Lloyd's Register and who became Chief Surveyor to the British Corporation, but sadly died at the early age of thirty-seven.

Biles became a member of the university staff in 1891 and brought distinction to the chair for the next thirty years. He was greatly respected and was an approachable teacher who took a keen interest in his students; a matter of real importance as during his years at Gilmorehill foreign students flocked to Glasgow and returned home to positions of considerable authority. His appetite for work was prodigious, and on many occasions he included undergraduates in his team, such as the experiments carried out in dry-dock on the hull of the destroyer HMS *Wolf*, the results of which were published by the Institution of Naval Architects in 1905. In 1907 he opened an office in London as a consulting naval architect, and for years regularly travelled between Glasgow and London without detriment to his work or health. This company, in changed form, continued in business until the end of the twentieth century.

With his wide experience, Biles was in demand as a consultant and sat on many committees. His public appointments included memberships of Lord Fisher's Committee on Ship Designs which heralded the Dreadnought battleship, and later he was an assessor at Lord Mersey's Inquiry into the loss of the RMS *Titanic*. On the death of Sir Edward Reed in 1906, the post of Consulting Naval Architect to the India Office became vacant, and again

Biles was appointed; this was of particular importance as within eight years Britain was at war and the river steamers of India and Burma became vital and many were transferred to work on the rivers of Mesopotamia.

Biles presented at least twenty papers to the Institution of Naval Architects, as well as a further five to the Institution of Engineers and Shipbuilders in Scotland. In 1921 he retired from the university with a knighthood (and was later made Knight Commander of the Order of the British Empire) as well as doctorates from Glasgow, Yale and Harvard. He died at Virginia Water in 1933.

SOURCES:

Biles, Sir John H
'The Strength of Ships with special reference to experiments and calculations made upon HMS *Wolf*'
Transactions of the Institution of Naval Architects 1905
Vol 47 Part 1 (1905)

———,
The Design and Construction of Ships
2 vols (London, 1911)

Reed, Sir Edward J
Report on the Daphne Disaster
London, 1883

William Fife III

1857–1944

FIFE OF FAIRLIE IS a name that ranks among the top yacht builders of all time. For a period of 130 years, the Company was headed by three generations in turn – a grandfather, a son and finally by a grandson. The yard came into being when William Fyfe (1785–1865), the son of a wheelwright, having made a success of building small rowing boats in his spare time, decided to set up a small boatyard at Fairlie in Ayrshire around 1810. His son William Fife (note the change of spelling) lived from 1821 to 1902, and was to put the yard not just on the map of 'North Britain', as was his postal address, but firmly on the gazetteers of Britain, Europe and the world. In turn William Fife III in the years between 1886 and his retirement in 1938 designed close on 700 sailing ships, two of which were America's Cup challengers and three of which were racing yachts for the King of Spain. A high percentage of his designs were built at Fairlie and a few others as far afield as Switzerland, the USA and Sweden. A handful of Fairlie-built yachts were designed by his friends and competitors, including G L Watson and A Mylne of Glasgow and surprisingly one by Captain O M Watts of London.

William Fife III was born in Fairlie in 1857 and after a long and most productive life was to die there in 1944. His formal education was at Brisbane Academy, Largs, but when aged a mere fourteen-and-a-half, he left school to serve a shipwright apprenticeship in the family yard under the watchful eye of his father. He then moved elsewhere on the Clyde, first to the small Paisley shipyard of John Fullerton & Co which built iron steamships for the coasting trade and launched them sideways into the River Cart. Fullerton's must have been a dramatic change from the family yard, but another stimulating experience was to follow with his appointment as manager of the tiny Culzean Shipbuilding Company at Maidens in Ayrshire. This was owned by an enthusiastic yachtsman, the Marquis of Ailsa, who had first set up a small boat building unit below his ancestral home at Culzean Castle (the original site is still distinguishable at the foot of the cliffs) but who later moved it to the village of Maidens. This gave Fife experience in design and building of quality craft, and introduced him to discerning and moneyed clients. Incidentally this small yard was to move again and became the Ailsa Shipbuilding Company of Troon.

Now what of William Fife's work? As mentioned above, on a numerical basis his output was prodigious, and while some designs would be re-used or be heavily modified reworkings of previously successful ships, he still managed to produce a new hull design every four weeks. As proprietor of a small shipyard with a tight-knit, locally-recruited workforce, he was aware of his responsibilities in securing orders and keeping them in work, and did not shrink from tackling hulls for local fishermen, while simultaneously moving the yard's emphasis towards the pleasure yachts that were to adorn the Solent and the Clyde from the 1890s until the outbreak of war in 1914. He was so successful that yachts built by Fife of Fairlie were seen all over

Europe as well as at Newport, Rhode Island for the America's Cup challenges.

From 1851 until 1983 the New York Yacht Club held the America's Cup (referred to by Sir Thomas Lipton as the 'Auld Mug'). Few pieces of sporting silverware have engendered such passion, and in the years since 1851 there have been thirty-one international challenges for the silver ewer presented by the Royal Yacht Squadron in 1851. To be asked to build or to design a contestant for this event was proof of one's supremacy in the business, as borne out by the names of the two Burgesses, **Nat Herreshoff**, Charles Nicholson, Olin Stephens, **G L Watson** and others. Several designers made attempts on this, the ultimate trophy, and William Fife was involved twice. The first vessel was Sir Thomas Lipton's *Shamrock* built by John I Thornycroft at Chiswick in 1899, and the second, again for Lipton, was *Shamrock III* built by William Denny and Brothers of Dumbarton in 1903. Both vessels incorporated aluminium, bronze and high-tensile steel in their structures and the latter design went through its paces at the still extant Denny Ship Model Test Tank in Dumbarton.

As an active yachtsman, Fife was prepared to conduct sea trials on newly-built yachts and when vessels failed to reach expectations would ask to be invited aboard during competitive racing to re-evaluate the design. He was conscious of the Yacht Rating Rules and during his time at the shipyard witnessed improvements such as the discontinuance of the old 'plank on edge' design of yacht where length and beam were incorporated in the formula but depth ignored. This interest as well as his attendance at all the major British regattas, enabled him to be an advocate for change and he had influence in the establishment of the Metre Rule – that is for the six, eight and other metre classes. Many well known 6- and 8-metre racers came from his board, and he designed a host of one-designs* including the Dublin Bay 25 and Belfast Lough classes. During the First World War the shipyard was involved in the building of seaplane hulls as well as cutters for the Admiralty. For this and other work William Fife received an OBE. Yacht building was to continue until 1938 but coupled with a change of both ownership and name the yard withered to a mere shadow of its previous greatness. In recent years, the restoration of Fife-built yachts has reached cult status, with enthusiasts looking for the carved dragon's head abaft the bow and at the fore end of the cut-in and painted sheer line.

William Fife was a quiet, reserved man from a humble background and never married. As his wealth grew, he decided to buy a fine mansion in Ayrshire, remaining there for the rest of his life despite some great personal sadness. In the shipyard he was a little aloof, not the practice of his father or grandfather, but he did attend to public duties with courtesy and grace. The grandson and the son of distinguished yacht-builders, he followed in their footsteps, and walked not only with some of the most distinguished people of his time, but also with kings.

SOURCES:

McCallum, May Fife
Fast and Bonnie: a history of William Fife and Son, Yachtbuilders
Edinburgh, 2002

Viner, Alan
A History of Yacht Rating Rules for Yachts 1854–1931
Maritime Monograph No 41
National Maritime Museum, Greenwich, 1979

Yachting
Badminton Library Vols 1 and 2
Longmans Green & Co, 1894

* One-designs are yachts that are built to identical plans and to exacting specifications. The purpose is to ensure that their use in yacht racing is on a level playing field and that success is through sailing skill, rather than technological advantage.

Rudolf Christian Karl Diesel

1858–1913

THE DEATH OF Rudolf Diesel is a beguiling and unsolved mystery. Born in Paris to German parents in somewhat straitened circumstances, he later bestrode the world of thermodynamics and to all intents and purposes invented the world's most ubiquitous prime mover – the diesel engine – and then perished in mysterious circumstances during the night of 29/30 September 1913.

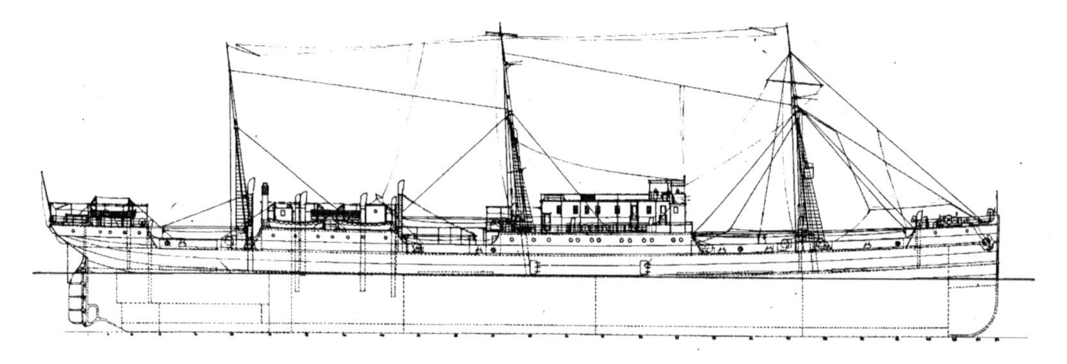

Profile of the Danish East Asiatic Liner *Jutlandia* built on the Clyde in 1912, just a few months after her sister-ship *Selandia* had been completed in Copenhagen. These pioneer diesel ships set a precedent in avoiding the use of the traditional smokestack. *(Author)*

Rudolf's father, Theodor Diesel, a bookbinder by trade, left Augsburg in 1848 and settled in Paris where he met a young lady, Elise, whom he married in the 1850s. Life cannot have been easy for the young couple, and Theodor had a variety of jobs while in Paris. They had to flee the country upon the outbreak of the Franco-Prussian War (1870–1) which led ultimately to the fall of the French Empire and the unification of Germany. The Diesels moved to London but shortly afterwards sent Rudolf to an uncle and aunt in Augsburg in order that he might continue to speak German, and also that he might benefit from his uncle's knowledge of mathematics. In 1873 Rudolf completed his secondary education with distinction, and then continued for another two years at a college of higher education. Having won a scholarship (and despite concerns expressed by his parents) Rudolf enrolled at the Munich Polytechnic and studied under Professor Karl von Linde, an authority on both thermodynamics and the associated field of refrigeration. Following practical work with Sulzer Brothers of Winterthur in Switzerland, he graduated with honours in 1880 and then returned to Paris where his former teacher had set up the Linde Ice Machine Company. Rudolf joined him, quickly rose to become manager of the firm and began to carry out fundamental research leading to several registered patents. Diesel married in 1883 and subsequently had three children.

In 1890 he decided to move to Berlin, and while there carried out his own research as well as representing von Linde. There were disagreements regarding the use of his patent rights and Diesel decided to branch out on his own; as he was well respected, help came from several companies which allowed him the use of their laboratories and workshops. He decided to move from the field of refrigeration to that of prime movers, as the low thermal efficiency of the steam engine indicated that new methods might be profitable. He considered several sources of energy and came on the idea of injecting fuel oil into air that had been compressed adiabatically to one-sixteenth of its volume and was then at 540°C – this was the basis of what is known now as the diesel engine. He was injured when one engine exploded, but continued his work, obtaining patents in several countries and publishing a definitive paper in 1893. MAN (Maschinenfabrik Augsburg Nurnberg) in Augsburg was particularly helpful and by 1898 Diesel had a demonstration engine on show in Munich and began licensing potential users like MAN and the Krupp organisation. Following lengthy technical correspondence with Burmeister & Wain of Copenhagen, they too became part of the small group of licensees, and they and MAN became major international players in the marine diesel business, currently marketing under the name MAN B&W. Alfred Krupp, a fanatical nationalist, was also interested and it is known that he gave financial support as he foresaw the need for mass production of diesel power units for submarines that were in the early stages of development. By 1897 Krupp had built a 32hp diesel motor.

Diesel became a salesman for the licensees and travelled extensively. He amassed quite a fortune and operated in several countries. His death has never been explained – at least publicly. On 29 September 1913 at Antwerp, he boarded the South Eastern Railway's cross-Channel packet *Dresden* bound for Harwich. After dinner he requested a early-morning call and retired for the night. He was never seen alive again, but a man's body recovered from the sea was identified as Rudolf Diesel by the contents of his pockets. In the 1913 hotbed of European re-armament, and with Diesel's involvement at the highest level with large companies and European governments and navies, only two theories have held ground, the first being a possible suicide and the second, a more likely murder.

SOURCES:
Day, L and McNeil, I
Biographical Dictionary of the History of Technology
London, 1996
Lehmann, Johannes
A Century of Burmeister and Wain
Copenhagen, 1948
Manchester, William
The Arms of Krupp
London, 1964

Henry Alexander Mavor

1858–1915

HENRY MAVOR'S PIONEERING work was the application of commercially-viable electric power to ships. In Stranraer in 1858, the Rev and Mrs James Mavor announced the birth of their son Henry Alexander. Both Henry and, in turn, his son Osborne were to leave two separate legacies to our nation: The grandson, Osborne Henry Mavor (1888–1951), became a well-known professor of medicine at Glasgow University, but is remembered better in international circles as the playwright who used the *nom de plume* 'James Bridie'. His father Henry (the subject of this article), however, is remembered as one of the great pioneers of electric propulsion in ships.

At the age of four Henry Mavor moved with his parents to Glasgow where after schooling he matriculated at the University as an undergraduate in the Faculty of Medicine. Undoubtedly he was influenced by both **Professor Macquorn Rankine** and **Lord Kelvin**, for he gave up medical studies and joined R E Crompton and Co, a happy situation which allowed him to earn badly-needed cash whilst attending evening classes in the city. Crompton's regarded him as a man suitable for fast-tracking and he travelled to many of the places where electrical installations were being commissioned, including two prestigious sites, first the 1881 Paris Exhibition and then the modernisation of Windsor Castle. In 1883, in partnership with a friend William Muir, he registered a new company, Muir and Mavor. Within a couple of years they had contracted for Glasgow Corporation's first electrical supply and this in turn induced them to take as partners W H Coulson, a person with some knowledge of financial matters, and Henry's brother Samuel, an experienced marine engineer.

In the 1890s, following the compulsory outright purchase of the city's power stations by the Corporation of Glasgow, the company, which had sustained a loss in this, had a reorganisation, was renamed Mavor and Coulson, and began to work as contractors for larger industrial companies including Sir William Arrol and several shipyards. Samuel Coulson concentrated on industrial applications, specialising in underground coal-cutting and transporting systems while Henry devoted himself to marine applications. In 1911 the company placed an order for the hull of a 15.2m (50ft) motor yacht with McLaren Brothers of Dumbarton which had an alternating current dynamo and electric motor of Mavor and Coulson manufacture and with prime power supplied by a Wolseley 6-cylinder petrol engine. The new ship, named appropriately *Electric Arc*, was an outstanding success and after proving the flexibility of marine electric propulsion went to work on the River Forth and was requisitioned for service in the First World War.

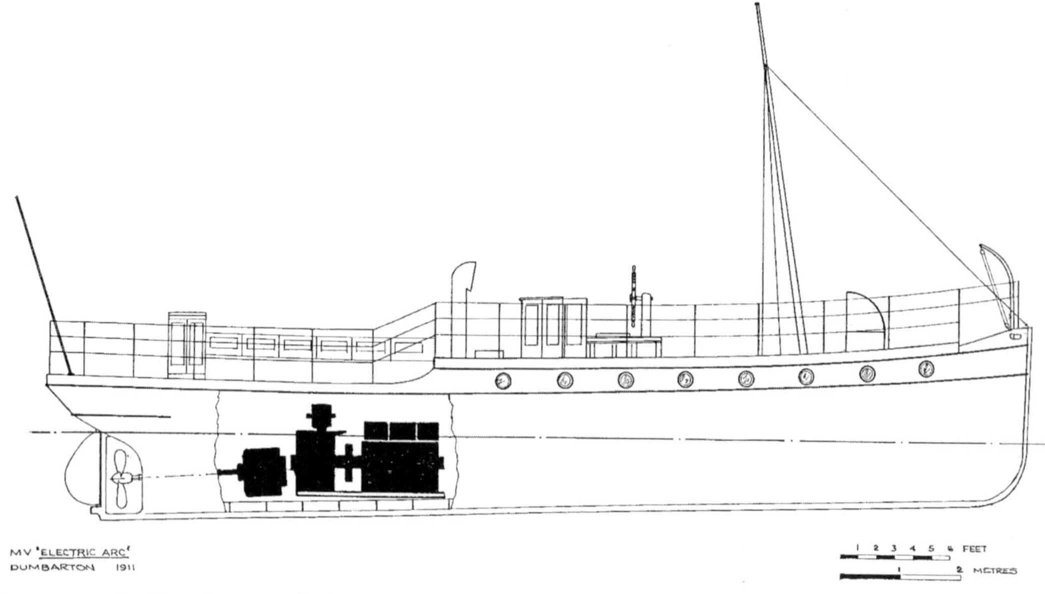

The motor yacht *Electric Arc* was built by McLaren of Dumbarton in 1911, and had an electric motor installed by Henry Mavor using a 45hp Wolseley six-cylinder petrol engine with a dynamo and motor. This little vessel was requisitioned and served throughout the First World War. *(Author)*

Henry Mavor served as Vice President of the Institution of Engineers and Shipbuilders in Scotland and has left in their *Transactions* (between 1890 and 1912) a total of six papers on electrical transmission and distribution as well as one on marine propellers. His health declined in the last years of his life, but his continued interest in cultural matters, his active membership of the Church and his service as an officer in the Lanarkshire Rifle Volunteers marked him out as a contributor to society. While less active with Mavor and Coulson, his role as an advocate for electrical machinery in ships came to the fore, particularly when asked to advise Swan Hunter of Newcastle on a new contract. Of greater importance was the assistance he gave to the United States Navy, first on their 19,000-ton deadweight collier *Jupiter* and later on the design of the turbo-electric driven *New Mexico* class of battleships, of which two were laid down in New York and one at Newport News in 1915. The thinking behind these three battleships was that the flexibility of electrical drive would enable optimisation of propeller speed to be achieved without the cost and added weight of gearing. Mavor did not live to see this dream become reality, dying at Mauchline, Ayrshire, in 1915.

SOURCES:
Lythe, S G E, and Black, Doris
'Henry Alexander Mavor'
Dictionary of Scottish Business Biography
Vol 1 (Slaven, Checkland, eds) Aberdeen, 1986
Walker, Fred M
Song of the Clyde
Cambridge, 1984

James Foster King

1862–1947

JAMES FOSTER KING was probably one of the hardest-worked naval architects of his generation. He was head of the British Corporation during the early years of the twentieth century when great battles raged between the Classification Societies.

He was born at Erskine, just outside Glasgow, in 1862 and received his formal education at the High School of Glasgow, before serving an apprenticeship with **Russell** and Company of Port Glasgow. At the

J Foster King, 1862–1947. Note the use of the Fullers Barrel Slide Rule – the most efficient hand-held calculating machine of all time. *(Lloyd's Register)*

end of the nineteenth century, this great shipyard was in continual contention for the 'blue ribband' for the highest shipbuilding tonnage production in the United Kingdom. They concentrated on the four-masted barques which made up the majority of the world's fleet of sailing bulk carriers and most of which had Glasgow as their home port. It has been said that as many as forty ships were completed from one scrieve board at the Russell yard, an early example of batch or mass production.

Another aspect of Russell's work which must have made an impression on the analytical mind of young Foster King, was the very high deadweight to overall displacement ratio of these ships which were unencumbered with machinery and boiler spaces. A surviving example is the three-masted barque *Glenlee*, now fully restored in Glasgow, and a product of Rodger's yard which was closely associated with Russell's; it has been calculated by the author that her cargo deadweight is almost two-thirds of full-load displacement, a remarkable achievement. On completion of his 'time', Foster King worked in Port Glasgow drawing offices before moving to Earle's of Hull and then to the dedicated White Star drawing office at **Harland and Wolff** of Belfast, then producing plans for the *Majestic* and *Teutonic*.

Many shipbuilders were concerned at the conservatism prevailing in ship design, and many were far from enthusiastic about what they saw as the deadening role of Lloyd's Register of Shipping. The 1880s had been a period of immense change in Britain with the complete and successful introduction of steel within the same decade that the triple-expansion steam engine had become the principal prime mover on all British-built ships. Many shipyard design teams felt that their hands were tied and that scientific progress was not being reflected in the Rule Book of Lloyd's Register. The matter was brought into the open and acrimonious debate followed when it was announced in Parliament that the only two authorities to be empowered to designate Load Lines were to be (first and naturally) the Board of Trade and then Lloyd's Register of Shipping. A powerful body of men, led by directors of the Allan Line and the Anchor Line of Glasgow and the shipbuilder Workman Clark of Belfast, assembled on Clydeside with formidable backing from Northern Ireland and the north-east of England. In 1890, a new Classification Society was formed in Glasgow, known as the British Corporation (BC). The enthusiasm and powerful lobbying of the new organisation was recognised, and before the final reading in the House of Lords of the Load Lines Bill, the names of the British Corporation and of Bureau Veritas were added to the list of the assigning authorities.

Foster King, with his state-of-the-art knowledge of steel hull structures, was invited to join the British Corporation as Principal Surveyor. He remained with them for fifty years, retiring laden with honours in 1940. Within a year of its incorporation, the British Corporation had issued their construction rules which undercut Lloyd's scantlings by around 10 per cent. In real terms, this meant a reduction of 300 tons of steel in a 10,000-ton freighter, with vast savings in first cost and fuel consumption and with corresponding improvements in cargo deadweight. Within a few years, BC had cut deeply into Lloyd's Register's market, and become an international force in the classification business. They allied with overseas groups (notably the Italians – builders of great passenger ships) and they introduced a market element into the business of ship investigation. The Turret Ships and many other innovative designs from the shipyards of the north-east were invigilated by BC and ultimately classed by them for insurance purposes. One or two pioneer vessels were built under survey by both Lloyd's and BC, and one in particular the SS *Turret* built in 1892 by William Doxford and Sons Ltd of Sunderland was not only surveyed by them, but was ultimately classed by the rival French organisation, Bureau Veritas.

Foster King was noted for his steadfast application in solving technical problems, and his prodigious work output. He was always at the forefront of technical thinking, an example being the willingness of BC to be the first Society to rethink effective hull girder design and classify new Atlantic liners being built without deck expansion joints. On a more personal note his office in Glasgow was known to be ruled with a rod of iron. BC were well served by him in the golden years before the First World War, and even more so in the difficult times of the Great Depression. On retirement he was appointed an Honorary Member of the British Corporation, a unique honour to be ranked alongside his CBE and Glasgow LL.D. James Foster King died in his native city in August 1947.

As a postscript, it is pleasing to record that the two great Societies, Lloyd's Register and British Corporation (which had worked harmoniously throughout two world wars) agreed to merge in 1947, the year of Foster King's death. The merger has been to the great benefit of shipping and shipbuilding world wide, and reinforced the merged British Classification Society's position in the world market. Initially, Lloyd's used both their name and that of their erstwhile rival, but understandably wishing simplification dropped BC from their title in the early 1960s. Few members of the staff of Lloyd's Register seem to have been aware of their debt to BC, the Society which forced them to sit up and take notice. Happily Lloyd's Register (now an organisation with a history spanning 250 years) is in process of producing their third in-house history, and this oversight will be remedied. The British Corporation, and Dr James Foster King, will be particularly remembered for introducing commercial reality into ship classification.

SOURCES:

The British Corporation Register of Shipping and Aircraft 1890–1946 – a brief history
Glasgow, 1946

Blake, George
Lloyd's Register of Shipping 1760–1960
London, 1960

Gray, L, and Lingwood, J
The Doxford Turret Ships
World Ship Society, 1975

Alexei Nicolaevitch Krylov

1863–1945

LIKE MOST OF HIS fellow Russian engineers, Alexei Krylov was a master not only of his branch of the profession – naval architecture in this case – but was also an outstanding mathematician. Throughout his long life his work and research were distinguished by a careful and rigorous approach.

Born in the small community of Visyoger in Siberia, his family arranged that his secondary education would be in France and Germany, after which he returned to Russia and entered the Naval College at St Petersburg in 1878, completing the course work six years later. In 1884 he was first employed at the Russian Hydrographical Institute, and then four years later returned to the Naval College to study ship design, combining this with a two-year course in mathematics at the University. By the early 1890s he had become an established figure in the world of naval architecture, presenting papers on ship motions to learned societies including three to the Institution of Naval Architects, the first in 1896 and the others in 1898. His 1898 paper, 'On Stresses experienced by a Ship in a Seaway', is regarded as work so fundamental that it was compared favourably with the publications of William Froude some twenty years earlier, drawing complimentary remarks from **R E Froude**, **J H Biles** and many others. For this and his other papers he was awarded the coveted Gold Medal – the first foreign national to be so honoured. Just before the turn of the century, he was asked to reorganise the teaching of naval architecture in Russia and to oversee such work both at the Naval Academy and the St Petersburg Polytechnic, later to become the world-renowned Leningrad Shipbuilding Institute, which was again renamed the State University of St Petersburg in 1992.

The procurement of ships for the Russian fleet in the early years of the century had been difficult with excessive bureaucracy and multiple overlapping committees, exacerbated by the bruising after-effects of the Russo-Japanese War and in particular the sharp learning curve brought about by the humiliating naval defeat at Tsushima in 1905. Further, the Russians had a unique system of purchasing large auxiliaries, potential armed merchant cruisers, transports and so on, known as the Volunteer Fleet and subscribed for largely by donations from well-to-do persons (often self-seeking) and public organisations – not a system geared for efficiency. Krylov was superintendent of the ship model testing facility at New Holland in St Petersburg from 1900 until 1908, and this ensured that he was in line to be appointed Chairman of the Marine Technical Committee as well as Chief Inspector of shipbuilding contracts for the Navy around 1908. With his acknowledged scientific leadership, encyclopaedic knowledge and above all his affability, much tedious bureaucracy was avoided, and he was involved in the design of many outstanding ships, including the four battleships of the *Gangut* class, all launched in 1911 at St Petersburg, and of which two survived until the late 1950s. In 1916 he was elected a member of the Russian Academy of Science

One can assume that life would have been difficult at the time of the 1917 Revolution, but Krylov seems to have weathered this well, and there is no record of his career being examined for political reasons. Again, his linguistic skills and sheer professionalism ensured that his services were indispensable; an example came in 1921 when he was asked to oversee the construction of new ships overseas, which in turn were used to import steam locomotives and other transport items into Russia. He learned to be a skilled negotiator with the shipyards of Britain, Denmark, France and Germany.

In 1932, a new scientific society was set up for shipbuilding and marine engineering, and in 1933 Academician Krylov was appointed its first president, a post he held until his death twelve years later. In the final years he wrote many papers and in 1942, during the 900-day siege of Leningrad, published *My Memories*, a volume that is popular with scientists and engineers in Russia. He served on the editorial board of *Sudostroenie*, the Soviet shipbuilding journal, and in addition has 500 papers ascribed to him, now enshrined in twelve volumes published by the Academy of Science. In September 1944, the British Ambassador to Russia presented Alexei Krylov with the diploma of honorary membership of the Institution of Naval Architects, an honour bestowed only on one other Russian, namely **Admiral Alexei Popoff** in the late nineteenth century.

On his death just after the end of the Second World War, he was buried at the Volkov Cemetery in Leningrad near the graves of fellow scientists. His greatest memorial comes through his name having been given to the scientific society that he led from the start, and is now one of the world's leading scientific organisations, the Krylov Shipbuilding Research Institute, St Petersburg.

SOURCES:

Krylov, A N
'A new theory of the pitching motion of ships on waves, and the stresses produced by this motion'
Transactions of the Institution of Naval Architects
Vol 37 (1896)

———,
'A general theory of the oscillations of a ship on waves'
Transactions of the Institution of Naval Architects
Vol 40 (1898)

———,
'Stresses experienced by a ship in a seaway'
Transactions of the Institution of Naval Architects
Vol 40 (1898)

Westwood, J N
Russian Naval Construction 1905–45
London/Birmingham, 1994

Frederick Lobnitz

1863–1932

LOBNITZ, A HIGHLY-DISTINGUISHED shipbuilding company, was a household name in the dredging industry for close on eighty years. The 'dynasty' was created by Henry Christian Lobnitz, born in Fredericia, Denmark, in 1831, and trained initially as a military engineer. With better professional opportunities across the water, Henry came to the United Kingdom to work with the engineering company Penn of Greenwich before going on to assist **John Scott Russell** during the building of the *Great Eastern* at the Isle of Dogs in London. In 1857, and by then a naturalised British citizen, Henry joined the staff of James Henderson's West Shipyard in Renfrew on the banks of the Clyde. Over the following twenty years, the shipyard was renamed three times, always coming more and more under the control of H C Lobnitz and in 1880 became Lobnitz and Company. Dredging is one the least well-documented engineering technologies despite having been invented by the Dutch as far back as the sixteenth century. The involvement of Lobnitz and Company stems from Henry's visit to Egypt in 1868, when on the invitation of Ferdinand de Lesseps he inspected the ongoing engineering works of the Suez Canal. At a subsequent meeting in Glasgow he expressed unbounded enthusiasm for this great civil engineering project.

Frederick, his son, was born in Renfrew, and received his early education in Scotland. His later studies were wide-ranging including two years at Heidelberg and Bonn, followed by an apprenticeship at **John Elder's** Shipyard in Govan. This period concluded with a period at the Zurich Polytechnic in Switzerland, and then some practical work on rock excavation and rock breaking in the Suez Canal. This training was vital, as Frederick Lobnitz (aged about twenty-five) then was assumed a partner in his father's company in 1888. His particular responsibilities included the design of new appliances for dredging and in maintaining the position of Lobnitz and Co as the world's leading designers and builders of rock breakers. With massive civil engineering, mining and canal projects underway throughout the world, this line of business had a real future, and in addition the trade in repairs and spares was nothing short of a goldmine.

On the death of his father in 1896, Frederick assumed full control of the shipyard and between then and his own death in 1932, the yard produced well over 500 hulls, most of which were dredgers, hopper/dredgers, hoppers or associated types of craft. It will not come as a surprise to learn that in the mid- and late nineteenth century the yard received many prestigious orders from Denmark. In 1914, one of the Lobnitz fleet, the floating crane *Alexandre Lavalley*, made history by being the first ship to pass through the newly-opened Panama Canal.

With his specialist knowledge, Frederick Lobnitz was appointed Deputy Director of Munitions for Scotland in 1915, reporting to Lord Weir, the future chairman of the Weir Group. For this he received a knighthood. At the end of the war he returned as full-time chairman of the shipyard, while simultaneously gathering a clutch of directorships and public appointments.

On reflection, it is amazing that the two greatest dredger builders in the world at the time (and the deadliest of rivals) had adjoining yards on the riverbank. William Simons and Company, Lobnitz's neighbour in the Renfrew East Shipyard, with a pedigree going back to 1810, was the shipyard which introduced hoppers with bottom-opening doors in the nineteenth century. Along with Lobnitz, they introduced steam-driven bucket dredgers. It was not until 1957 that the yards merged becoming Simons-Lobnitz Ltd. Shortly thereafter and for a less happy period, they were part of the Weir Group. At the time of their merger, Lobnitz had completed nearly 1,200 hulls and Simons around 800.

SOURCES:
Cooper, H R
Practical Dredging
Glasgow, 1958
Lobnitz, H C
'On the Nature and Progress of Works on the Suez Canal'
Transactions of the Institution of Engineers and Shipbuilders in Scotland
Vol 11 (1867–8)

David Watson Taylor
1864–1940

CONSTRUCTOR REAR ADMIRAL David Watson Taylor was one of the most distinguished naval architects of the twentieth century; his name and his work are widely known and yet his fascinating personal history remains very private. Both in the United States and the United Kingdom, he was

Admiral D W Taylor USN, 1864–1940.
(The Royal Institution of Naval Architects)

recognised as a man of outstanding intellectual capability, straightforwardness of purpose and considerable charm.

Taylor was born on a farm well inland in Virginia and remained there until the age of thirteen, when he was enrolled at Randolph-Macon College. At around the age of seventeen he decided on his future career, joining the United States Naval Academy at Annapolis, from where he graduated as an engineer in 1885 at the top of his class. Three months of sea time followed on the old wooden steam frigate *Pensacola* before he was appointed a student at the Royal Naval College, Greenwich. While in Britain he became fascinated with ship model testing and in particular the work of the Froudes. Three years later he completed the Constructor course with the highest marks ever achieved by any student, British or foreign. To round off his training the following two years were spent as a Construction Officer at Mare Island, the former Navy Yard in the Bay area of California.

From 1894 onwards, Taylor was to have a life busy and fulfilling life. He was transferred to the Bureau of Construction in Washington D.C. and from then on was completely immersed in ship hydrodynamics. In 1895 the Institution of Naval Architects awarded him its Gold Medal, he being the first American to receive it, for a paper on 'Ship Shape Stream Forms'. Possibly with the kudos of this medal, he persuaded the authorities that a ship model testing tank was essential for the United States Navy and once the finances were authorised, was asked to oversee both the design and construction at a site in Washington. This was the first tank in the United States coming on stream shortly before the tank at Ann Arbor, Michigan, and well before the one at MIT, Cambridge.

For fourteen years, Taylor ran the department and amassed an enormous data bank of information which led to his best-known book *The Speed and Power of Ships*, which was revised at least twice and then republished after re-analysis in 1954. Just before the First World War, Taylor received a great compliment in being asked to represent the Admiralty in a legal case with the White Star Line following the collision in 1911 between HMS *Hawke* and the new liner *Olympic*. The argument hinged on interaction between ships in fairly shallow water, one of the first instances of this phenomenon becoming widely known. Incidentally, the Admiralty won the case, although to this day the decision of the court has been regarded as controversial.

In December 1914, Taylor was appointed Chief Constructor of the US Navy, a post he held for eight strenuous years, during part of which the USA was at war and at a time when 1,000 ships amounting to 1.2 million tons were being constructed under his authority. Furthermore from 1915 until 1921 the design and construction of naval aircraft was designated as the responsibility of the Chief Constructor. As in the Second World War, the American authorities were not found wanting in their shipbuilding for the Allied cause, providing a wide range of standard vessels, including the charismatic 3,500-ton steam freighters built of indigenous North American timber. Admiral Taylor played a key part in this great venture.

One matter which caused Taylor and others considerable vexation was the cancellation of the United States' post-war warship building programme, following the 1922 Washington Naval Conference. Work was well in hand for the final authorisation of close to half a million tons of warships, a very large amount of intellectual investment.

On his retirement from the Navy, Taylor became a consultant with the New York naval architects, now known as Gibbs and Cox, and also advised on aeronautics and shipping for various US Boards. He was to enjoy a diverse and busy retirement with many honours coming from all over the world. In Britain he became Honorary Vice President of the Institution of Naval Architects, again a 'first' and graduated Honorary LL.D. from Glasgow University. Despite his close affinity with the United Kingdom, there can be little doubt that the honours which gave him greatest pleasure were those in North America. The Society of Naval Architects and Marine Engineers named their Gold Medal after him and in 1937 the United States Navy named their research facility in Maryland the 'David W Taylor Model Basin'.

SOURCES:
Taylor, D W
The Speed and Power of Ships – a manual of marine propulsion
Washington DC, 1933

Sir James Caird

1864–1954

JAMES CAIRD HAD A charmed life, making money and latterly spending it for the benefit of the United Kingdom. While it was unsuccessful, his setting up of the Standard Shipbuilding Company at Chepstow was the first serious attempt in Europe to apply modern production methods to shipbuilding.

The son of a Scottish solicitor, Caird was born in Glasgow in 1874 and educated at Glasgow Academy. While the connections are unclear, he was related to the Cairds of Dundee, a family renowned for gifts to that city and to the Church of Scotland, and also less directly with the proprietors of the Caird Shipyard in Greenock – the company which for fifty years had a near-monopoly of building ships for P&O. Despite these connections, James Caird was to make his own way in life, and on leaving school joined an East India merchant, William Graham, and worked in his Glasgow office for about eleven years before moving to the London offices of Turnbull, Martin and Company, managers of the Scottish Shire Line.

The Scottish Shire Line (not to be confused with the Shire Line which merged later with the Glen Line and ultimately Blue Funnel) had been founded in 1877 and was prominent in the Australian trade. In 1884 they built the *Elderslie*, one of the first ships for the frozen meat trade, and were well established in this business when Caird joined them in 1890. Within twelve months, he had been made a manager and after only thirteen years service had become sole partner and owner. The ships of the line were unmistakable, all of considerable deadweight and many with four masts, indeed the classic profile of the large pre-First World War freighter. During his London shipping years, Caird built up a large network of directorships and connections, and was instrumental in opening-up the meat trade from South America.

Upon the outbreak of hostilities in 1914, James Caird proposed that a shipyard for standard cargo vessels be built in a location safe from enemy attack be it by sea or air. For rather complicated reasons, the chosen site was Chepstow on the Welsh borders and in 1916 a vacant site was purchased on the banks of the River Wye. The funding and back-up came from Caird's own resources as well as those of the ship repairer John Silley and a few of his shipowner friends. Shortly thereafter the Bridge Engineering Shipyard of Edward Finch and Company was added to this portfolio of assets, and in April 1916, the whole was registered as the Standard Shipbuilding & Engineering Company. The issued capital was 300,000 shares valued at £1, and these were snapped up by shipping interests throughout Britain. The Edward Finch name was retained for the construction of non standard craft. James Caird was elected Chairman of the new companies, but very much against his own wishes.

Trouble was to come, with labour shortages heading the list, and the construction of the first three 10,000-ton ships had to be delayed – an embarrassment to the new management. Local susceptibilities were inflamed when permission had to be obtained to destroy a scheduled ancient monument within the works, and equally annoying developments required that some facilities in Chepstow, including the cattle market, had to be resited. In 1917 another and totally unexpected turn of events was to create further problems for the shipyard. Major General Collard, the Deputy Controller of Auxiliary Shipbuilding, proposed employing German prisoners of war in certain shipyards, which would be publicly owned and manned largely from this fairly sizeable source of labour. The Standard Shipyard was selected for purchase by the Government, but strangely Finch's yard was to remain under private control. All shareholders were bought out at a premium of 80 per cent above their original investment.

The yard proved a costly government mistake with little good production to its name. The Standard Shipbuilding Company produced no ships at all, while Finch's works produced a stream of standard vessels, mostly of the 'C' and 'H' classes. After several changes, the two yards were merged again and became the Monmouth Shipbuilding Company, part of the ill-fated Northumberland Shipbuilding Group. They ceased production in the 1920s and the works were taken over as a fabricating facility by the Faifield Company of Govan and continued as Fairfield Chepstow for some years, and happily are still operating, although under a slightly different name.

At the end of the war, with business becoming difficult, in part caused by dramatic increases in shipbuilding prices and a lack of good tonnage, the Clan Line (a fairly far-sighted organisation which desperately required more ships to make up war losses) purchased the name, ships and goodwill of the Scottish Shire Line outright. Following this, James Caird found himself in an unusually strong financial position, and for the next thirty years devoted much of his time to the setting-up of the National Maritime Museum at Greenwich. When it was opened by King George VI in April 1937, Caird (now Sir James) had given well over £1 million to this new organisation, the equivalent of well over £100 million today.

The formal memorial to Sir James Caird of Glenfarquhar is in two parts: first a bust executed by Sir William Reid Dick RA, placed in a rotunda at Greenwich, which in turn was designed by Sir Edwin Lutyens. The second memorial came through the naming of the unit at the heart of all research in the Museum, the Caird Library, and also the main research fund at Greenwich – the Caird Fund.

The National Maritime Museum, Greenwich, may not have lived up to Caird's expectations – certainly not in recent years – but as a major sponsor of the Museum said to the author of this book some years ago: 'Despite ups and downs, Greenwich is bigger than any director, any member of staff, or you or me – it will survive all of us.' For this we should remember Sir James Caird with sincere thanks.

SOURCES:
Bowen, Frank C
'Shipbuilders of other Days; the Chepstow Shipyards'
Shipbuilding and Shipping Record
14 December 1950
Littlewood, K, and Butler, B
Of Ships and Stars
London, 1998

James Rennie Barnett
1864–1965

JAMES RENNIE BARNETT was a man devoted to the profession of naval architecture, and who by his six presentations to the Institution of Naval Architects and the Institution of Engineers and Shipbuilders in Scotland has left a clear picture of yacht design in the late nineteenth century, and the development of the inshore and offshore lifeboat in the early part of the twentieth century.

He was born at Johnstone in Renfrewshire in 1864 and would die in nearby Glasgow just over 100 years later. It appears that the whole of his career was spent in the service of **G L Watson**, the well-known naval architects, including an apprenticeship during which time he was granted leave of absence to attend Glasgow University. Watson's clientele included many of the world's greatest yachtsmen, and Barnett received a good grounding in both sailing and steam yacht design, as well as on lifesaving craft for the Royal National Lifeboat Institution as Watson's were their retained consultants. On the death of George Lennox Watson in 1904, two of his main jobs, first Principal of G L Watson and Co and secondly the post of Consulting Naval Architect to the RNLI, passed to Barnett and he would hold both these positions until his retirement in 1947, when he was in his early eighties.

Three of Barnett's papers to the Institution of Naval Architects (between 1910 and 1929) give a clear indication of lifeboat development in the early part of the century, and introduce later readers to the long-running argument of the time about the benefits and otherwise of self-righting and non-self-righting lifeboats. Taking the risk of being simplistic, Barnett's view was that self-righting boats were for shallow and inshore waters, while deep-water lifeboats need not be self-righting, but designed with a positive righting lever well beyond 90°. In his 1922 paper to the Institution of Naval Architects he presented a lifeboat stability curve with high initial stability and positive righting levers through 180. Unfortunately the situation was such that when larger boats capsized completely, they were unable to recover, and this matter caused considerable heart-searching not only in the United Kingdom, but in Europe and North America as well. In Britain the matter came to a head with the loss of the Fraserburgh Lifeboat (a Watson non-self-righting type) during freak North Sea conditions in 1970, and the decision was taken to change all the RNLI fleet in Britain and Ireland to self-righting boats by 1980.

On assuming his role with the RNLI in 1904, he was instrumental in starting in-depth studies on the best ways of powering lifeboats with internal combustion machinery. Matters such as safety cut-outs, effective air intakes and tunnelling round propellers had to be thought through and then designed. Like Watson before him and **R A Oakley** who came after him, he had a lifeboat class named after him. Despite his unusually advanced age when standing down, Barnett is remembered for his meticulous care in maintaining the high levels of skill and craftsmanship which were the hallmark of Watson's. As well as being awarded an OBE, he was to receive the Gold Medal of the Royal National Lifeboat Institution.

SOURCES:

A total of six papers by J R Barnett were published in the trans actions of the Institution of Naval Architects and Institution of Engineers and Shipbuilders in Scotland between 1899 and 1929.

Evans, Clayton
Rescue at Sea
London, 2003

Richard Oakley

1906–1988

THE ROYAL NATIONAL Lifeboat Institution has antecedents going back well over 250 years, and in that time has accumulated a great wealth of technical knowledge and experience, although until well after the Second World War, the responsibility for lifeboat design was let out to consulting naval architects from well-known British firms. The first 'in-house' RNLI naval architect was not appointed until 1963, a man who in a remarkably short space of time re-invigorated the design philosophy of the organisation.

Richard Oakley served an apprenticeship with the now-defunct shipyard of S E Saunders Ltd of Cowes, later known as Saunders Shipyard Ltd, a division of Saunders Roe Ltd. Here he gained experience in the meticulous and painstaking work of building lifeboats, ships which were 'over-designed' to ensure they could withstand every conceivable contingency at sea. There is little doubt that this time influenced his decision to apply for the job of Assistant Surveyor of Lifeboats with the RNLI; appointed to this post in 1928, he began thirty-eight years of dedicated service. Promotion was steady as he rose through the ranks, becoming Chief Draughtsman and then at the age of thirty-four Surveyor of Lifeboats, a position of considerable authority, and one which would bring him into close contact with **James Barnett**, the naval architect and Principal of **G L Watson** and Co.

Barnett's view was that self-righting lifeboats were excellent, provided the cost in other aspects of stability were not compromised. Self-righting was a contentious issue in the period between the wars, and the protagonists from almost every shipping country in Europe, were serious and caring professionals, but at a time when risk analysis was unknown. Deep down Oakley felt that self-righting was correct and with mounting losses of personnel on non-self-righting vessels the RNLI was beginning to consider the situation. In 1953, work started on a new design of boat, suitable for launching from open beaches, but with the added benefit of having self-righting qualities. From this came the vessel now known as the *Oakley* 37 and which led the Institution back into having all its vessels self-righting.

The *Oakley* 37 was a major step forward in ship design owing to the very strict limitations placed on a vessel of under 10 tonnes. The self-righting was achieved by water transfer systems which were both ingenious and complex, with full use being made of the shape of the hull. Oakley was appointed Naval Architect of the RNLI in 1963, just three years before his retirement, and had the satisfaction of seeing his views accepted as the policy of the RNLI.

SOURCES:
Evans, Clayton
Rescue at Sea
London, 2003

Oscar Kjellberg
1870–1931

THE PIONEER OF ELECTRIC arc welding, Oscar Kjellberg was born in Arvika, a small town in the county of Värmland, midway between Stockholm and Gothenburg. Prospects in nineteenth-century rural Sweden were unpromising and in his teens, after leaving home to earn a living, he ended up as a farm hand in Kristinehamn on the shores of Lake Vänern. His hard work, kindly ways and gentle spirit endeared him to the farmer and his wife, and later when Kjellberg decided to seek his fortune elsewhere, they provided the financial support which allowed him to begin further education classes in Gothenburg. He signed on as fireman on a small Göta Canal trading ship and after a short period obtained his Second and subsequently his Chief Engineer's Ticket. Over the next few years he travelled in Europe and is known to have studied at Lubeck Polytechnic in Germany, where his interest in metallurgy was aroused.

Jane Hay, an Oakley 37 lifeboat, built in 1964 for the St Abbs Station in Scotland. (© *RNLI*)

For centuries, men have searched for improved means of bonding metals. An early literary reference is found in the fourth chapter of the Old Testament Book of Genesis where Tubal Cain is mentioned as 'the forger of all instruments of bronze and iron', and certainly over the following few thousand years, smith work has gained in scope and efficiency. During the eighteenth, nineteenth, and early twentieth centuries the rate of progress in metallurgical research increased dramatically thanks to the work of scientists such Volta, Wilde, Wilson, de Bernardo, Slawianoff and Coffin.

The Russians were quick to introduce welding in the Baltic shipyards, but owing to the cumbersome equipment of the 1890s, coupled with high costs and poor results, they discontinued this after some years. Early welding processes suffered from the inability of operators to shield the edges being

A first for the British Army. The launch of the world's first large all-welded hull on 11 June 1918, a sea-going barge built by the Royal Engineers at Richborough in Kent. *(The Royal Institution of Naval Architects)*

fused from the air, which caused oxidation and a weak, porous weld. The process was understood, but the practicality of achieving it was a different matter. While many people were involved, it is correct to say that efficient welding began with the work of Oscar Kjellberg.

Around 1900, Kjellberg experimented with arc welding in the repair of ships' boilers. Initially he achieved only poor results owing to porosity, but then hit on the idea of what we now call a welding rod, a steel electrode covered with a layer of chemical products which under intense heat produces inert shielding gas and liquefied slag to exclude the air. Modern welding had been born. A patent was granted in 1906, and by then Kjellberg and associates had founded ESAB, a company name taken from the initials of their name (in Swedish) – Elektriska Svetsning AB – the Electric Welding Co Ltd. At first the new company, which was concentrating on ship and boiler repairs, expanded slowly, but once the manufacture of welding plant and consumables was commenced, growth was significant. Subsidiaries were set up in Germany and in the UK, under the well-remembered name of Anglo-Swedish. The speed of development increased once classification societies expressed interest in the work, and the First World War had broken out.

The war offered opportunities for the company to show its worth. Jobs included emergency boiler repairs to the Swedish America liner *Stockholm* in 1917, the re-joining of a ship split in two by battle damage, and most significantly, the building at Richborough, Kent, of a fully-welded 38m (124ft 8in) barge for the British Government.

Kjellberg admitted later that research in welding fell behind in Sweden during the war owing to their neutrality, but in reality his company had capitalised on unexpected demand. ESAB purchased two small powered wooden hulls and renamed them *ESAB I* and *ESAB II* respectively. They were used as floating workshops, carrying electricity-generating equipment and steam heated ovens to keep electrodes dry. When one was sold in France, the company in 1920 proceeded with the building of a fully-welded barge named *ESAB IV* which is now on display in Gothenburg.

One of the earliest seagoing all-welded ships was Cammell Laird's *Fullagar* of 1920. She had very early diesel machinery supplied by Beardmore's of Glasgow and was classed +100A1 by Lloyd's Register. The effectiveness of good welding was demonstrated in 1930, when after hitting a rock in British Columbia, head-on and at full speed, only her forepeak bulkhead was shattered. All hull welds remained intact and a mere 4 per cent of her bagged cement cargo was lost. To conservative shipowners this assurance regarding weld quality should have been sufficient but in a world-wide recession, welding had to wait years for general acceptance.

In the 1920s Oscar Kjellberg was awarded the medal of the Swedish Academy of Science. This was greatly appreciated as it gave formal endorsement (if such were needed) of his life's work. He died in 1931. Around 1940, a Kjellberg Commemorative Medal was instituted by the Swedish Academy of Sciences, and the President arranged that one be given to the old farmer in Värmland, then aged ninety-two, in recognition of his support of Kjellberg as a young man.

SOURCES:

Caldwell, Captain James R E
'Notes on Welding Systems'
Transactions of the Institution of Engineers and Shipbuilders in Scotland
Vol 61 (1917–18)

Denny, M E
'A Diesel-Electric Paddle Ferry Boat'
Transactions of the Institution of Engineers and Shipbuilders in Scotland
Vol 78 (1934–5)
This interesting paper compares two sister ships, one welded and the other riveted.

King, J Foster, and Montgomerie, J
'Electric Arc Welding in Ship Construction'
Transactions of the Institution of Naval Architects
Vol 74 (1932)

McKeown, D
'Welding – the quiet revolution', in Walker and Slaven (eds)
European Shipbuilding: One Hundred Years of Change
Greenwich, 1983

Sir Joseph Isherwood

1870–1937

WHILE REMEMBERED AS one of the major industries of Hartlepool, shipbuilding was carried on there for only a relatively short period, no more than 125 years. The *Castle Eden* built by Parkin and Richardson in 1836 is regarded as the first 'newbuild' and the motor-ship *Blanchland*, built in 1961 for Stephenson Clarke by William Gray and Co, was the last hull to be built there. These somewhat dry and dismissive facts conceal the town's exciting history and the tremendous output of ships and of marine engines in the late nineteenth and early twentieth centuries. Like other ports on the northeast coast, Hartlepool had a massive coal export trade which in turn supported ship repairing. The four or five shipyards concentrated on fishing craft, colliers and to an overwhelming extent the ubiquitous British three-island tramp ship for which the shipbuilders of Hartlepool were in direct competition with Sunderland and Newcastle-upon-Tyne.

Shipyards are good training grounds for those destined to accept responsibility in industry, and here Hartlepool was well to the fore. One such man was Joseph Isherwood, the son of a Hartlepool grocer, who joined the shipyard of E Withy and Co in 1885, and after eleven years of intensive training in office and yard left the service of the yard which by then had been renamed Furness Withy and Co Ltd. While the details of his night school training are not known, it is clear that Isherwood had an excellent foundation in mathematics and structures as he was appointed an Assistant Surveyor to Lloyd's Register of Shipping, initially based in West Hartlepool, but soon thereafter moving to the head office London, where he worked on the approval of plans and reported directly to Benjamin Martell, the Chief Surveyor.

Isherwood worked for Lloyd's for a mere ten years, and during this period gained a masterful appreciation of the qualities as well as the weaknesses in the structure of ship hulls. His analytical mind assessed the methods of the time; to him the traditional means of transverse hull framing seemed inefficient, and after thorough intellectual

Sir Joseph Isherwood, 1870–1937.
(Sir Joseph Isherwood Limited)

consideration he developed a new means of longitudinal framing, a method which before long became known as the Isherwood System. He kept Lloyd's informed of his researches, but protected his intellectual property by patenting the framing system, and then submitted it to the Society. Before long an opportunity came to build a ship in this manner at the Middlesbrough yard of R Craggs and Sons, and at this point Isherwood resigned from Lloyd's and shortly after was appointed a director of Craggs. The ship was a 6,000-ton deadweight tanker, the *Paul Paix*, for the Lennard's Carrying Company, and here Isherwood made a masterstroke in arranging that the ship was built under survey not just by Lloyd's Register but also by Bureau Veritas and by the new and very progressive Glasgow-based British Corporation. This ship was followed immediately by another longitudinally-framed shelter-decker *Gascony* for the well-known Liverpool ship-owner David MacIver.

Isherwood was confident in his ability to make the new system viable and in 1906 set up Joseph Isherwood and Company, naval architects, a company that made an impact on tanker and dry cargo shipping and also made him a wealthy man. The concept of longitudinal framing was far from new, and a form of this had been used by John Scott Russell and Isambard Kingdom Brunel in the construction of the *Great Eastern* at the Isle of Dogs in 1857. But the Isherwood System was fundamental and by early 1914, over 276 ships had been delivered, representing over one and a quarter million gross tons, and by 1921 over 1,400 ships had been delivered. In 1921, he was honoured by King George V by being made a Baronet. In the same year, Sir Joseph Isherwood's friends entertained him to a Testimonial Dinner at the Waldorf Astoria Hotel in New York with over a hundred of the great and the good from the North American shipbuilding scene present. At this dinner, a biography made available stated that '... on a total output of approximately 12,000,000 tons, the Isherwood System had saved over 250,000 tons of finished steel ... and increased deadweight carrying capacity by 300,000 tons ... which equals the output of any of the busiest shipyards in Great Britain'.

The consulting company was responsible for several innovative developments in ship construction, all of which emanated from the Isherwood System. On the structures side, bracketless construction was proposed, being a means of increasing the efficiency and oil-tight qualities of riveted joints in tankers. In a paper presented before the Institution of Engineers and Shipbuilders in Scotland in 1926, this was well received and had a generous review from **Foster King** of the British Corporation, a matter not lost on Lloyd's Register which had introduced a major rule review for oil tankers in 1925. With the economy in downturn, many shipbuilders were seeking out simpler and less expensive forms of construction such as straight-frame ships and hulls designed to use standard plate sizes.

One further major initiative was to come from Isherwood's offices, the design of a ship with a highly rounded midship section, significant tumblehome and a prismatic co-efficient of 0.70. After ship model tank tests at Teddington, Washington and Wageningen, it was agreed that the hull, with less than normal wetted surface, would be more fuel-efficient. Three 7,000-ton deadweight freighters of this design were ordered from yards in three ship-building rivers, namely Short's on the Wear, Furness on the Tees and Lithgow's on the Clyde. At a paper presented to the North East Coast Institution of Engineers and Shipbuilders in May 1934, the trials performance of the lead vessel *Arcwear* was presented and in the coming months several similar ships were constructed. There has been no detailed analysis of the class of ship since then, but it is likely that the additional building costs coupled with the greater difficulty of stowing break bulk cargo in a highly-shaped ship discouraged ship-owners from building to what became known as 'Arcform'.

Sir Joseph Isherwood remained at the helm until his death from pneumonia in 1937. The company, now Sir Joseph Isherwood Limited, continues in business to this day at North Shields as a marine systems support organisation.

SOURCES:
Isherwood, J W
'A New System of Ship Construction'
Transactions of the Institution of Naval Architects
Vol 50 (1908)
———,
'The Bracketless System'
Transactions of the Institution of Engineers and Shipbuilders in Scotland
Vol 69 (1925–6)
———,
'The Arcform Ship: Trials and first voyage performances'
Transactions of the North East Coast Institution of Engineers and Shipbuilders
Vol 50 (1934)

Robert MacGregor

1873–1956

FOR CENTURIES, LONDON'S insatiable need for coal was met by a fleet of intrepid coastal colliers, making the tough voyage from small coal ports in Fife, the Lothians, the north-east coast and Yorkshire to the capital. Before the days of steam, most colliers were brigs with a deadweight of a few hundred tons and were hard-pressed to make this arduous round-trip four times a year. The trade changed in the mid-nineteenth century with the introduction of iron construction, the acceptance of the steam engine and ultimately improvements brought about by advanced design which enabled colliers to self-trim and to maintain longitudinal trim almost irrespective of their condition of loading. This latter quality was introduced by **Palmers** of Jarrow who introduced the 'flatiron' in 1878, thereby laying the foundation for the late-nineteenth and early-twentieth century sea coal trade to London.

A Hebburn man who was to have influence on the safety and viability of this massive coastal fleet, was Robert MacGregor born in 1873. As was the tradition of the time he followed his father Sandy MacGregor as an apprentice at the great shipyard of Palmers of Jarrow, and on completion of his indentures had become Queen's Prizeman of the Worshipful Company of Shipwrights. This helped pave his way to becoming a successful naval architect. To gain experience, he worked in drawing offices in Glasgow, Hull and Newcastle before going across the Channel to Dunkirk. Here he gained a good grounding in French which was to stand him in good stead when at the age of thirty-three he was appointed Chief Draughtsman of the Antwerp E. & S. Company. He stayed in Belgium until 1914 when invited back to the UK as manager of James Dible on the River Itchen at Southampton. This was a small yard which had just switched from building coastal sailing topsail schooners to barges. A strange posting, but possibly MacGregor was tasked with the yard's modernisation. He remained with them until 1923 and between 1919 and 1923 registered ten patents in his own name.

In 1924, Robert MacGregor set up his own business as a naval architect, known for a few years as MacGregor and King. The main activity was collier design, a demanding task with considerations of cargo ventilation, self trimming and ease of unloading. The early twentieth century flatirons were designed to proceed up river fully laden at high tide, with minimum ground and bridge clearances. As the return journey was in light condition and at low tide, the ships had to maintain their trim, and hence the development of the 'raised quarterdecker'.

Single pull steel hatch covers on MV *Wilmington* 1969. (Author)

Between 1922 and 1925, no fewer than forty-five colliers foundered, for a variety of causes, ranging from human error through to hatch failures. Hatch design had remained unchanged for decades and was as basic as fitted short planks laid on a steel grid over the hatch mouth, and then covered by two layers of tarpaulins held down by bars and wedges. For security many ships had additional chains and wires held taught by slips, wrenches and similar tackle. Robert MacGregor gave close consideration to the hatch problem and by 1927 was designing a steel hatch, which was to be patented the following year. Steel hatches may seem obvious now, but was not the case when looking at early twentieth-century coaster design, with varying sheer and cambers. The new hatches had to be an accurate fit, watertight and if possible they should contribute to the strength of the hull girder. All colliers worked to tide-based schedules with loading and discharging deadlines. It was essential to have expeditious hatch removal.

In the conclusion to his 1931 Institution of Naval Architects paper 'Seaworthiness of Collier Types', Professor Burrill stated that '. . . the only solution to the problem [of collier losses] will be the introduction of some form of steel hatch cover'. This was the endorsement that MacGregor and the shipowners needed and was to be backed up by the Load Line Committee's report which stated that hatch failure was the cause of no less than 13 per cent of ship losses at sea. An order from Cory Colliers for two hatches each for two new-buildings began the changes and soon these owners moved over 100 per cent to steel hatches. During the war, it was found that ships with steel covers had a better chance of staying afloat after being torpedoed than those with wooden ones, which would be blown to pieces, losing any hope of retaining hull integrity.

The 1930s were difficult times and in 1937 MacGregor's agreement with King lapsed. He invited his brother Joseph (1883–1967) to join him and they worked from a tiny drawing office, and in 1939 formed MacGregor & Co (Naval Architects) Ltd of Whitley Bay with a capital of £300. Joseph with wide ship repair experience was an asset to the business. They targeted the collier business the main stay of Austin's Shipyard in Sunderland, closely followed by Burntisland, and the Aberdeen yards of Hall's and Hall Russell. Despite universal acceptance of steel covers and of their proven expertise in collier design, profits were slim, and the brothers decided on radical business changes including the appointment in 1945 of the Austrian-born Henri Kummerman (1908–84) as their sales agent for Europe. Over the years Kummerman increased his control of the business and was a major contributor to the long-term success of MacGregor & Company. In the 1960s they produced the single-pull cover, one of the greatest aids to speedy cargo handling.

Robert MacGregor died at Whitley Bay in October 1956. He had been a major player in the campaign for safety at sea; his business had made key contributions to the new study areas of cargo handling and safe stowage. His contributions and his prestige are embedded in the MacGregor Organisation now operating on a world-wide basis.

SOURCES:

Burrill, L C
'Seaworthiness of Collier Types'
Transactions of the Institution of Naval Architects
Vol 73 (1931)

Guglielmo Marconi

1874–1937

AT HIS DEATH IN ROME in 1937, Marconi was one of the world's most successful men, having reached this eminence through a combination of scientific inventiveness and natural business skills. For those with some knowledge of his family background, this is of little surprise, as his parents were quite singular people. His mother Annie Jameson was the daughter of a well-to-do Scots family involved in whiskey distilling in Dublin. She had been sent to study music at the Conservatoire at Bologna, and while there met a wealthy Italian widower Giuseppe Marconi. They fell in love, Annie hurried home to obtain parental permission to marry, which not unsurprisingly was withheld as Giuseppe was old, 'second-hand' and above all a foreigner. To take her mind off the unwelcome Italian, Annie was introduced to all the eligible young men in Wexford and Dublin society, but to no avail, and on reaching the age of consent, she fled to Boulogne where her suitor awaited her. They returned to Italy as Signor and Signora Marconi. On 25 April 1874, their second son Guglielmo was born in Bologna.

Probably owing to the differences in their ages, Marconi's parents, while devoted and faithful to one another, did spend lengthy periods apart, and as Annie was anxious that her son should speak English as fluently as Italian, she took the children for some very long periods to the United Kingdom. With an affluent background, the children lacked for little and young Marconi soon proved himself as an experimenter in the young and exciting field of electricity, an interest his father found difficult to understand. Education followed at Leghorn Technical Institute and then at Bologna, the doyen of European universities.

He used the family home at Villa Grifone for his researches and in 1895 managed to transmit a wireless signal over 2 kilometres. The field was wide open and many people were struggling to be the leader in radio communications including the Russian Popov, the Dane Poulsen and the Welshman Sir William Preece, with each man contributing something of value to the new science. Marconi was one of the first to establish the importance of the configuration and positioning of aerials. The world was ready for a more flexible form of communication, and Britain in particular with the Royal Navy and the world's largest merchant fleet could see the benefits of ship-to-ship communication over long distances, a science that would eventually replace flag signalling and the short-lived 'truck semaphore' of the latter years of the nineteenth century. Furthermore, with the introduction of high-speed fleet manoeuvres with destroyers and similar craft, efficient communication had become essential.

Marconi's father came to recognise his son's ability and also the market value of the new product. The two men felt for patriotic reasons that this intellectual property should be offered to the Italian government with agreed terms for development and exploitation, but despite Marconi being a nominal officer in the Italian navy, they were rebuffed and in 1896 Marconi made his way to his second home in Britain, and started to file patents. The Chief Engineer of the GPO was impressed and offered assistance and encouragement, such that within a short time Marconi had sent signals across the Bristol Channel, to be followed by the English Channel as well as offering useful help to the British Army. In 1897 the Wireless Telegraph and Signal Company (shortly after renamed Marconi's Wireless Telegraph Co Ltd) was formed and the new organisation set about winning the greatest prize, that of sending telegraphic signals across the Atlantic. In an amazingly short time, indeed on 12 December 1901, this was achieved when a morse message was sent 3,400km (2,113 miles) from Poldhu in Cornwall to St John's, Newfoundland.

Wireless telegraphy (WT) was installed in many ships, and there are many stories about the efficacy of the new means of communication in saving lives. The greatest endorsement of WT came from the rescue of around 750 persons following the collision of the White Star liner *Republic* and the Lloyd Italiano ship *Florida* with 800 emigrants on board, off Nantucket in January 1909. With the help of WT, five ships came to the rescue and the total complement of the stricken *Republic* were placed aboard the *Florida* and then later re-distributed around the other five ships. Casualties were minimal; six persons from the two ships were killed and two injured.

The establishment of British and American telegraphic companies by Marconi was far from easy, and in both cases vested interests opposed the young Italian businessman. In Britain there was a scandal when it was discovered that members of Lloyd George's government had purchased shares in Marconi's Imperial Wireless Scheme just prior to an announcement that the government would back and subsidise it. However, by the end of the First World War, the Marconi companies were almost international, and Marconi himself both wealthy and influential. He served as an Italian delegate at the Paris Peace Conference and started to enjoy the role of statesman. In 1919 he purchased a beautiful steam yacht, built by Ramage and Ferguson of Leith in 1904, and after renaming it *Elettra*, used it more often than his home, with his time divided between his cabin, the wireless office and the study where his piano was installed.

His first wife was Beatrice O'Brien, the daughter of an Irish peer. They had children, but were divorced in 1924. His second wife was to be an Italian beauty less than half his age, and their wedding took time to plan owing to the opposition of the Church authorities in Italy. Marconi did join the Fascist Party, but seems to have had little interest in it and in later years had reservations about Mussolini. Little by little he stood back from commercial life, and was able to view the remarkable way his name had become world famous in the maritime world. Honours were heaped on him; the title of Marchese (Marquis) and elevation to the Italian Senate in 1929, doctorates from Oxford and Glasgow as well as the surprising election by the undergraduates of St Andrews as their Lord Rector. In 1909 (when aged only thirty-five) he had received (jointly with K F Braun) the Nobel Prize for Physics.

SOURCES:

Jolly, W P
Marconi
London, 1972

Shirley Brooks Ralston

1874–1952

WHEN S B RALSTON began his apprenticeship in the Glasgow office of **G L Watson** and Company around 1890, little did he or any of his contemporaries realise that on his retirement over sixty years later, the name Ralston would be known around the world!

In the last years of the nineteenth century, Watson's were producing plans for some of the finest steam yachts of all time, and all apprentices gained a broad appreciation of naval architecture. Further education was encouraged; indeed it was regarded as a necessity for advancement. After completing his indentures, Ralston moved to the drawing offices of Alexander Stephen & Sons at Linthouse, and there his college education coupled with experience gained at Watson's was utilised when the head of the Company asked him to assist in the design and building of **Alexander Stephen**'s own 350-ton steam yacht *Calanthe*. This beautiful ship was completed in June 1898. In 1902, Ralston moved to Southampton as shipyard manager of little-known yard of Summers and Payne Ltd, but within two years had returned to the Clyde and to Stephens where he rose rapidly to chief draughtsman and ultimately to naval architect.

In the early years of the twentieth century, knowledge of the stability of operating ships depended on the ability of the ship's officer to interpret the paperwork issued to the ship on handover from the shipyard, and the skill of the shipyard in supplying easily-understood stability books. This was not always satisfactory, and Ralston hit on the idea of a mechanical means of deducing mean drafts, trim and metacentric height. For this he used a brass balance table on which was engraved a vertically-exaggerated profile of the ship. This table could be balanced delicately in both the vertical and also the horizontal axes. Small brass weights representing the mass of fuel, stores, cargo and passengers were then applied at the appropriate centres on the plate, and after finding a balance and then applying information from additional curves, the ship master could be appraised of the current condition of his ship. Within a few years many ships had these supplied and right up till the advent of the shipboard computer, almost all shipyards supplied an accurately drawn inboard profile to the Ralston Company, and later to their successors, Kelvin Hughes.

In 1921 Ralston's ability received formal recognition by the award of a seat on the shipyard board. He was to remain in harness until 1952 when forced to retire through ill health, but by then with an astonishing fifty consecutive years of work at Linthouse to his credit. Later that year he died at his home in Bearsden.

SOURCES:

Carvell, John L
Stephen of Linthouse 1750–1950
Published by the shipbuilders

Ralston S B
'Description of a stability and trim indicator',
Transactions of the Institution of Naval Architects
Vol 53 (1911)
Ralston gave two papers to the Institution of Engineers and Shipbuilders in Scotland, namely 'Method in ship design' in 1932, and 'A note on the block coefficient of a ship' in 1947.

A P Møller

1876–1965

ONE OF THE WORLD'S largest and most celebrated transport concerns, with over a thousand ships on its books, was founded largely through the efforts of one man, Arnold Peter Møller. Born in 1876 at Dragør, a pretty town south-east of Copenhagen on the Island of Amager, both sides of his family had connections with the sea. Early in his life the family moved to Svendborg in central Denmark, which to this day remains a shipping and shipbuilding centre, and from where his father (Captain Peter Mærsk Møller) commanded and part-owned the 320-ton deadweight steamship *Laura*. A P Møller and his brothers and sisters often sailed on this little vessel and were imbued with a love of the Baltic and of the sea. From the outset, their father was set on establishing a family-run shipping business, and structured the education of his children with this end in view.

A P Møller, 1876–1965. *(A P Møller-Mærsk, Copenhagen)*

Møller served a commercial apprenticeship of three years, before being sent in turn to shipbrokers at Newcastle, Königsberg (now Kaliningrad) and finally St Petersburg where he had the good fortune to work on chartering for well-known Russian and Danish companies. In 1904, having gained a good working knowledge of English and other languages, he joined the staff of C K Hansen in Copenhagen with a clause in his agreement allowing him to manage ships on his own account. In 1904, along with his father and several other citizens of their home town, the Svendborg Steamship Company was set up with a two-year-old steamer built by John Crown of Sunderland; it was renamed *Svendborg* and this was the start of the mighty Møller-Maersk empire. Another move, and a most critical one, came in 1912, when the 'Steamship Company of 1912' was founded. By then Møller had raised enough money to be a major shareholder and ensured that the Articles of Association allowed him freedom of operation, and having resigned from Hansen's he could concentrate on the building-up of these closely related yet rival companies. Throughout his life Møller insisted on ploughing reserves back into the firm and not enjoying quick profits; his successful management of the 1912 Company bears this out.

The First World War caused endless problems for neutral shipowners. Most Danes were sympathetic to the Allied cause, but were conscious of their border with Germany, and fearful of a repetition of their long-standing nineteenth-century conflicts over Schleswig-Holstein. In a nutshell the problem was that the British demanded the use of 25 per cent of their fleet in return for coal, while the Germans demanded a guarantee that ships built with German steel would never work on behalf of the Allies. With great difficulty the two company fleets continued but lost two of their twenty ships to hostile action.

While in the UK, Møller had been impressed by the Ropner Company of West Hartlepool which managed both a shipyard and a considerable tramp fleet. He realised that with an ever-increasing fleet, an in-house yard could depend on regular orders and improve the recovery of overheads. In 1917 a shipyard was set up at Odense on the Island of Fyn, originally with two berths, but quickly expanded to three and for a short while to four with side launching into the Odense Canal. There were a few turbine ships, but most were diesel-driven, often omitting the funnel as was the early-twentieth-century Danish custom. In 1932, work ran out and until 1937 the yard sustained massive losses. Møller faced up to the problems and in-depth meetings were held with workforce and unions. Despite suspicion and hostility on all sides, concessions were made and with great fortune orders were received in 1933 and work recommenced. Owing to the complexity of serving both owners and builders, Møller insisted that dealings not only had to be above board, but they must be transparent.

From 1928, the Maersk companies entered into liner operations and they also took shares in many marine developments such as whaling in the Antarctic. One particularly close relationship was with the Isbrandtsen Lines of New York, with the Danish company managing ships on their behalf from time to time. The German invasion of Denmark on 9 April 1940 instantly divided the Maersk fleet in two. The overseas fleet, which amounted to thirty-six vessels of over a quarter of a million tons dwt, worked for the Allied cause and was to lose twenty-five ships and 148 seamen. Great distress was felt in Copenhagen and London when several ships that had been requisitioned by the British and given to the French were later handed over to the Germans by the Vichy government. Møller's son Mærsk McKinney Møller hurriedly moved to New York, armed with the power of attorney for his father and started to plan for the resumption of normal trading once the war was over. Throughout the war A P Møller refused to compromise himself with the occupying power, and in 1943 published a robust letter of praise for the Danish sailors in wartime, who were 'staking their very lives for freedom'.

Møller was seventy the year after the end of the war, but he remained in full control for some years although gradually handing over to his son. The future of the Odense Shipyard was given deep consideration and in 1957 following a share transfer with the shipping companies the go-ahead was given for a new shipyard at Lindø near Odense, involving building docks and introducing revolutionary shipbuilding methods. In October 1962 the first ship was delivered and the yard has continued successfully working in close co-operation with several builders in other countries. Some years ago at the Odense Steel Shipyard, after a shipbuilding crane (built in Britain) collapsed and recriminations and ill-will abounded, A P Møller made a quiet and considered comment: while the incident was regrettable, blame has to be across the board, as management has the responsibility to act 'with constant care'.

In the early 1960s, the Maersk shipping companies controlled eighty-eight ships of over 1.7 million tons dwt, managed a world-class shipyard and had moved into oil exploration, offshore work and other businesses. With the full consent of his family, in 1953 Møller had placed the massive wealth he had built up into a trust fund to avoid the work of a lifetime being squandered by speculators. This fund is now a primary shareholder of the organisation and has the task of ensuring the companies are run according to the principles of the founder. Until his death in 1965, he continued to attend the office and on many days would sail from his home in Charlottenlund by yacht to the Langelinie Harbour, beside the Little Mermaid in Copenhagen. Stories about A P Møller and his operations are legion. Clearly he was conservative in approach, and possibly aloof, but he has to be admired for fearlessness, integrity and above all an abiding loyalty to Denmark. At all times he was opposed to moving his ships from Scandinavian or British flags to countries of convenience.

As a postscript, how did the A.P. Moller-Maersk Group come by their now ubiquitous seven-pointed white star on a blue background? Many years ago, the author was told by a lady (whose father who was a Maersk Chief Engineer) that the points represent the working days of the week! Amusing though this may be, the reason is straightforward; the symbol was on the funnel of SS *Laura* in 1886 when she was purchased by Captain Peter Mærsk Møller, a deeply religious man. One night, his wife who was accompanying him was very ill, and Captain Møller, who was deeply distressed, prayed for her. The star which always reminded him of that night and of her recovery, was retained and since then has been used throughout the fleet.

SOURCES:
Hornby, Ove
With Constant Care ... A P Møller: Shipowner 1876–1965
Copenhagen, 1988

Sir Westcott Abell, 1877–1961.
(The Royal Institution of Naval Architects)

Sir Westcott Stile Abell

1877–1961

IN 1948, CAMBRIDGE University Press published *The Shipwright's Trade*, the last of three important books written by Sir Westcott Abell and which were described after his death as 'a fitting memorial, demonstrating his deep knowledge of ships and shipbuilding and attachment to his profession'. Few naval architects have had such a varied and productive career as Abell, and few have had to work against such terrible odds. In his twenty-first year, while lighting fireworks for Queen Victoria's Diamond Jubilee, he suffered several injuries including the loss of his right hand, but this was no deterrent to him as he learned to write with his left hand and continued his professional training as a naval architect.

Abell was born in Exmouth, Devon and in 1892 at around the age of fifteen entered the Royal Navy Engineering College as a cadet destined to spend two years on the bench and in the fitting shop, before being offered a studentship in naval architecture at Devonport Dockyard. He was to spend three years at Plymouth and in 1897 was informed that he had gained admission to the Royal Naval College, Greenwich where he might undertake training as a probationary assistant constructor. What a challenge to a highly-motivated young engineer! The accident in 1898 was a serious setback, but Westcott took this in his stride and within three years had obtained a first class professional certificate and was appointed a member of the Royal Corps of Naval Constructors.

His first job was that of professional secretary to **Sir Philip Watts,** then Director of Naval Construction, which included being part of the internal Corps enquiry into the reasons for the lack of stability of the new Royal Yacht *Victoria and Albert* which had been launched at Pembroke in 1899. This must have been a time of great embarrassment for the

RCNC officers as A/S Burmeister and Wain of Copenhagen had just built the very similar but highly successful yacht *Shtandart* for the Russian royal family. Following this Abell held the post of Lecturer at the Royal Naval College, Greenwich.

The year 1910 marked Westcott Abell's entry into the first of the three jobs that would bring him to the very forefront of his profession. His first major appointment was elevation to the chair of naval architecture at Liverpool University, a post he held until 1914 when he accepted the post of Chief Ship Surveyor to Lloyd's Register of Shipping, in succession to Dr Thearle. He was to remain with Lloyd's for fourteen years – years that were important for two reasons, first the requirement to combat the inroads into their business brought about by the commercial drive of their closest rivals, the British Corporation based in Glasgow, and secondly the stress placed on all the Classification Societies during the First World War. The revisions to Lloyd's Rules advocated by Westcott Abell would decrease ships' lightweight conditions and simultaneously increase the structural efficiency of longitudinally framed tankers. All this was to prepare him for appointment in 1928 as Professor of Naval Architecture at Armstrong College, then part of Durham University, a post he held with great distinction for many years.

Two features of the life of Sir Westcott (he was knighted in 1920) have to be mentioned: first his service on many committees and public enquiries, an examples being the Load Line and the Safety of Life at Sea Committees. Secondly he was responsible in the late 1920s for the design of the train ferry *Twickenham Ferry* built for the Southern Railway's service between Dover and Dunkirk. This was a difficult task, with design constraints of a very high order, however using the principles laid down in the nineteenth century by **Robert Napier**, these highly successful ships were successfully completed and operated. The overnight 'sleeper' (something London and Glasgow had enjoyed for the best part of a century – and still do) became the *chic* way to travel between the British and French capitals!

Westcott Abell died in 1961 leaving a wonderful legacy of written material. He produced papers for the North East Coast Institution and for the Institution of Naval Architects as well as several books. In particular one paper for the Institution of Engineers and Shipbuilders in Scotland entitled 'The Ancient History of Ship Regulations', published in 1920 is a tour de force: It established the author as a naval architect who not only knew the 'rule-book' but who understood how it came about. His words in the preface to *The Shipwright's Trade* may help us to understand the man and to appreciate his depth of thought: '... since the shape of any ship is bound to conform to certain laws of nature, the basic technique, begun in Tudor times and "brought to rule" under the Stuarts, must persist, even though the work itself be shared with less skilled workers ... the manner of the building of ships remains with us in essence as it was some 400 years ago.'

SOURCES:
Abell, Sir Westcott S
The Ship and her Work
1923
———,
The Safe Sea
1932
———,
The Shipwright's Trade
Cambridge, 1948

Sir Thomas Henry Havelock
1877–1968

THOMAS HAVELOCK WAS described once as in the first rank in applying mathematical methods to the solution of the seemingly intractable problems of naval architecture and especially hydrodynamics. He was known to and worked from time to time with a remarkable group which included G S Baker, W C S Wigley, J F C Conn and Professor Carl Prohaska from Denmark.

Havelock was a native of Newcastle and had his early undergraduate training in mathematics at the Durham College of Physical Sciences, Newcastle upon Tyne before moving south to St John's College Cambridge where he graduated as Wrangler in 1900 and was awarded a Smith's Prize. After a period of research at Cambridge, in 1906 he was appointed lecturer in applied mathematics at the now-renamed Armstrong College, Newcastle (then awarding degrees from Durham) and in 1915 was elevated to the Chair of Applied Mathematics. An injury sustained at Cambridge many years earlier precluded him serving in the forces during the First World War, but he served as a senior researcher in optics and what was to become his special preserve, hydrodynamics. Here he presented many closely argued and detailed papers on a wide variety of subjects including heave and pitch, wave patterns and the effect of boundary layer on wave resistance. Indeed he produced over ninety papers of the highest academic quality over a 55-year period.

In 1941 he was appointed acting Head of the Department of Naval Architecture at King's College, Newcastle (now the University of Newcastle upon Tyne) and held this post until close to the end of the War. It led to many notable honours including honorary fellowships and degrees from Cambridge, Durham and Hamburg. His unique role as a scientist/mathematician was recognised by the Institution of Naval Architects in the award of Honorary Membership in 1944, when the President pointed out that this was a rare event and placed Sir Thomas (he was to be knighted the following year) along with the two great physicists **Lord Kelvin** and Lord Rayleigh in the Institution's Roll of Membership. Incidentally he was awarded the first Institution of Naval Architects William Froude Medal in 1956.

Havelock was appointed a Fellow of the Royal Society in 1914, and had steadily published papers in their Journals. These, coupled with those from the Institution of Naval Architects and other societies, were gathered together by the Institution of Naval Architects around 1958. The United States Navy Department were to publish a full set later. On a personal basis, he remained unmarried and became an establishment figure at Newcastle, and in recognition of this a student hall of residence is named Havelock Hall in his memory.

SOURCES:

Wigley, C
The Collected Papers of Sir Thomas Havelock on Hydrodynamics
Office of Naval Research, Arlington, VA, 1965

Sir William Wallace

1881–1963

ON 29 JANUARY 1917, the Fairfield-built submarine *K 13*, one of the new and fast steam turbine boats, was completing sea trials on the Firth of Clyde. On a dive in the Gareloch, the after end of the boat flooded and she grounded in about 20m (65ft) of water. A massive rescue operation mounted by the Navy, civil organisations and the Clyde shipyards enabled the fore end of the ship to be brought to the surface and within three days forty-six of her complement of seventy-seven were saved. Among the survivors were two notable members of the Institution of Naval Architects: the first was Professor Percy Hillhouse of Glasgow University, who also acted as naval architect to Fairfield of Govan, and the second was a younger man, William Wallace, destined to make his mark in the history of maritime technology.

Born in Leicester in 1881, William Wallace came north with his family and received his education at Paisley Grammar School and thereafter at Anderson's College (later Strathclyde University), while serving an apprenticeship with the now-defunct Paisley shipyard of Bow McLachlan. On completion of his indentures he joined the British and Burmese Steam Navigation Company, better known on the Glasgow/Liverpool/Rangoon trade as Paddy Henderson's. By the age of twenty-nine, a remarkably short time in those years, he came ashore with the rank of Chief Engineer, and was to work for the rest of his life with Brown Brothers of Edinburgh, bringing international renown to its already distinguished name.

Joining the company in 1910, his skill as a draughtsman, but even more his inventiveness and originality, brought him to the attention of the Brown family, and in 1916, at the age of thirty-five, he was invited to become Managing Director. In this capacity he attended the trials of HM Submarine *K 13* to witness the operation of Brown Brothers hydraulic gear, then a fairly new development in the shipping world. The war years enabled Wallace to develop a good relationship with the Admiralty, and after much effort, in 1932 Brown

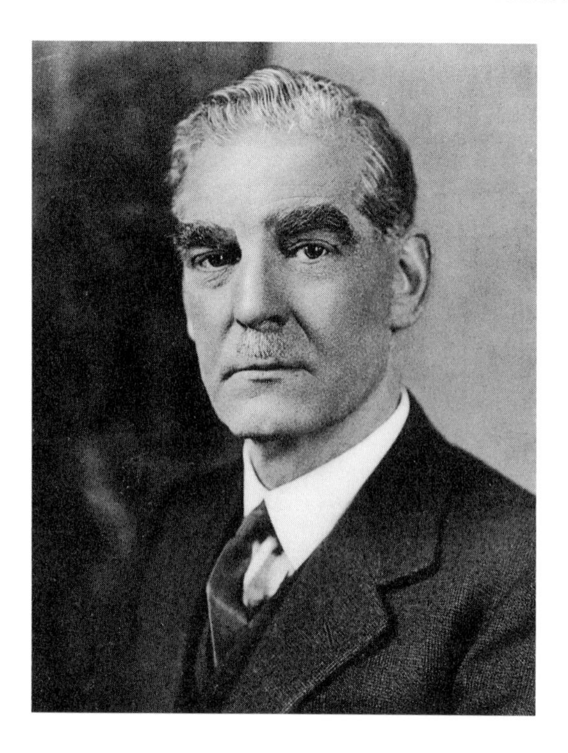

Sir William Wallace, 1881–1963.
(The Royal Institution of Naval Architects)

Brothers were awarded the contract to design the first aircraft catapult for Royal Navy aircraft carriers. This work has continued and the vast bulk of steam catapults used by navies throughout the world are manufactured in Edinburgh.

From 1922 to 1952, the great shipyard Denny of Dumbarton was under the chairmanship of **Sir Maurice Denny**. He and Wallace enjoyed a friendly relationship, and from the 1920s investigated mechanical methods of stabilising ships in a seaway. The earliest attempts had been made (and patented) in 1898 by a chemist, Dr Andrew Wilson of Stirling, and this work was further developed by Dr Shintaro Motora of Mitsubishi Shipbuilding in 1920. As Wallace and Motora knew one another, the path for Brown Brothers was clear, and with the use of the internationally-known Denny ship model testing facility, the result was a predictable and unqualified success. Wallace and Denny realised that full-scale testing was needed and approached the Southern Railway Company, offering to fit stabilisers on one of their ferries, and further, to meet two-thirds of all costs. This was a major proposition for the two engineering/shipbuilding companies, both struggling in the worst industrial depression known in Britain. The Railway Company responded favourably and offered the *Isle of Sark*.

This ship, a Channel Islands steam turbine passenger ship, had been built by Denny Brothers and engined by its associate Denny & Co, both of Dumbarton. In 1932 she was at the forefront of technology, having had the Maier Hull Form incorporated in her design. The stabiliser trials took place in early 1935 and the results were moderately satisfactory, and certainly good enough for the Admiralty to order similar equipment for the sloop HMS *Bittern*, making her the world's first stabilised warship. Brown Brothers capitalised on this success, and in particular the ease of retrofitting the *Isle of Sark* was a major selling-point.

The Denny-Brown stabiliser became one of the greatest British maritime successes of the twentieth century with larger and larger units being developed for every type and size of ship afloat, including Cunard's two *Queens* serving on the unforgiving North Atlantic run. From time to time there were problems, one being the New York arrival of the new Cunard liner *Media* when it was discovered that she was minus one stabiliser! Wallace had the knack of turning potential disasters into triumphs, and launched a design enquiry, the results of which ensured that fin structures could withstand all foreseeable externally-imposed loads.

Wallace, now knighted, relinquished the post of managing director in 1957 when he was seventy-six years old, but continued as chairman for two more years. By now he was a Fellow of the Royal Society of Edinburgh and had been President of both the Marine Engineers and Scottish IES as well as Vice President of the Institution of Naval Architects. The University of Edinburgh awarded him an honorary LLD. Sir William Wallace died in Edinburgh in 1963.

Brown Brothers came under the management of a syndicate of British shipbuilders before becoming part of the Vickers Group in the 1980s, and then in 1999, part of Rolls-Royce while still maintaining a

25 per cent share of the international ship stabiliser market. One interesting connection is that in the 1960s, the managing director was Willie Walker, a former director of William Denny and Brothers and one of the most popular presidents of the Scottish Institution.

SOURCES:

Allan, J F
'The Stabilization of Ships by Activated Fins'
Transactions of the Institution of Naval Architects
Vol 87 (1945)

Everitt, Don
The K Boats
London, 1963

Hay, Marley F
'The Maierform of Hull Construction'
Transactions of the Institution of Naval Architects
Vol 73 (1931)
This paper describes the theory propounded by Mr Maier of Austria, who suggested a soft-shaped forefoot designed to enable an easy flow of water along the bow and buttock lines.

Pugh, Peter
The Magic of a Name: The Rolls-Royce Story
Volume 3 (Cambridge, 2002).

Wallace, Sir William
'Experiences in the Stabilization of Ships'
Transactions of the Institution of Engineers and Shipbuilders in Scotland
Vol 98 (1954–5).

Watson, Nigel
Brown Brothers: A Company History 1871–1996
Edinburgh, 1996

Marie-Augustin Augustin-Normand

1881–1964

ON THE DEATH OF Monsieur Augustin-Normand at Le Havre in 1964, French industry lost the sixth and last generation of his family to have directed shipbuilding in Normandy. The family business began in 1728, when François Normand, a ship's master and deep sea pilot, set up a shipyard on the banks of the Le Claire River near Honfleur. This business flourished, but owing to the silting of the nearby waters and the growth of Le Havre as the seaport to the Seine, it was decided to transfer business there. The first ship built in 1819 was the 384-ton whaler *Harponneur*, a fair-sized ship for the time. Early on, both steam propulsion and iron construction were adopted and the shipyard carved a place for itself in the market for packet steamers and larger coastal vessels.

In the late nineteenth century, the company was headed by Augustin Normand (grandfather of the above Marie-Augustin). He was an active naval architect and was one of the earliest members of the Institution of Naval Architects, presenting a paper in London in 1866. Both he and his son pursued orders for fast naval craft and won a fine reputation as builders of torpedo boats and torpedo boat destroyers. Their 120-ton displacement twin-screw torpedo boat *Forban*, completed in 1895 reached the then-incredible speed of 31 knots on trial, and was recorded as the first ship in the world to travel faster than 30 knots. The Normand yard was now in the forefront of the international small craft arms race, and they were consulted by the Russians and many others with regard to both ship design and the development of shipyard plant.

Marie-Augustin was marked out to succeed both his grandfather and father and his education was planned accordingly. An apprenticeship was served with **Yarrows**, first on the Thames and then on the Clyde after the shipyard had been moved lock, stock and barrel to Glasgow. On the death of his father in 1906, Marie-Augustin took the reins and with the approval of his two aunts (the only other stock holders) he reorganised the yard and arranged that it be registered as a Société Anonyme (SA), the Continental equivalent of a Limited Company. The functions of the company were thought through and appropriate heads appointed for the departments, enabling the new board of directors to take a broader view of their work. The manufacture and repair of diesel machinery was introduced and even more daring, the manufacture of submarines commenced.

Export work was maintained from the early 1900s until the outbreak of the Second World War. In 1940, after the German occupation of France, the yard continued working but the slowness of production and the sabotage of plant and work in progress caused serious problems locally, and were the cause of a short term of imprisonment for Marie-Augustin. Nearing the time of the Allied invasion of Normandy, the works were bombed heavily. On the return of peace, the yard was quickly restored and continued as a quality traditional yard through to the 1960s, but then like many other businesses of this kind found trading difficult and had to close.

SOURCES:
Obituary for M-A Augustin-Normand
Transactions of the Royal Institution of Naval Architects Vol 106 (1964)

Sir James Lithgow

1883–1952

AT HIS DEATH IN 1952, Sir James Lithgow presided over the world's largest shipbuilding group in private hands. This situation had come through adroit management and a strong work ethic by first William Todd Lithgow (1854–1908) of **Russell & Co** of Port Glasgow, followed by that of his sons James and Henry Lithgow, who took over the business and worked harmoniously together until their deaths a few years after the Second World War.

James Lithgow was born into an affluent but hard-working family. While his father ensured that all members of the family were set up financially, he also determined that his sons had a clear understanding of the meaning of duty, loyalty and service; in this he did not fail and both Henry and James showed exemplary integrity in their business dealings. James Lithgow's education was similar to that of many able Scottish children of the time, attending local Renfrewshire schools and then finishing at Glasgow Academy before travelling to France for a year of special tuition. At this stage James Lithgow made the decision to eschew tertiary education and to enter his father's shipyard as an apprentice in 1901. His 'time' was barely complete when his father, discovering that he was terminally ill, took him on as a partner. James Lithgow little realised that within months the ownership and full responsibility for management of the yard would fall on his 25-year-old shoulders and those of his brother Henry, just three years younger.

From one point of view, the takeover of Russell & Co by the young brothers was timely, as the Clyde (and other areas) was recovering from a few years of economic depression and optimism had returned to British shipyards. Russell's built two standard cargo ships, allowing the brothers time to learn their 'new trade' of shipyard management, unencumbered by design and estimating problems. In 1911 a further stroke of good fortune came with the closure of the Bay Shipyard in Port Glasgow – the neighbouring yard of Russell's and one which had Lithgow family connections. The brothers seized the opportunity and purchased the yard, and the growth of what was to become the Lithgow Group had commenced. Within a few years acquisitions included Robert Duncan of Port Glasgow, the builders of the first Cunard steamship *Britannia* of 1840 and then in 1917 the marine engine builders David Rowan of Glasgow, which for the first time enabled the group to quote for combined ship and machinery contracts.

While still an apprentice, James Lithgow had joined the Volunteer Royal Garrison Artillery, later to be part of the Territorial Army. At the outbreak of the First World War, his unit was mobilised for active service and then served in France from 1916. Lithgow, who had been commissioned, rose to the rank of Colonel, before being recalled to the UK in 1917 to undertake the role of Director of Merchant Shipbuilding under Sir Eric Campbell Geddes, the Controller of Merchant Shipbuilding. In this position, he worked closely with a diverse group of people including Lord Weir and Lord Pirrie, all of whom widened his knowledge and experience. Throughout the period from 1914 until 1919, when James Lithgow returned, the shipbuilding businesses at Port Glasgow and elsewhere had been managed almost single-handedly by Henry Lithgow.

For a year or two following the Armistice, there was a feeling of cautious optimism in the shipyards, and the Lithgows acquired the two Port Glasgow shipyards of William Hamilton and Co Ltd and Dunlop, Bremner and Company giving them almost total control of shipbuilding in the town. This was followed by the long-established marine engineering business of Rankine and Blackmore. The decision was taken then to rename the former shipyard of Russell and Co as Lithgows Limited, and to use the new collective name of the Lithgow Group – a name it was to retain until the 1960s although several companies including Hamiltons (the preferred builders for the Brocklebank Line) continued to trade under their former names. Clearly James Lithgow had learned from his experiences in London; he realised that secure steel supplies were an essential part of a successful industrial enterprise and set about obtaining the interests of James Dunlop and Co who were major steel and coal merchants in Scotland. This move later led to the merger of Dunlops with the massive steel manufacturers Colvilles of Motherwell in 1931, with the two Lithgow brothers on the Colvilles Board. A further twist to the story came a year or two later when James Lithgow was given the opportunity to purchase another major steel manufacturer, the Steel Company of Scotland. This placed Colvilles in an invidious position as they could ill-afford to lose the business generated by the Lithgow shipyards to the 'Steel Company' as it was known in Glasgow. The merger of the two steel companies was inevitable. It went ahead, and the Scottish steel industry underwent rationalisation, again with Lithgow interest at board level.

Two further crises occurred on the Clyde in the 1930s: first the giant Beardmore Company, suppliers of steel, ships, castings, guns and machinery was in trouble, and here the rationalisation of the steel industry added to the pressure, which ultimately led to the closure of most of the Beardmore Group before the outbreak of the Second World War. The other problem was the great Govan shipyard of Fairfield which had been dragged down by the insolvency of one of their most prestigious clients, the Anchor Line. With direct help from the Bank of England, it was made possible for the Lithgow Group to add Fairfield to their portfolio of businesses, giving them access to builders of naval and high-quality mixed tonnage.

Throughout the inter-war years James Lithgow (now a baronet) represented the United Kingdom as a delegate at the International Labour Organisation in Geneva. He held several government advisory posts and was President of the Federation of British Industries in the difficult years between 1930 and 1932. He was an extremely hard worker and constantly commuted between the west of Scotland and London. Without Henry in place in Port Glasgow it is unlikely that he could have achieved as much. The brothers discussed and agreed policies which had to be implemented by Henry with the backing of a few trusted staff. With Lithgows' tramp and tanker production, good relations had to be established with likely competitors such as the Burntisland Shipyard operated by the **Ayre Brothers**.

Undoubtedly Sir James Lithgow's most difficult task was setting-up British Shipbuilders Security Limited, an organisation charged with the long-term aim of improving shipbuilding competitiveness, in part by the elimination of inefficient shipbuilding capacity: At the time this was highly controversial, and even today, opinions are divided on this organisation. It is described briefly elsewhere in this volume.

Lithgow enjoyed living in the country and had estates in the west of Scotland. He was an active Churchman giving much support to the Church of Scotland, and also to the Iona Community which had been founded by the former minister of Govan Parish Church, the Rev George F MacLeod; the two had different views politically and otherwise, but over the years became friends. (MacLeod became a Moderator of the Church of Scotland and most unusually for a Scots divine took his seat in the House of Lords as the Very Rev Lord MacLeod of Fiunary.)

The outbreak of hostilities in 1939 came to him as a bitter blow, but within months he had become Controller of Merchant Shipbuilding and Repairs with a seat on the Board of Admiralty. He proposed the Anglo-American discussions which in the fullness of time led to the Liberty Ship programme, and gave his all for Britain's war effort. At the conclusion of the Second World War, James Lithgow returned to Port Glasgow shipbuilding with a lighter heart and knowing that he had served his country faithfully. Misfortune awaited him, as in early 1948, his brother Henry who had 'held the fort' in Port Glasgow over the war years, died probably due to exhaustion. Sir James then had the hard task of guiding the Group in the changing world of the late 1940s, and sadly in 1952 he died while still at the head of a massive steel and shipbuilding empire.

SOURCES:
Reid, J M
James Lithgow, Master of Work
London, 1964
Slaven, Prof A
'Sir James Lithgow'
Dictionary of Scottish Business Biography
Vol 1 (Aberdeen, 1986)

Vladimir Ivanovitch Yourkevitch
1885–1964

'SCIENCE AND ENGINEERING are international and the ocean which divides nations also unites them.' These words, written to the author by the late Alexander Kholodilin, Professor at the Leningrad Shipbuilding Institute, aptly describe the life and times of Russian naval architect Vladimir Yourkevitch.

Born in Moscow, Yourkevitch came from an academic family with no maritime connections, but he seems to have made an early decision to be a shipbuilder. After secondary education at Moscow, he travelled west and matriculated at the St Petersburg Polytechnic. On completion of studies, he joined the Baltic Shipyard and commencing the professional training which led to becoming a member of the Russian Corps of Naval Constructors – and by the age of twenty-five. The early 1900s were a fascinating time in Russia, with the navy coming to terms with its massive defeat at Tsushima and with the Dreadnought race on all over Europe.

Yourkevitch was appointed to a senior position in the design team for the fast battleships of the *Borodino* class, then due for completion before 1920. The British contenders for the subcontract work – Brown's, Beardmore and Vickers – had been eliminated and any overseas contact was with Germany, giving Yourkevitch the unexpected opportunity of viewing the work of the Norddeutscher Lloyd Tank in Bremerhaven and revising his thoughts on optimum underwater hull shape for large, fast ships. This influenced the design of the four ships which might

The *Normandie* hits the water at St Nazaire, France on 29 October 1932 and becomes the world's longest ship afloat. Yourkevitch incorporated features to the hull which came from the Russian *Borodino* class battleships coupled with innovations he had seen in the German Norddeutscher Testing Tank at Bremerhaven. *(Arnold Kludas)*

well have become the super-battleships of the twentieth century, had it not been for the Russian Revolution of 1917 and the cancelling of work in the Baltic and Admiralty Shipyards. The first of the class to be launched, *Izmail*, remained incomplete until 1931 when she was finally broken up, and the claim that she required about 10 per cent less power than any comparable vessel remains unsubstantiated.

Yourkevitch left Russia in 1918, passing through Constantinople and eventually reaching Paris as a refugee. He took work wherever it was offered and in the 1920s must have felt his life's avocation ended. Happily an unexpected introduction to the Chairman of the St Nazaire Shipyard enabled him to resume work as a naval architect at the time the French Line's flagship *Normandie* was being designed. His connections with the German testing tanks and his experience on the *Borodino* class led to the hull shape of the French flagship being altered with an extra fine entrance and run, and the addition of a small but nonetheless significant bulbous bow. The French Line claimed that their power requirement was 10 per cent less than that of their deadly rival – the Cunard liner *Queen Mary* – for identical service. The *Normandie* surpassed all expectations achieving 30 knots on the North Atlantic and winning the Blue Ribband on her first crossing.

Yourkevitch then set up a naval architects' business and in 1937 moved to the United States where he enjoyed mixed fortunes. During the fire on the *Normandie* in 1942 which was handled ineptly by the New York Fire Authorities and the US Navy, Yourkevitch begged to be allowed aboard to direct matters, maintaining that the ship could be made to sink on her bottom. The request was refused and the ship turned over on her side. He tried to raise cash to have her rebuilt, but despite the sympathy and help of the American authorities time ran out and the wonderful *Normandie* was scrapped in 1946. One sympathetic ship-breaker remarked that he had witnessed the breaking of Yourkevitch's heart.

One design was yet to come from his offices; the concept of a mega-liner possibly of 50 per cent greater tonnage than the *Queens* carrying several thousand passengers 'across the pond' at an economical fare. This proposal was initiated during lecture sessions at both the Ann Arbor School of Naval Architecture in Michigan and also at the Massachusetts Institute of Technology. With aircraft travel in the ascendency, no shipping line was prepared to take on this very direct challenge, and it has been left to the cruise liners and to Cunard with their new *Queen Mary 2* (built at St Nazaire) to construct these large hulls.

Vladimir Ivanovitch Yourkevitch died in North America in December 1964.

SOURCES:
Correspondence between the late Professor Alexander Kholodilin of St Petersburg and the author.

The Ayre Brothers of Burntisland

The Burntisland Shipbuilding Company was one of Britain's more remarkable twentieth-century industrial enterprises. Founded on a greenfield site in 1919, the shipyard was to give continuous employment in the Kingdom of Fife for exactly fifty years and to deliver more than 300 ships, that is one every eight working weeks. The yard was founded by two young men from South Shields, Amos Ayre born in 1885 and his brother Wilfrid born five years later. The sea was in their veins as generations of their family had served as river pilots on the Tyne.

The brothers served apprenticeships in the now-defunct shipyard of Wood Skinner and Company of Bill Quay-on-Tyne and both studied with distinction at Armstrong College, Newcastle before progressing to other places of employment throughout Great Britain and Ireland in vastly differing jobs, that were to give them the background and breadth of experience for their ultimate roles in British shipbuilding. Around 1914 Amos became Manager of the new Employment Exchange in Govan, Glasgow, before being given responsibility for fleet coaling on the River Forth during the First World War and finally being appointed Scottish District Inspector for shipyard labour. After gaining experience on the Tyne, Wilfrid joined the Aberdeen Company of John Lewis and instigated the expansion from engineering and trawl ownership into shipbuilding. As he admitted later this opportunity gave him the confidence to begin shipbuilding at Burntisland some years later. (Incidentally many of the Lewis facilities survive on the River Dee, now part of the Wood Group.)

In 1918, the brothers set up of the new Burntisland Shipyard on the River Forth, with a publicly subscribed share capital of £120,000 and with the Lord Lieutenant of Fife, Sir William Robertson, as chairman. The strategy was to build ships of 6,000 tons deadweight, designed for ease of construction and economy of operation. Despite difficulties, they succeeded in this and by the mid-1920s the shipyard was established as the supplier first of 'Burntisland Economy' ships, and secondly, raised quarterdeck flatirons for the London 'sea-coal' trade. Bearing in mind that the United Kingdom was heading into economic depression, this was real success. Their cost-cutting methods were complemented by elegant and simple designs, all backed up by published work and careful record-keeping. The late **Sir Maurice Denny** in a tribute to

Sir Amos Ayre described him as 'The prize empiricist in the best sense of the word'. On the death of Sir William Robertson, the chairmanship was taken by Amos whilst retaining the joint Managing Director's status with Wilfrid.

Sir Amos Ayre (1885–1952)

During the 1920s Amos Ayre became deeply immersed in work for national and international committees, such as the Conference on Safety of Life at Sea, while chairing the League of Nations Committee on Shipbuilding Statistics. As the storm clouds of the late 1930s approached and British industrial output slumped to all-time lows and the threat of world war loomed ever more closely, Amos Ayre was offered the Chairmanship of the Shipbuilding Conference, a full-time appointment making him the undisputed spokesman of the industry. His remit was to plan the strategy to be adopted by shipbuilders in response to the demands of the coming world war. A knighthood followed. From 1939 to 1944 he was Director of Merchant Shipbuilding, reporting to the overall Controller Sir James Lithgow.

In a paper published in 1940 he pointed out that in 1933 only 5 per cent of UK shipbuilding capacity had been used, while seven years later the industry as a whole was working at full stretch. He asked how many industries could endure such fluctuations. At his own request he rejoined the Conference in 1944 and started planning for shipbuilding's return to normality, and presented an excellent contribution on the work of merchant shipbuilders during the war to the Institution of Naval Architects in 1945. Probably remembering his time at Burntisland, he took an especial interest in the Admiralty Ship Welding Committee, and contributed regularly to the transactions of the engineering institutions. While kindly and genial, he was noted for a sharp intellect and a desire to have information presented in a clear and logical fashion; sloppily presented results – especially ship model tank results – irritated him. He received many awards including a DSc from Durham University and was elected President of the Institute of Marine Engineers for the years 1946 to 1948. He died in office in 1952.

Sir Wilfrid Ayre (1890–1971)

In 1936, Wilfrid Ayre took over the Chairmanship of the Burntisland Company and was to make his mark as a forceful leader. The pre-war output had been tramps and colliers, with economy of operation as the prime consideration, but at the end of the conflict, the Company recognised that there would be changes in demand, with ships became costlier and more sophisticated. The Company bought over Alexander Hall of Aberdeen (one of the world's oldest shipyards) and shortly thereafter their immediate neighbour Hall, Russell with the inevitable merging of these yards. This gave the group a wide range of products, and at its peak a workforce numbering several thousand.

To ensure continuity of supply of diesel engines an interest was acquired in the British Polar Company, and like all successful industrialists Wilfrid Ayre expanded his network of directorships, non-shipbuilding appointments and government advisory bodies. He worked hard at obtaining orders from Norwegian Companies and Hall Russell found themselves as licensees for the Fredriksstad steam motor, several of which were fitted on this unusual type of ship where the boilers were fitted at shelter-deck level.

In 1963 Wilfrid Ayre retired with a knighthood and the satisfaction of having seen the integration of three shipyards and their change from steam to diesel and from riveting to welding. He died in 1971, but sadly after one disastrous contract for Karachi owners had forced the closure of the Burntisland yard. Fortunately, the group was not endangered as control had passed to Hall Russell in Aberdeen, and under its chairman John Wright this yard was still to build some great ships.

SOURCES:

Ayre, Sir Wilfrid
A Shipbuilder's Yesterdays
Aberdour, 1968

Denny, Sir Maurice E
'The First Amos Ayre Lecture – the Man and his Work'
Transactions of the Institution of Naval Architects
Vol 97 (1955)

Henry J Kaiser

1882–1967

IT IS DOUBTFUL IF ANY single person has had such a massive impact on steel ship production as Henry Kaiser. Despite having had neither naval architecture nor shipbuilding training and experience, for the last three years of the Second World War he directed several companies and newly-constructed shipyards which together produced over 1,500 standard general cargo ships, amounting to close on 28 per cent of the United States Maritime Commission's emergency merchant shipbuilding output.

Kaiser had been born near New York in 1882 and started training as a photographer with such good effect that by the age of twenty he was manager of his employer's business. By judicious changes of occupation, he found himself with just enough capital in 1914 to found a road-paving company on the US west coast, which in turn thirteen years later led to work in Cuba on land-contracting projects. Steady growth, coupled with good labour relations and timely completion of work enabled one of his companies to become prime contractor for the massive Hoover Dam and then later the Bonneville and the Grand Coulee Dams. These projects demanded logistical and leadership skills of a high order and his name became well known in North American industry.

Following the entry of the United States into the Second World War, the US Maritime Commission planned the opening of new shipyards and the extension of old ones. The Americans were experienced in this having had a highly successful shipbuilding programme for the Allies in 1917–18, and in 1941 were resolved to improve on even that! About thirty yards on both sea coasts were earmarked, some placed in the hands of existing shipbuilders like Bethlehem Steel while others were leased out to new and untried organisations amongst which was the Kaiser Corporation with control of about six yards in California, Oregon and Washington State.

The emergency shipbuilding programme commenced with sixty ships to the design of J L Thompson of Sunderland, but with minor changes in design to suit the style of work in American yards, and to avoid the need for the furnacing of hull plates. The negotiations for this vital order for Britain were handled by **Sir Amos Ayre**. Thereafter the following 5,700 ships, including the famous Liberty Ships which differed somewhat from Thompson's design, were built to standard plans with emphasis on exact repetition and adherence to welding throughout. The naval architects were Gibbs and Cox Inc, and it is recorded that when production was at its peak, the naval architects were issuing 700 acres of ship plans every year. Kaiser's built about 1,550 ships or nearly 29 per cent of the total output and manned their yards with a high percentage of personnel with no previous knowledge of ship-building. Richmond, the site of yards in California (close to Oakland where Kaiser's administration was based) had a population of 23,000 in 1940, but by 1943 when ship construction was at full tilt, the population was over 100,000. With such a large number of launches, sponsors were picked from a wide stratum of society, and each launching was treated as a public event with strict rules governing matters like the value of the gift which was not to exceed $500 in value. All the shipyards were at pains to make any celebrations inclusive of the entire workforce.

The first Liberty Ship was the SS *Patrick Henry*, built by Bethlehem-Fairfield, which entered service in 1942, and survived the war despite voyages to Murmansk and elsewhere. By 1943, the shipyards which were each producing many ships a month had lowered the building time on berth to a mere twenty-eight days and outfitting afloat to ten days. The shortest time on the ways is believed to be that of SS *Robert E Peary* which required only fours days and 15½ hours from lay-down to launch at the Richmond No 2 Shipyard.

The introduction of welding caused problems, with several ships having severe hull cracks both at the fitting-out quay and also at sea in low temperature conditions. It is believed, however, that no ship on the programme was lost outright through notch sensitivity of steel. The welding improved with advanced training and improved rod and flux quality. The design of stress points was investigated

The ss *Marchovolette* of Cie Maritime Belge, seen leaving the Schelde in July 1963. This highly successful steam turbine Liberty ship was built by Bethlehem Fairfield, Maryland, in 1945. *(Author)*

and higher steel qualities introduced at hatch corners and areas of similar risk.

At the end of the war most of the shipyards were mothballed, and Henry Kaiser moved on to pastures new. He went out to Hawaii and became involved in real estate. He died in Honolulu in 1967, remembered as a man who had made a massive contribution to the Allied war effort.

SOURCES:

Lane, Frederic C, *et al*
Ships for Victory
Baltimore, 1951

Mattox, W C
Building the Emergency Fleet
Cleveland, Ohio 1920

Sir Maurice Edward Denny

1886–1955

WHILE THE DENNY FAMILY has been associated with Dumbarton for centuries, it was only at the beginning of the nineteenth century that they came to the fore as shipbuilders, then operating several small yards in the shadow of the ancient Burgh's historic Rock and Castle. One William Denny had been employed by **Robert Napier** as a yard manager, but in the early 1840s joined with his two brothers Alexander and Peter to form a ship design business, known as Denny Brothers in Glasgow. However, the idea of building hulls haunted them and in 1844 (the date now accepted as the commencement of the business) William Denny and Brothers returned to Dumbarton and laid the keel of the iron paddle steamer *Loch Lomond*. This was the first of close on 1,500 hulls which were constructed in the ever-growing shipyard at Dumbarton, which continued until 1962.

From around 1880 until the early 1950s, the name Denny of Dumbarton was synonymous with the highest standards in research, design and quality of product. In 1883, the shipyard commissioned the first commercial ship model tank testing facility in the world and through this were able to obtain an order for the Belgian cross-Channel paddle steamer *Princesse Henriette*, a ship of revolutionary design which achieved over 21 knots on trials, thereby ensuring Denny's sixty-year domination of the cross-Channel market. The company were the first to fit Parsons steam turbines on a commercial ship (*King Edward* of 1901), they introduced welding in the 1930s and wisely held large shareholdings in many companies including the largest inland fleet in the world – the 600-ship Irrawaddy Flotilla Company operating out of Rangoon. They were known as fair employers and were supportive of undergraduates, often employing as many as the remaining Clyde yards put together.

Maurice Denny, a grandson of Peter one of the founding brothers, was born in Dumbarton in 1886, and until 1911, had a remarkably wide-ranging education. Schooling was at Tonbridge in Kent, followed by two years at the University of Lausanne in Switzerland and then one year at Heidelberg in Germany. Then he embarked on a 'sandwich' apprenticeship, for four years shuttling backwards and forwards across the Atlantic between the shipyard in Dumbarton and the Department of Naval Architecture at the Massachusetts Institute of Technology, from where he graduated in 1909. A short spell followed at the Sunderland shipyard of William Doxford, then noted for elegant solutions to ship design problems and which was beginning a long and successful association with the diesel engine. Maurice Denny immersed himself in the technical side of the shipyard upon his return to Dumbarton, but at the outbreak of the First World War found himself in France as a member of the Machine Gun Corps, where he rose to the rank of Major, but before hostilities ceased he was asked to return to London and join the staff of the Controller General for Merchant Shipbuilding (for which he received the CBE). In 1918 the Dumbarton shipyard became a limited liability company with Denny being appointed a director, then two years later Vice-Chairman and in 1922 on the death of his uncle being appointed Chairman, a position he retained for thirty hard-worked years until his retirement in 1952. Subsequently he was succeeded as Chairman by Edward Denny and he received the honorary position of President of the company.

During his thirty-year stint there, great emphasis was placed on the work of the model tank, and with the skills there coupled with the engineering expertise of Brown Brothers of Edinburgh, the Denny-Brown ship stabiliser was developed, the first being a 'retro-fit' in the 1934 Southern Railway Channel packet *Isle of Sark*, which had been built in Dumbarton in 1931. Incidentally, this was the first British ship to have a Maierform hull. In 1934 the shipyard delivered two novel diesel-electric paddle ferries for use on the Queensferry Passage beside the Forth Rail bridge; they were the all-welded *Robert the Bruce* and her riveted sister-ship *Queen Margaret* of which all comparative details were presented by Maurice Denny in a paper to the Institution of Engineers and Shipbuilders in Scotland. Many other innovations were recorded including the building of the world's first high-pressure turbine ship *King George V* in 1926, described by many engineers at the time as a full-size working model, and a ship that was to serve on the Clyde and the Hebrides for over forty years. The marine engine building aspects of the Company were not overlooked as Denny was a well-known builder of the Sulzer diesel under license.

His public work was immense, and included serving on the Advisory Committee on Merchant Shipbuilding during the war, whilst chairing the Shipbuilding Conference. In 1944 he helped establish the BSRA, the British Shipbuilding Research Association, and became the first chairman of the Research Board as well as being chairman of the technical committee of the British Corporation, the Glasgow-based rival to Lloyd's Register and with which it later amalgamated. At the end of the war he received a KBE, but his title did not change as in 1936 he had inherited his father's baronetcy. He also was honoured with an LLD from Glasgow University as had both his father and grandfather before him.

It is possible that what gave him most satisfaction in later years was the series of full scale tests carried out on the hull of the redundant paddle steamer *Lucy Ashton*. This former Clyde steamer was stripped of all appendages and machinery and powered with Rolls Royce jet engines was used for the reanalysis of hull friction coefficients and other matters. Geosims of the highest degree of accuracy were tested in various ship model test tanks throughout the world and from the accumulated results, the famous Lucy Ashton papers were prepared. The first paper was presented in 1951, the Festival of Britain year. The following year he left office and after a very short retirement died at Drymen in Stirlingshire in 1955.

SOURCES:

Denny Dumbarton 1844–1932
Privately published history of the Shipyard and the Company

Denny, Sir Maurice
'BSRA Resistance experiments on the *Lucy Ashton*. Part 1 Full scale measurements'
Transactions of the Institution of Naval Architects
Volume 93 (1951)

Sir James McFadyen McNeill

1892–1964

JAMES MCNEILL WAS naval architect of John Brown and Company of Clydebank during an interesting period when their products included the two *Queens*, the last British battleship HMS *Vanguard* and the Royal Yacht *Britannia*. He was typical of many twentieth-century shipbuilders in being a 'single company' man, as apart from his army service he remained with Brown's throughout his working life (1908 to 1962).

The Clydebank Yard was unusual in that it had been constructed on a green field site on the north bank of the Clyde about 9km (6 miles) west of the centre of Glasgow by James, and George Thomson, when they had to move their business (known as the Clyde Yard) from the centre of the city as the docks were enlarged. The new establishment was named the Clydebank Shipyard, which gave its name to the new town which sprung up around the shipyard and the works of the other main employer, the Singer Manufacturing Company. To ensure that the workforce of Thompsons were willing to move with the yard, the company built traditional, elegant sandstone blocks of flats near the river, buildings that have stood the test of time and now are known as the Clydebank tenements. As the Glasgow boundary was then just short of Clydebank, all the employees were at pains to say their ships were from Clydebank and not from Glasgow! In 1897 following change of ownership, the shipyard was renamed the Clydebank Engineering and Shipbuilding Company and two years later, when it was taken over by a firm of steel makers from Sheffield, it became John Brown and Company Ltd.

James McNeill was born in Clydebank and commenced his education at Clydebank High School, before moving to the renowned Alan Glen's School in Glasgow. In 1908 he was accepted by John Brown's as an apprentice and within a couple of years was earmarked for higher education and encouraged to matriculate at Glasgow University under the then unique 'sandwich' system of training with six months of the winter at the University and then spending the long summer vacation in the shipyard. He graduated in 1915 with a multitude of prizes, and immediately volunteered for the army. On demobilisation in 1918 he had achieved the rank of Major in the Royal Artillery and had been awarded the Military Cross, the first of his many honours.

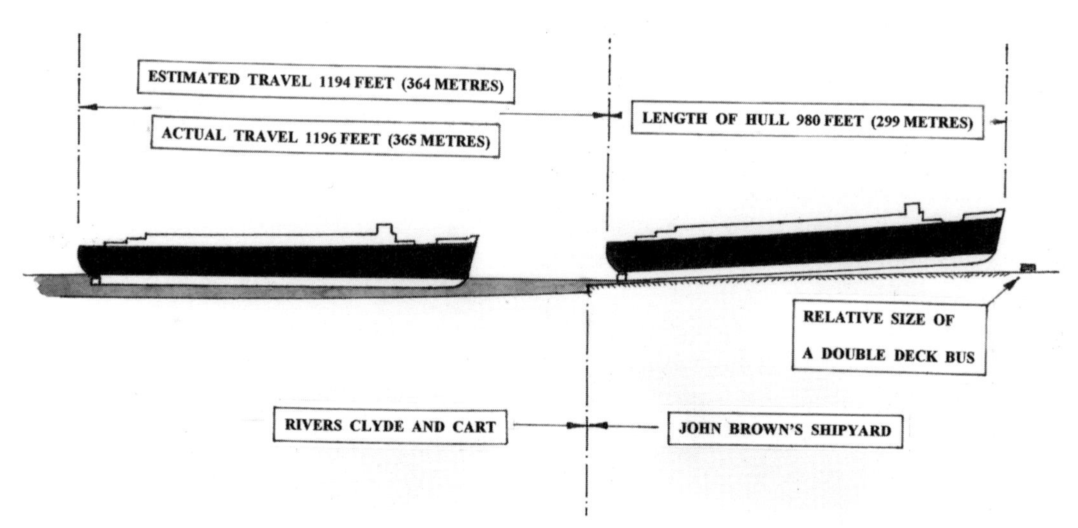

An illustration of the remarkable launch of *Queen Mary* at Clydebank in 1934.
(Drawing based on a sketch in the 1935 INA Transactions)

On return to Clydebank, he was appointed Assistant Naval Architect and ten years later became the Chief Naval Architect. Initially the yard was under pressure, with owners clamouring for the replacement of tonnage lost in the war, but as the 1920s went on and the economic situation deteriorated, the work of the naval architects and estimators became the unending drudgery of preparing designs and costs at short notice and of applying ever-reducing margins. The Clydebank shipyard built a surprisingly wide range of high-class tonnage and of naval ships, but the greatest contract of them all was the ship known as 534, later named *Queen Mary*. Her story is amazing, and for many reasons the design work was protracted and owing to the recession in industry the hull remained in the yard longer than foreseen. The delays were financially costly to all parties in terms of finance, and involved central government and the merger of the Cunard and the White Star Lines. Among McNeill's assistants was the late Jack Brown, later to be Sir John Brown; in a conversation with the author a few years ago, he described this time as a golden opportunity which enabled the *Queen Mary* to be designed to nothing short of superlative standards. The Clydebank shipyard was further aided in this by having one of the two in-house ship model tank testing facilities on the Clyde.

In the presence of the King and Queen in 1934, the largest dynamic launch to date took place when the ship and ways displacing 37,900 tons slid from the yard across the River Clyde and up the entrance of the River Cart. It had been predicted by McNeill and his team that the ship would travel 1,194 feet, and in the event, it travelled 1,196 feet. The launch was described in possibly the best paper ever published in the *Transactions of the INA*: in the discussion Percy Hillhouse said, 'I can honestly and enthusiastically say that never in my life have I seen a more perfect or a more beautiful launch' – praise indeed as Hillhouse was naval architect of the Fairfield Shipyard, Clydebank's deadliest rival, and also Professor of Naval Architecture at Glasgow University. From this work came McNeill's energy equations for which he received an LL.D. from his *alma mater*, and was later made a Fellow of the Royal Society.

McNeill was appointed a local director in 1934 working under the American-born managing director Dr Stephen Pigott. In 1941, the Burgh of Clydebank paid a severe price during the Blitz with 448 of the population killed and only four houses left undamaged. The shipyard was relatively unharmed, however, although other yards and ships on the river were to suffer more. The shipyard was of an unimaginable size and complexity, with in fact two shipyards operating side by side and a total labour force at times nearing 5,000 people; despite this, the workforce's loyalty to the yard and to Clydebank was always of a high order. McNeill was appointed managing director in 1949 and during the following ten years helped set up a new company known as John Brown & Co (Clydebank) Ltd which led to the separation of the Sheffield and Clydebank divisions, and he initiated the first phase of the yard's post-war modernisation. He resigned as deputy chairman in 1962. He must have appreciated the knighthood received from the Queen on completion of the Royal Yacht *Britannia*; other honours included Presidency of the Institution of Engineers and Shipbuilders in Scotland, Vice Presidency of the INA and appointment as a Royal Designer to Industry. McNeill, who died in July 1964 was a gentle man, an Elder of the Church of Scotland and devoted to his profession.

SOURCES:

Johnston, Ian
Ships for a Nation, John Brown and Company Clydebank
West Dunbartonshire Libraries, 2000

McNeil, J M
'Launch of the quadruple-screw turbine steamer *Queen Mary*'
Transactions of the Institution of Naval Architects
Vol 77 (1934)

Walker, Fred M
Song of the Clyde
Cambridge, 1984

Part 5
A Global Profession
1950–2000

Growth in ship size

The second half of the twentieth century witnessed an unprecedented growth in ship size. In particular oil tankers were built that had extraordinary lifting capacities, some of over half a million tonnes; these ships were specialist animals requiring close and constant invigilation. The almost exponential growth in tanker size was exacerbated by the Six Day War of 1967 which in turn led to the eight-year closure of the Suez Canal, and the need to haul much of the world's oil round the Cape of Good Hope. The Canal crisis forced ship owners to plan for economies of scale, leading to the massive half million tonne deadweight vessels. Reminiscent of **Brunel**'s *Great Eastern* a century before, the very largest tankers (many with drafts of over 25m [82ft]) had limited routes and ports of call, and as a result ships of this size have not been built recently.

Post-war shipyard reconstruction

The end of the Second World War not only gave great relief to the hard-pressed merchant navies of the world, but it inspired their crews with feelings of optimism brought about by a return to normality. The shipbuilders of the world geared up for a massive workload as replacements were ordered, dilapidated tonnage restored and long-delayed routine maintenance made good. The British and European shipyards welcomed these years with enthusiasm, and manfully struggled with shortages of steel and other raw materials. In Britain there was little in the way of shipyard rebuilding until the 1960s, and most of the early changes came through amalgamations and the rationalisation of plant. In the 1950s, the Swedish and Danish shipyards were among the first to invest in shipyard reconstruction, and often taking the opportunity to reinvent systems of construction. Most German shipyards had rebuilt in the early 1950s, though few had taken the courageous path of their Scandinavian neighbours. From the early 1960s the Japanese shipbuilding industry commenced an almost unstoppable rise and was to become both America's and Europe's deadliest commercial rival. Now, South Korea currently dominates the global shipbuilding industry.

The reduction in the number of shipbuilding sites throughout the world was not unrelated to the growth in ship size. Learning from the wartime experiences of the Americans, many shipyards in Europe, and later in the Far East, pinned their hopes on greenfield sites with an infrastructure based on a high throughput of steel. This was most successful for those shipyards enjoying lower than normal labour costs or which were in receipt of government subsidies. It placed pressure on the yards working in a niche (and usually high-quality) market as they had to justify their inevitably higher technical and labour costs.

In Britain, the emphasis during the post-war years was on technical efficiency and cost cutting, with little thought being given to the building of enduring relations with the workforce, although Britain is far from being the only country that allowed management arrogance coupled with trade union inflexibility to develop to an extent that it strangled the shipbuilding industry at a most critical time. The last twenty-five years have seen great changes for the better, but possibly too late. Sadly the Nationalisation Act of 1977 suffered from lack of political consensus and, much worse, the sell-off of the yards back to the private sector some years later was an unmitigated disaster.

Shipyard administration

In Britain, the shipbuilders under considerable political pressure agreed to form groupings for administrative and marketing purposes. All the shipyards on the Tyne formed one trading group and a similar group was formed on the River Wear by the Sunderland shipbuilders. The Clyde shipyards formed two groups, one in Glasgow and the other 24km (15 miles) west on the lower reaches at Inverclyde. This was the springboard for nationalisation which took place in 1977.

In most parts of the world, shipyards specialising in warship production have remained rather separate and have become dedicated military builders. Such yards include Bath Iron Works in Maine, USA, and the yards in Britain formerly known as Yarrow of Glasgow and Vosper-Thornycroft of Portsmouth.

Marine engineering

Great steps forward have been made by the increasing efficiency of the slow-speed two-stroke diesel engine. Similarly there has been a new approach to the powering of smaller ships with the introduction of medium speed diesels operating with gearboxes and controllable pitch propellers. Such packages can weigh surprisingly little – often less than 2 per cent of the total displacement of a ship of under 500 tonnes displacement.

The navies of the world enjoyed a new tool, the gas turbine. There are many variations on this theme, all of them expensive both in fuel and in first cost, but the advantage is reliable ship machinery that can be started up 'from cold' within minutes, and then will give high performance.

The building of submarines has changed beyond all recognition. The American, British and French nuclear programmes were and are of singular magnitude. New management control systems were established and computer aided systems like

Network Analysis had to be developed to keep control of extraordinarily complex building and testing systems. Welding of very specialist steels was a challenge, and in this area the Barrow shipyard of Vickers did pioneer work directed by Sir Leonard Redshaw. Some navies have dispensed with submarines and others maintain fleets of conventional diesel-electric boats.

Structural changes in the freight sector

In the late 1940s the massive United States emergency fleet was withdrawn from service with some ships being laid up and a controlled number released onto the second-hand market. The lifespan of the Liberty Ships became limited as great strides were being made in cargo handling. With the widespread introduction of roll on-roll off (ro-ro) and containerisation in the 1980s break bulk cargo became a thing of the past. The saddest part of this was the disappearance of the well-established cargo lines such as Blue Funnel of Liverpool, the East Asiatic Company of Copenhagen, Wilhelm Wilhelmsen of Oslo and the Clan Line of Glasgow. The container ships now dominate the non-bulk cargo market; currently the largest container ships can lift 10,000 TEUs (Twenty Equivalent Units) or in plain English 10,000 containers each of 6m x 2.4m x 2.4m (20ft x 8ft x 8ft) or an equivalent combination. The cargo revolution continued with the construction of many specialist vessels for services as diverse as vehicle transportation and livestock carriage.

There are vast numbers of ships at sea which are designated as bulk carriers; they are the workhorses of the world carrying ore, coal, grain and similar cargoes where required. While their appearance may leave much to be desired, their design can be sophisticated, and most are driven by turbocharged two-stroke diesel engines of remarkably high thermal efficiency, as twenty-five years ago the major diesel-engine builders passed the 50 per cent thermal efficiency barrier.

Safety at sea

The public agenda now is one of safety at sea and of the protection of the environment. Increased powers for the newly-named Maritime Coastguard Agency and added responsibilities for the three Central Lighthouse Authorities (CLAs), Trinity House, Northern Lighthouse Board and the Commissioners of Irish Lights, make this possible. The CLAs are tasked with maintaining safe sea lanes, an example of which is the English Channel – the busiest seaway in the world frequented by many ships drawing more than 20m (65ft).

The International Maritime Organisation (IMO), a United Nations non-governmental body based in London, has developed quite substantial powers and now requires close invigilation of all shipping. The Register of Ships published by Lloyd's Register has close to 100,000 ships listed, and all with a unique IMO number. Despite this, however, ships still go missing for reasons other than foundering or bad weather. The days of the 'coffin ships' may be over, but piracy and ship theft are still rampant.

The Hong Kong registered *OOCL Shenzhen* leaving Hamburg in July 2007. This 8,063 box (TEU), 25-knot and double-skinned vessel was the largest container ship in the world when built in 2003. It is powered by a single twelve-cylinder B&W type two-stroke diesel engine. *(Author)*

Hydrodynamics

During the last half of the twentieth century other technical changes took place. On the hydrodynamics front the *Lucy Ashton* tests on the Clyde may take pride of place – they were to re-establish understood coefficients for skin friction, and were the feather in the cap of the great shipbuilder **Sir Maurice Denny**. Ship model testing was boosted by the building of many tanks in research institutes and universities throughout the world, but this method of testing may have peaked as other methods of predicting resistance and powering, using numerical analysis, are coming on stream.

The most noticeable change in the appearance of ships during this half-century is the fitting of bulbous bows to almost every commercial ship at sea. This is an 'invention' claimed by several people, but in reality is the natural use of a phenomenon noticed by **William Froude** and **Lord Kelvin** in the nineteenth century. In simplistic terms the principle of the bulbous bow is that it sets up a wave train as the ship moves through the water, whilst the hull generates another set of waves. The naval architect's task is to ensure that in normal working circumstances, these two sets of waves cancel each other enabling the ship to leave calm water behind. The real bonus is a significant reduction in the wave-making resistance of the hull.

Classification

The classification societies, Lloyd's, Norske Veritas and all the others, have changed their approach in recent years. The traditional responsibility of classification societies had been to ensure the safety of a crew, their ship and its cargo, but now the wider issues of protection of the environment and health and safety are being considered. Some years ago Bureau Veritas started to purchase and absorb key engineering consultancies, in keeping with the view of the Classification Societies that their future should be as 'Quality Assurance Organisations'. Lloyd's Register, which invigilates many areas including railways, introduced the innovation of preparing Rules for the Construction of Naval Vessels. This was promulgated thirty years earlier when Hall, Russell of Aberdeen accepted a seven-ship contract for Royal Navy offshore patrol vessels all based on commercial terms.

Marine disasters

This fifty-year period saw several marine disasters, of which two were especially notable. In January 1953 the cross-Channel ferry *Princess Victoria*, then of modern ro-ro design, foundered in the North Channel between Scotland and Ireland, with the loss of 133 lives. In March 1987 another ro-ro, the *Herald of Free Enterprise*, was lost in Zeebrugge Harbour with 193 fatalities. In both cases, the free surface effect of loose water on the car deck was found to have diminished stability.

The America's Cup

On a sporting note, the Australians, represented by the Royal Perth Yacht Club, won the America's Cup in 1983 with the **Ben Lexcen**-designed *Australia II*, with its radical winged keel, thereby ending 132 years of dominance by the New York Yacht Club. Yachting has exploited many of the new materials that have become available, including aluminium and sundry forms of fibreglass and the sport has been an invaluable catalyst in the development of new compounds that give the necessary qualities of strength or flexibility.

Environmental issues

Finally, and in keeping with current international concerns, we must look at changes in geography and the climate. In 1958 history was made by the signal '*Nautilus* 90 North' as the world's first nuclear submarine, the USS *Nautilus*, broke through the ice and surfaced at the true North Pole. Since then the Arctic, the North-West Passage and the North-East Passage are becoming safer for ships as ice cover reduces and the capability of ice-class vessels increases. Several major civil engineering projects have revolutionised forms of travel; these include the St Lawrence Seaway opened in 1959, the Channel Tunnel between England and France opened in 1994 and the recent opening of the sophisticated Øresund link between Denmark and Sweden. All of these have impacted on merchant shipping, and have reduced the potential demand for short sea ferries.

One growth area is the increasing number of vessels which are classed for working in ice conditions. The retreat of the ice caps is a two-edged sword; as the ice diminishes ships are able to reach places yet unexploited like the bed of the Arctic, but in so doing they risk damaging some of the few places on earth still in their natural state.

KEY DATES

1951 The *Lucy Ashton* experiments on the Firth of Clyde.

1953 TSMV *Princess Victoria* founders between Scotland and Ireland with loss of 133 lives.

1955 Patents for hovercraft filed by Sir Christopher Cockerell.
The first jack-up drilling rig built in the United States.

1956 The Suez Crisis involving Egypt, UK, Israel and France.
Japan becomes the world leader in shipbuilding on a tonnage basis.

1957 Founding of the International Association of Lighthouse Authorities (IALA).

1958 US nuclear-powered submarine *Nautilus* reaches the North Pole – '*Nautilus* 90 North'.

1959 Opening of the St Lawrence Seaway (USA and Canada).
Re-discovery of the 1628 Swedish warship *Vasa* in Stockholm Harbour.
Discovery of many Viking ship hulls in Roskilde Fjord, Denmark.
First hovercraft flight across the English Channel.

1960 Launch of the French liner *France* at St Nazaire.

1967 North Sea gas begins to flow.
Launch of the Cunard liner *Queen Elizabeth 2* at Clydebank.
Start of the Six Day War – the Suez Canal closed from 1967 until 1975.
Tanker *Torrey Canyon* strikes Seven Stones off the Scilly Isles. 60,000 tons of oil spilt.

1969 First commercial oil strike in the North Sea.
US tanker *Manhattan* successfully navigates the North-West Passage.

1970 British Royal Dockyards end their tradition of shipbuilding.
Royal National Lifeboat Institution decrees that all their future vessels be self-righting.

1977 Introduction of the 200-mile EEZ.
British Shipbuilders formed by Act of Parliament.

1980 Tanker *Seawise Giant* is converted to world's largest at 565,000 tonnes deadweight.

1983 *Australia II* wins the America's Cup, breaking 132-year American dominance.

1986 Northern Lighthouse Board converts lighthouses to solar power.
The Chernobyl Disaster.

1987 International Maritime Organisation (IMO) adopts an unique and immutable numbering system for all ships on a worldwide basis.

1993 Launch of replica of Captain Cook's *Endeavour* (1764) at Fremantle, Australia.

1994 Opening of the Channel Tunnel.

1998 All lighthouses in the United Kingdom and the Republic of Ireland are unmanned.

2000 Lloyd's Register publish rules for naval ships.

William Hovgaard
1857–1950

WILLIAM HOVGAARD WAS BORN in Århus, Denmark, in 1857 and while in his teens was sent to the Royal Danish Naval Academy in Copenhagen, from where he graduated as a commissioned sea officer in 1879. Sea time followed, including serving on the Danish voyage in 1882 to St Croix to witness that year's Transit of Venus. He had experience in several jobs for the navy, and having an acute and sharp mind was seconded to the Royal Naval College at Greenwich around 1884 to study naval architecture, foreign students then being accepted in limited numbers. He passed in 1887 and returned to dockyard service in Denmark until 1895 when he asked to accept a line manger's post in the great Burmeister and Wain Shipyard in the City centre. This was the only 'pure management' job during his lifetime, and as it ended two years later, clearly it was not to his taste.

While in Copenhagen he carried out a complete design exercise for a submarine, and shortly afterwards the navy sent him to Cambridge, Massachusetts, where submarine design was part of the course at the new MIT Naval Architecture Department. Some dates are difficult to pin down here as Hovgaard was appointed to the staff of MIT but failed to resign his Danish commission until later. The United States would remain his home from then on, and from 1905 until his retirement in 1933 he remained Professor of Naval Design at Cambridge, Mass.

His prolific publications brought him a worldwide following and many honours including a Knighthood from King Christian X of Denmark and an Honorary Membership of the Institution of Naval Architects. Once at MIT a popular vote was taken to find the best English speaker, and here William Hovgaard came top of the list; he read to his children every day and also listened to their reading, and had one other habit, that of carrying a notebook in which he wrote down any word that was new to his already massive vocabulary.

The value of his writings is that they give closely-reasoned comment on the engineering and ship systems relevant at that time. In 1917 he was appointed an adviser to the US Navy Bureau of Ship Design, and at the end of the First World War became a naturalised American citizen. He died at Summit NJ in 1950.

SOURCES:
Hovgaard, William
Modern History of Warships
London, 1920

Anton Flettner
1885–1961

THE CITIZENS OF BREMEN were treated to a most unusual sight in 1926 when the experimental rotor ship *Barbara* was delivered from the Weser Shipyard. This ship of 2,000 gross tons was driven in a conventional manner by twin diesel engines geared to a single shaft, but her claim to fame were the three rotors on her weather deck designed to give additional thrust from the wind using the then well-established and understood Magnus Effect.

The system's inventor was Anton Flettner, who from an early age had been enthusiastic about the use of wind-power for ships – probably the result of having sailed from Germany to Australia and back on a windjammer. As an engineer specialising in aeronautics and hydraulics he worked with the Zeppelin Company and investigated the possibilities of using radio-controlled airships as guided missiles, and also worked on servo-control systems.

In 1924, the four-year-old schooner *Buckau* was fitted with two large 15m (49ft) high vertical rotors which were turned at 140rpm by a 45hp motor. The ship was driven by a 200hp diesel motor and by manipulation of the ship's heading in the wind the propeller thrust was augmented by the thrust from the rotors. Flettner always insisted that the rotors were auxiliary systems, not the prime mover. Two years later the *Barbara* was delivered new, sporting three 16m (52ft 6in) high and 4m (13ft 1in) diameter rotors, each weighing one and half tons. The main machinery could drive the hull in windless conditions at about 10 knots but in optimum wind conditions another two or three knots could be added, although the ship might have to make slight tacks, but often as close as 25° to the wind.

Many people have expressed the view that with better marketing and a clearer understanding that the Flettner Rotors were not the prime mover, this system might have become established. Flettner, who was then running his own business, was undaunted, and he designed and patented a rudder before turning his attention to rotary-wing aircraft, producing the single-rotor and twin-propeller Fl 185 which was unsuccessful, but then mastering the principle with the twin-rotor Fl 265 which was ordered by the German Navy. This led to the Fl 282 which was the only helicopter to be used operationally during the Second World War.

At the end of the war, Flettner was recruited by the Americans, crossed the Atlantic and worked in the USA. He died in New York in 1961. Apart from research work at a few university and yachting establishments, the marine rotor has been consigned to the history books.

SOURCES:

Winchester, Clarence (ed)
Shipping Wonders of the World Vol 1
London, c1938
This is a very well-known research tool based on a bound series of magazines published by Fleetway House London, before the Second World War.

Cuthbert Coulson Pounder

1891–1982

THE LEADING BRITISH exponent of two-stroke marine diesel engines of the 1950s and 1960s, Cuthbert Coulson Pounder was born in the then-bustling shipbuilding and industrial town of Hartlepool in May 1891. He attended local schools before becoming indentured to one of the leading marine engineering companies in the north-east, Richardsons, Westgarth and Co Ltd. 'Richies', as they were known, were not the largest company of their kind, but they employed several thousand people and did produce a new set of triple-expansion engines every two to three weeks in addition to a considerable quantity of other marine and non-marine work. Such a background was more than useful to young Pounder, as most of his life was to be dedicated to the development of big two-stroke diesels.

Shortly after completing his apprenticeship he joined the marine engineering branch of the Harland and Wolff shipyard in Belfast. He would stay with them for around fifty years until his retirement in the early 1960s. A well-read man, suited to scientific leadership, he commenced a literary career while in his twenties, and continued producing textbooks and scientific papers for close on sixty years. His progress in the shipyard engine design office was steady, and at a fairly early age he became chief draughtsman and some years later head of engine design with ultimate responsibility for operational efficiency of the two-stroke diesels built in Belfast (and Glasgow), nearly all licensed from Burmeister and Wain of Copenhagen. His literary skills enabled him to have a devastating turn of phrase, an ability which enabled him to defuse disputes in an amicable manner!

Between the wars, the Harland and Wolff organisation was enormous with shipbuilding facilities under their own name in both Belfast and Glasgow, as well as owning A & J Inglis in Glasgow and for a while other, smaller yards on the Ayrshire coast. On the ship repair side they had yards with the H&W name in London, Liverpool and Southampton as well as that of D & W Henderson in Glasgow. There were extensive machinery-erecting facilities and also foundries in Belfast and Glasgow. In general in the 1930s shipbuilding costs were lower on the Clyde, whilst Belfast, aided by higher capitalisation, reigned supreme in diesel-engine manufacture. Incidentally, H&W had considerable control of David Colville and Sons, the Motherwell steel manufacturer.

Pounder was an advocate of airless injection, and quietly introduced this and many other improvements in large engine design and manufacture. (The White Star liners *Britannic* and *Georgic*, built in 1930 and 1932 respectively, had the last Harland-built engines with blast injection.) As the engine works had earlier been identified as the biggest drain on company resources, this turnaround in efficiency

A bulk carrier makes its way along the North African coast. Driven by efficient slow-speed, two-stroke diesel engines, these modern workhorses can carry cargoes of a magnitude undreamt of in years gone past. This vessel is 'gearless', having no cargo-handling facilities aboard. ***(Author)***

and productivity was critical at the time and enabled Belfast to compete for the new generation of diesel ocean liners of the 1930s. At this time, all engines were built on license from Copenhagen, under an arrangement which had come about in the First World War. In 1911 and 1912, the first three diesel ships for the Danish East Asiatic Company had been built in Copenhagen and the Clyde, and shortly after, A/S Burmeister and Wain had set up a subsidiary based in Glasgow. For a variety of reasons including the outbreak of war this had been unsuccessful and B&W decided to withhold all patents until a licensing system had been developed. Once this had been done, Harland and Wolff had primary rights for B&W types for the Empire and Commonwealth. (Sub-licensees included John G Kincaid & Co Ltd of Greenock and the Hong Kong and Whampoa Dock Company.)

Despite the benign back-up from Copenhagen, many major decisions had to be taken by the licensees, and on one occasion Pounder was put in the hot seat when faced with the desire of the directors of H&W to build three Atlantic ships with the (then) largest diesel engines in the world, all well beyond the accepted safe levels of extrapolation from existing designs. The successful outcome of such difficult projects augured well for the 1940s when H&W had to operate entirely on its own. On 9 April 1940, Denmark was occupied by the Germans and for the next five years B&W Copenhagen struggled to remain intact, while their partner H&W Belfast manfully built engine after engine and ship after ship for the Allied cause. Pounder revelled in this and during this five-year period built up an enormous store of information and experience. Shortly after the liberation of Europe, the B&W licensee system was re-established.

Personality conflicts occur in many shipyards, and H&W was no exception, as the chairman Sir Frederick Rebbeck and Pounder did not work well together. The engine design side of the business became remote from the rest of the business and in his later years Pounder was accused of setting his own agenda with regard to design practices, product appearance and possibly unnecessarily high quality levels. During this period, the weight saving in two-stroke diesels reached the remarkable level of 15 per cent; however, it is possible that production costs and long-term engine maintenance had been overlooked. In the early 1960s, Pounder (then nearing seventy) reluctantly accepted retirement. R S Punt was appointed in his place, and an era in the history of shipbuilding in Northern Ireland was ended.

The legacy of C C Pounder was of national importance. Many honours came his way including first the Presidency of the Institute of Marine Engineers and later an appointment close to his heart as an honorary companion of the City and Guilds of London Institute. His real memorial is the list of publications which include his frequently republished magnum opus, *The Marine Diesel Engine*.

SOURCES:

Griffiths, Denis
Power of the Great Liners
Yeovil, 1990

Hogg, Peter L
'Richies' a History ... Richardsons and Richardson Westgarth 1832–1994
Hartlepool Borough Council, 1994

Lehmann, Johannes
A Century of Burmeister & Wain 1843–1943
Copenhagen, 1948

Moss, Michael, and Hume, John R
Shipbuilders to the World: 125 years of Harland and Wolff, Belfast 1861–1986
Belfast, 1986

Edmund Victor Telfer

1897–1977

EDMUND TELFER, A NOTED academic and a founder of the International Towing Tank Conference, was born in Hartlepool, and following a highly-successful school career, became an apprentice at William Gray's shipyard, then moved to the Naval Yard at Walker-on-Tyne, returning later to Gray's to 'go outside' as an assistant manager. However, his real success lay in his studies which were spent at Armstrong College, Newcastle from which he gained in the first instance a degree in Naval Architecture from the University of Durham. By sheer hard work, coupled with supportive scholarships, Telfer continued to distinguish himself and his college by gaining a total of four degrees between 1920 and 1927, the last one being a Doctorate of Science.

His postgraduate research honed his interest in ship model testing, and in particular his master's degree was based on the methods to be used in presenting and extrapolating model data. This intense interest in hydrodynamics ensured that most of the fifty papers he presented (mostly to the INA and to the North East Coast Institution in Newcastle) were on related subjects, and he became accepted by the profession as a leader in this field. For a while he was assistant naval architect to a shipping company, a period that clearly inspired him to set up on his own as a naval architecture consultant. After setting out independently, he had considerable success with, firstly, his own design of rudder, which became known as the Duplex Rudder, and secondly the design of a new type of propeller which was widely used up to the time of the Second World War and was marketed under the name of the Heliston. His knowledge and understanding of ship motions ensured that he was retained by the Admiralty to advise on the collision between the liner *Queen Mary* and HMS *Curacoa* in the entrance to the North Channel in October 1942. Incidentally, on the same matter the Cunard line retained Professor Robb of Glasgow University.

At the end of the war he was invited to accept the Chair of Naval Architecture at Istanbul and set off for Turkey in 1946. Undoubtedly his happy knack for linguistics helped here and also during a short period in western India around 1951 advising on the setting-up of ship model testing facilities. The academic task for which he is best remembered came in 1951 on being appointed Professor at the Technical University of Norway where he remained until around 1968, having decided to return to the UK at the age of seventy. Some more consulting followed and in 1976 he was awarded a well-deserved Froude Medal by the Royal Institution of Naval Architects. He was a family man with very wide range of interests including philology, and is reputed to have coined the test-tank word 'Geosim' – geometrically similar model!

Throughout his life he advocated the exchange of ideas on ship testing, and was instrumental in helping set up the International Conference of Ship Tank Superintendents. He remained on the councils of this for many years, and was to see the name change to International Towing Tank Conference (ITTC).

SOURCES:
Robb, A M
'Inter-action between ships'
Transactions of the Institution of Naval Architects
Vol 91 (1949)
This paper describes the phenomenon of inter-action between ships and describes the terrible collision between RMS *Queen Mary* and HMS *Curacoa* in the North Channel in 1942.

Hyman G Rickover

1900–1986

HYMAN RICKOVER IS A true representative of the 'American dream'. Born in Russian-controlled Poland to Jewish parents, he emigrated with his family to the United States in around 1906, and settled in Chicago, Illinois, where his father found work as a tailor. From this less than promising start, Rickover was to become one of the world's outstanding naval engineers, and in later life was charged with the task of introducing nuclear propulsion to the United States Navy.

In 1918, he entered the US Naval Academy to be commissioned Ensign in 1922. From that time it is clear he was earmarked for fast-track education, experience and training, as in the 1920s (following considerable sea time) he attended Columbia University obtaining a master's degree in electrical engineering. An interesting development occurred when Rickover was placed on the submarine training programme, which led in 1937 to his command of USS *Finch*. Truly a unique and rounded career, which was to give him the breadth of experience necessary for higher command. Late in 1937, he was directed to the engineering branch and became an Engineer Duty Officer for the 'boats' of the USN, a position he was to retain for the remainder of his long service career. At the outbreak of war Rickover was appointed head of the electrical section of the Bureau of Ships and later as commanding officer of the ship repair base at Okinawa.

In a move that is still not common knowledge, as early as 1939 the United States Navy had commenced top-secret research into the design and operation of nuclear-powered submarines. Shortly after the end of hostilities, Rickover was assigned to the Atomic Energy Commission in Tennessee and in 1949 was appointed Development Director giving him full charge of the preparatory work for the world's first nuclear-powered submarine, USS *Nautilus*, which was to be constructed at the Electric Boat Co. of New London, Connecticut. The magnitude of a task of this nature must have been daunting, especially as the Chief of Naval Operations initialled the project in August 1949 with instructions that the boat had to be at sea by January 1955. Despite all the problems of building a new type of vessel with untried propulsion systems, this was achieved and *Nautilus* sailed from New London on 17 January 1955 and then sent the historic signal 'Underway on nuclear power'. The *Nautilus* went from strength to strength, and just three years later (in 1958) surprised the world by completing an underwater passage from the Pacific to the Atlantic under the Polar icecap and thereby re-awakening interest in the commercial usage of the North-West Passage. The *Nautilus* was at the North Pole on 3 August 1958 and sent another historic signal: '*Nautilus* 90 North.'

Rickover became the effective leader of the entire United States nuclear submarine programme. One of the mysteries, as yet unanswered, is how did he remain an active four-star admiral at the age of eighty-two, with sixty-three years of service to his credit and having served thirteen presidents in all? Clearly his unorthodox and direct dealings gave him power, and his success rate in building vessels that can be described only as diabolic weapons of destruction made him a required member of the senior staff. On the downside he was known as being awkward and pugnacious, a

The launch of the world's first nuclear-powered vessel, the submarine USS *Nautilus* (SSN-721), at the Electric Boat Division of General Dynamics Corporation. *(United States Naval Institute)*

matter compounded by his small and slim stature, and his final years in office were clouded by several controversies. His disregard for uniform was legendary and in earlier years his promotion had been blocked on more than one occasion. On the international front, his perceived unfriendliness to the Royal Navy was a fairly long-standing cause of irritation, as were the host of restrictive agreements (of his making) which hampered international nuclear engineering for many years

On a more positive note, one has to appreciate that, under his leadership, one of the world's most advanced weapon systems was produced along with a host of by-products ranging from network analysis through to advanced hull constructional techniques. The long-term relationships between Rolls Royce Associates and their American counterparts were established, and the British nuclear deterrent was given considerable support. While Rickover was single-minded and nothing short of forthright, he did have the utter loyalty of many younger officers, possibly brought about by his practice of interviewing every prospective officer for a nuclear vessel personally. It is doubtful if any other could have seen through such a complex programme as the complete re-equipping of the United States Submarine Service in a mere twenty years.

In civilian life his principal pre-occupation was education, where he believed in what in the UK is now known as elitism. He was awarded many medals, honours and honorary degrees. On his death in 1986, he was buried in the Arlington National Cemetery.

SOURCES:
Anderson, W R, and Blair, C
Nautilus 90 North
London, 1959
Baker, Sir Rowland, and Rydill, L J
'The Building of Two Dreadnoughts' in Walker and Slaven (eds)
European Shipbuilding – one hundred years of change
National Maritime Museum, Greenwich, 1983
Pocock R F
Nuclear Power: its development in the United Kingdom
Unwin & Inst. of Nuclear Engineers, Old Woking, 1972
Pugh, Peter
The Magic of a Name: the Rolls Royce Story
Vol 2 (Duxford, 2001)

Peter Du Cane

1901–1984

THE NAME OF Vosper & Co, originally of Portsmouth, is connected with two men, first, Herbert E Vosper (c1850–1934) the innovative founder of the company, who made advances in steam engine design in the 1870s and has more than one patent to his credit. The second is Peter Du Cane, their managing director for over thirty years, and who is associated with the design of high-speed planing hulls. Du Cane joined the Royal Navy as a thirteen-year-old cadet, and in 1916 on being appointed Midshipman joined the battleship HMS *St Vincent*. At the end of the First World War, he found himself a student at Greenwich and then was seconded to the engineering branch. He served for a few months on Yangtze Flotilla gunboats stationed near Nanking (now Nanjing), a posting which he found boring and distasteful, but then work in the fleet followed which culminated with his appointment as senior engineer aboard the light cruiser HMS *Emerald*. Du Cane admitted to feelings of frustration with the peacetime service and in 1928 resigned his commission.

Bluebird II taking the world water speed record on Lake Coniston in 1939. (BVT Surface Fleet (Portsmouth) Ltd)

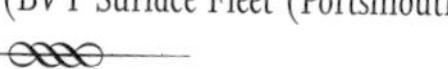

In 1929 he joined the Royal Auxiliary Air Force (RAAF) and after investing in private flying lessons, became a pilot in what later became 601 Squadron RAAF, serving at first under Lord Edward Grosvenor, an uncle of his wife and – as Du Cane less modestly admits – a fellow member of White's, his London club. Clearly he was of independent means, was able to fly for pleasure and covered his expenses by sundry consulting tasks. Around 1930, a former naval colleague Commander Glen Kidston asked Du Cane to join him at the Vosper Shipyard, a company he was planning to purchase outright. Du Cane's job seemed to be something equivalent to Contract Executive, but this is of little matter as shortly after Kidston was killed in an air crash in South Africa, and the ownership of Vosper went through several changes. In July 1931, to his great astonishment, Du Cane was invited to become managing director, a position he accepted knowing that with the current economic climate, any of his efforts could only improve shipyard productivity and profitability. In addition he retained the responsibility of Chief Designer, enabling him to keep his finger on the pulse of the Company at all times. Through a strange sequence of events, it became possible for Du Cane to invest in Vosper and by the early 1930s he owned about two-thirds of the equity with Philip, Earl of Hardwicke, holding the remainder.

The whole marketing strategy of Vosper changed and Du Cane was single-minded in steering the yard towards the construction of high-speed vessels and the introduction of both stepped and un-stepped planing hulls. Undoubtedly he was influenced by his most serious rival Hubert Scott-Paine, the principal of the British Power Boat

Company situated just a few miles away and who was courting the Royal Air Force in the hope of obtaining orders for small, very fast vessels. While the two shipyards were out-and-out rivals, their presence on the same river made the south of England the undisputed centre of small high-speed craft development in Britain.

The two main contenders for the world water speed record worked with Du Cane at different times. Sir Malcolm Campbell broke the record in 1939, just one week before war was declared, with *Bluebird* achieving 227km/h (141mph) on the smooth surface of Coniston Water, for which much credit must go to Dr Gawn of the Admiralty Experiment Works, Haslar, and to Du Cane for design work and support during *Bluebird*'s test runs on Lakes Leman and Lucerne in Switzerland. The relationship between Campbell and Du Cane was never happy and in the 1940s the two men parted company; similarly in the post-war years Du Cane and Campbell's son Donald did not see eye-to-eye and they too drifted apart. The building of *Crusader* for John Cobb was more pleasant with Cobb and Vosper working closely together. The job was complex and required extensive research and testing, and in September 1951 the boat made the required double run on Loch Ness reaching nearly 333km/h (207mph) on her first run, but on the return and just before the mile ended the boat porpoised and broke up. Cobb, killed outright, was robbed thereby of the world water speed record. Du Cane, who had witnessed the crash, was devastated and decided henceforth that he would avoid this kind of venture.

In 1938, the company had to vacate their shipyard near the Portsmouth Naval Base, and by early 1940 the new Portchester shipyard was in operation. From this site some trend-setting fast craft emerged including a long series of motor torpedo boats (of which close to 100 were built), Air Sea Rescue launches and others. Before long most hulls were of the un-stepped variety and from this Vosper produced some truly great hulls including the 'Bold', 'Gay' and 'Brave' classes of fast patrol boats for the Royal Navy in the late 1940s and the early 1950s.

On reading the accounts of Du Cane and others, one is impressed by their willingness to take calculated risks whilst pushing their scientific knowledge to the limit. However, some of the hulls for the Royal Navy did not reach their optimum speeds and this disappointment was considered in depth. The causes were believed to have been caused by propeller cavitation, and Vosper decided that research into propellers was a real priority. With advice from the Admiralty Experiment Works, a new cavitation tunnel was ordered from Hamburg in the early 1950s. Many more innovations were to follow, including the Vosper roll damping fin which was the small-ship equivalent of the then-popular Denny-Brown retractable fin stabilisers.

In today's parlance, Vosper's would be described as a 'niche' market and at all times it required the close personal attention of Du Cane as Managing Director. Valued clients included the navies of Denmark, Sweden, Malaysia and Brunei. In 1958, Vosper became a subsidiary of another company for the first time in its history and in 1963 became part of the David Brown Corporation with Du Cane appointed deputy chairman and research director, and shortly after appointed a CBE. A more significant change took place in 1973 when Vosper and the nearby shipyard of John I Thornycroft merged, creating a power in naval shipbuilding. Commander Du Cane died in 1984.

SOURCES:

Dawson, Christopher
A Quest for Speed at Sea
London, 1972

Du Cane, P
An Engineer of Sorts
Lymington, 1971

———,
A History of the Principal Activities and Achievements of Vosper during the Period 1931–1969
Manuscript held by the Library of Vosper-Thornycroft, Portsmouth

Scott-Paine, H
'Some of the Aspects and Problems of the Development of High-Speed Craft and its Machinery' The Institution of Mechanical Engineers, the Eleventh Thomas Lowe Gray Lecture (1939)

Howard I Chapelle

1901–1975

THE HISTORY OF NAVAL architecture has been enriched by a few persons who have devoted their lives to recording and questioning the systems, the methods and the conventions of ships and the sea. Historians are indebted not only to them, but also to the early pioneers who recorded technical details and systems on old ships and vernacular craft before they had disappeared without trace. These early researchers not only gathered records, but they established the principles of recording and of conservation, although the word 'conservation' was not used in earlier times!

Howard Irving Chapelle was born at Tolland in Massachusetts in 1901. While little is known of his early years, it is clear he had an interest in the sea as in 1919 he enrolled at the **Webb** Institute in New York, and graduated in 1923. He worked for a series of companies, some shipbuilders, others designers and by 1936 felt confident enough to set up his own design company. Here he had the good fortune to obtain an appointment as head of the New England Section of the Historic American Merchant Marine Survey, a 'New Deal' project designed to give employment to out-of-work shipbuilders. Here his latent interest in the history of naval architecture came to the fore and he embarked on his parallel career of writing.

With the outbreak of the Second World War he joined the US Army, becoming head of their ship and boat-building programme, with the rank of Lieutenant Colonel. In 1950 he was awarded a Guggenheim Fellowship and travelled to the United Kingdom where he researched American colonial ship design, mostly at the National Maritime Museum, Greenwich. In the 1950s he worked for some time for the United Nations Food and Agricultural Organisation and was seconded to Turkey to advise on fishing boat construction. On his return to the States he joined the staff of the Smithsonian Institution, Washington as a museum curator responsible for transportation, but rose to the position of Senior Historian. He commenced the task of building up and of recording the vast National Watercraft Collection, while at the same time maintaining his prodigious writing output. He retired from the museum service in 1971 and died in Delaware four years later.

SOURCES:

Among Chapelle's books are the internationally-known titles:
Yacht Designing and Planning
New York, 1936
The History of the American Sailing Navy
New York, 1949
American Small Sailing Craft
New York, 1951
The Search for Speed under Sail
New York, 1967

Sir Christopher Sydney Cockerell

1910–1999

CHRISTOPHER COCKERELL, the inventor of the hovercraft, was one of the distinguished sons of Sir Sydney Cockerell, former Director of the Fitzwilliam Museum in Cambridge. He grew up in Cambridge in an artistic family, but despite this he enrolled at Peterhouse College and studied engineering. On graduation he joined the Radio Research Company and then in 1935 joined the Marconi Wireless Telegraph Company, remaining with them for sixteen years. While with Marconi during the war, he worked in a small team developing radar, work of which he was immensely proud, and on leaving them knew that he had patented no less than thirty-six inventions.

With a small family inheritance on his wife's side, he purchased a boatyard in Norfolk. It did not blossom into a great undertaking, but it allowed Cockerell to test some of his then-unusual scientific ideas. The most significant of that time was to lift hull forms off the water by a cushion of air, and his first working model was a hull made from tin can, with an air blower and rubber curtains or 'skirts' as they were to become known. The reduction in drag was significant and the idea of the hovercraft took off. Incidentally the name was coined by Cockerell, and is now an accepted word in English and other languages!

An SR.N4 hovercraft leaving Dover Harbour while operating services across the English Channel. These large passenger and vehicle carrying craft were built by the British Hovercraft Corporation, and they operated on the Channel run for more than thirty years before the advent of the Channel Tunnel finally rendered them unprofitable. The SR.N4 was also considered for minesweeping but the idea never progressed beyond the concept stage. *(J Mannering)*

To develop the hovercraft concept, Cockerell set up a small company known as Ripplecraft, but on obtaining the necessary patents was held back by the British government's anxiety that this valuable form of transport remain secret, and that development be along military lines. Only in 1958 did full government backing become available and the National Research Development Council gave funding for a prototype to be constructed by Saunders Roe. In the summer of 1959 this seven-ton 6.5m (21ft 4in) long prototype flew and the hovercraft age had begun, and even more remarkable on 25 July 1959 the first hovercraft flight took place across the English Channel, exactly fifty years to the day since Bleriot's historic aircraft crossing. Several developments continued in parallel, including the unsuccessful attempts by the shipbuilders Denny of Dumbarton to develop the sidewall vehicle. Following disagreements, Cockerell resigned from Hovercraft Development, but he was not forgotten and in 1969 was knighted for his services to scientific development.

The largest commercial hovercraft was known as the SR.N4 with the ability to carry over 400 passengers and more than 60 cars at over 70 knots, and these worked for many years on the English Channel. The United States Navy is the largest user of hovercraft today, which have been seen in almost every theatre of war in the past two or three decades. The story of the hovercraft is far from over, and although Cockerell died in 1999, he must be described as the man who made this revolutionary form of aquatic transport a reality.

SOURCES:

Jacobs, W
The Oxford Encyclopaedia of Maritime History
Vol 1 (New York, 2007)

William Avery Baker

1911–1981

WILLIAM A BAKER, OR BILL as he was known to his friends, was born in New Britain in Connecticut and from the earliest years, his skill as a draughtsman was admired, not only at the engineering drawing board but also on the sketch pad. His desire to become a naval architect led to his enrolling at the Massachusetts Institute of Technology, graduating in 1934. He joined Bethlehem Steel and worked both at Quincy, Mass., and San Francisco, gaining practical experience in welding and steelwork assembly before being appointed to the drawing office and then spending fifteen years at the Quincy Technical Department. His old college invited him back as a lecturer in naval architecture, a position he held from 1963 to 1981.

The naval architecture school at Cambridge, Mass., is fortunate in having an 'in-house' museum, known as the Francis Russell Hart Nautical Museum. This small but fascinating place is a great draw to all ship-lovers in the area, and naturally in addition to his teaching work, Bill Baker was appointed Curator, a task in which he was assisted ably by his wife Ruth. Baker continued in both posts until his death in 1981.

Baker's interests were wide-ranging and he advised many historic ship projects in different parts of the world, one of which was the restoration in Oslo in the late 1940s of Amundsen's *Gjøa*, the first ship to transit the North-West Passage in 1904, for which Baker received the St Olav Medal. With ever-increasing interest in seventeenth- and eighteenth-century American pioneer life it was not long before he found himself working on the conjectural

Bill Baker's masterpiece, the replica *Mayflower* leaves Britain for the United States in 1957. Since then the building of authentic replicas has gathered apace, and research and development has been applied to the ships of every era. (*Author*)

designs for a replica of the *Mayflower*. His academic work was carefully annotated and later published, and it was decided to produce working plans and to raise funds. In 1955, the keel was laid of a full-scale replica in the Plymouth Shipyard of J W and A Upham Ltd. Historic working replicas were then a novelty and Baker's groundwork was to stand many people in good stead over the coming years.

One of the great contributions that William Baker made to his profession was devising means which enabled the key dimensions and shapes of ships (for which there were only sparse records) to be visualised. He regarded replica ships not so much as museum artefacts, but as working hulls which enabled a greater understanding of ship science in earlier years.

SOURCES:
Baker, William A
Colonial Vessels: Some Seventeenth-Century Sailing Craft
Barre, Mass., 1962
Baker, William A
A Maritime History of Bath, Maine & the Kennebec River Region, 2 vols
Bath, Maine, 1973
Ronnberg, Erik A R Jr,
William Avery Baker: A Tribute from His Friends
Rockport, Mass., 1982

James J Henry

1913–1986

INNOVATION WAS ONE of the greatest qualities of the man known in the American shipbuilding industry as J J Henry. In his early twenties he graduated from the Webb Institute, then in New York, and then throughout the late 1930s was involved in the Bureau of Marine Inspection, an agency now subsumed into the United States Coast Guard, and then in 1938 joined the staff of the U.S. Maritime Commission, where he gained experience and built up a close knowledge of many of the American standard ship types then being built in massive numbers for the War Emergency Programs. These included standard troopships as well as the ubiquitous C1 'Liberty' cargo vessels. Following the end of the war, he branched out into consultancy, and in 1951 incorporated the business that would bear his name, J J Henry Co Inc.

Three matters were of particular interest in the early years: First the alteration of standardised tonnage to new peace time purposes, such as conversions of T2 tankers into bulk carriers, a very necessary stop-gap as western nations were struggling with severe material shortages. At this time the oil companies were investigating the carriage of liquefied gases at cryogenic temperatures and near atmospheric pressures, and the J J Henry Co designed the pioneer LPG Carrier *Bridgestone Maru*, a ship that would lead to a multitude of further design contracts. Of greatest long term importance was the company's contribution to the development of the container and of the shipping required in this new mode of transprt.

Particularly interesting and novel designs were the barge carriers for Lykes Brothers and the quite revolutionary 33-knot transatlantic container ships for Sea Land. These and similar ships were benchmarks in the shipping industry of the 1960s and 1970s and at a time when high speed was the unquestioned prerogative of the containership operator. In his later years he served on many technical committees including that of the United States Coast Guard. Undoubtedly the task which must have given him maximum pleasure was Chairman of the Board of Trustees of the Webb Institute, now moved to their new home in New Jersey.

SOURCES:
Article in *Lloyd's List* 26 November 1986

Sir Iain Maxwell Stewart

1916–1985

IN 1901, THREE BROTHERS, Alexander, Maxwell and Frederick Stewart founded Thermotank, a small ventilating company in Glasgow. Over the years it flourished, and by the time of the Second World War was one of the most important heating and ventilating companies operating in the marine and other fields. Two brothers died quite young and Frederick ran the company until his death in 1950 when the managing director (and later chairman) was his nephew Iain Maxwell Stewart.

Iain Stewart was born in 1916, educated at Loretto School, Edinburgh, and then studied engineering at Glasgow University. He served an apprenticeship with Thermotank before joining the armed forces, and then returning to Govan at the end of hostilities. He had full responsibility for the day to day running of a large and complex organisation by the time he was in his thirties, and had the privilege of being able to spend time considering the subject of what is now called human resources, while simultaneously building up a group of directorships in companies which ultimately included British Caledonian Airways and the Weir Group.

In the early 1960s a conference was held at Marlow in Buckinghamshire, when men (from politics, the churches, industry, education and the trades unions) discussed the need in Britain, indeed in Europe for all individuals to feel and accept personal responsibility for society. The paper became known as The Marlow Declaration and for many young people, especially in industry, it was a breath of fresh air, introducing logical thinking to working relationships. It defined privileges and responsibilities, and every level of the workforce was considered – directors, shareholders, employees, senior managers and workers' representatives. Iain Stewart was one of the twenty-six signatories.

A file recently 'unearthed' in the Institution of Engineers and Shipbuilders in Scotland, laid out three of the main Marlow principles:

> The need to give as much thought to human engineering, or the right use of people as we do that of machine operation.
>
> The need for study of redeployment and retraining of the workforce at all levels, and the consideration of any psychological issues involved.
>
> Education of the public to the significance of industry, as public awareness is conditioned by ignorance, emotion and PR Techniques.

This was fairly unusual management thinking for nearly fifty years ago.

Sir Iain Stewart, 1916–1985. *(Sketch by the late Emilio Coia)*

Following consultations with the Bank of Scotland, the long-established Fairfield S & E Co Ltd of Govan called in the receivers on 15 October 1965, and Britain had one of the biggest industrial collapses for many years on its hands. Following moves in every level of society and industry, means were found to re-establish the shipyard with shares held by the government, industry, some individuals and to a lesser extent by trades unions. The new company known as Fairfields (Glasgow) Ltd, had the aims of introducing improved industrial relations, work measurement and vastly enhanced internal communications. The Fairfields Experiment, as it became known, was a test bed for later Employment Acts, and certainly was a very good training ground for younger managers. The new board of directors represented a wide range of British cultural interests and was chaired by Iain (later Sir Iain) Stewart.

All young managers at Fairfield, the author among them, passed through a period of retraining and adaptation. Formal training was instituted in management techniques and every manager and supervisor learned the need for good communication, as well as the fundamentals leading to the Industrial Relations Acts that followed shortly after. Attitudes changed and little by little the trained shipbuilders and naval architects stopped regarding the 'work study experts' and others as brash, while these incomers learned some respect for good shipbuilding skills and mellowed their view that old hands were 'ignorant and arrogant'. All the shipbuilders did learn that to be professional they had to understand their profession in depth and they had to be courteous in all dealings in the shipyard. The experiment was never concluded as the untimely merger of Upper Clyde Shipbuilders in 1968 made logical and comparative studies impossible. A change in the attitudes of British industry was needed at the time and this was stimulated by the Fairfields Experiment. Sir Iain Stewart's short time at the head of the quasi-nationalised shipyard may not have pleased everyone, but he did something that was ground-breaking.

Sir Iain was President of the Institution of Engineers and Shipbuilders in Scotland, a learned body that has an annual lecture on Human Resources. In 1977 he gave the Institution the substantial sum of £10,000 to underwrite the aptly-named Marlow Lecture, an important event in Scotland's calendar.

SOURCES:
Stewart, Sir Iain M
'Redundancy – the scrap heap or a new job opportunity?', Fifth Marlow Lecture
Transactions of the Institution of Engineers and Shipbuilders in Scotland Vol 116 (1972–3)

Ben Lexcen

1936–1988

Ben Lexcen can best be described as a legendary Australian. In fifty-one years, he was to overcome a deprived background, and change the face of one of the world's most conservative and money-driven sports, that of the 'big yachts'. Until recently little was known of him, but now his name is enshrined in the America's Cup Hall of Fame at Bristol, Rhode Island, along with **Herreshoff**, Lipton, Sopwith, Vanderbilt, **Watson** and others.

Ben was born in New South Wales at Boggabri, a desolate outstation, the son of Edward and Doreen Miller; he was christened Robert Clyde Miller, a name he would change in his thirties. His father who was employed as a timber cutter in the gangs supplying jarrah wood to the State Railways for sleepers, was nomadic in outlook, given to drinking and violent disagreements with his wife. Following the declaration of the Second World War, he joined the Royal Australian Air Force and disappeared for ever from the life of his wife and son. Despite the short time he had to endure the rigours of the bush, Ben never forgot the sights, smells and sounds of the outback, memories that would strengthen him in the difficult years that followed. For seven or eight years he was moved from one relative's house to another, with little stability in his lifestyle, becoming in his own words '... a bloody embarrassment to the family'. The depths were plumbed when he was admitted to a Roman Catholic home for difficult boys, and there endured repression and cruelty. Two redeeming feature of this period were his developing interest in yachts through reading back numbers of yachting journals in the library, and his ability to gain comfort from classical music.

His life changed when he went to live with his widowed maternal grandfather in Newcastle, New South Wales, and for the first time experienced caring attention and personal freedom. He wandered round the docks, honed his love of small ships and began to dream of ship design. On being given a dollar by his grandfather, he purchased a toy yacht that did not sail well, but he carved out the solid hull, added ballast and produced a creditable sailer. At the age of fourteen he left school and started work as an apprentice moulder in a brass foundry, but shortly after joined the railways and soon became a fitter apprentice. Every spare moment was spent at sailing clubs hoping for crewing positions. In 1954 he designed and built a 7m (23ft) hard chine sailing craft and fitted it with a revolutionary independent spade rudder, explaining why he became known as 'The Professor' at the

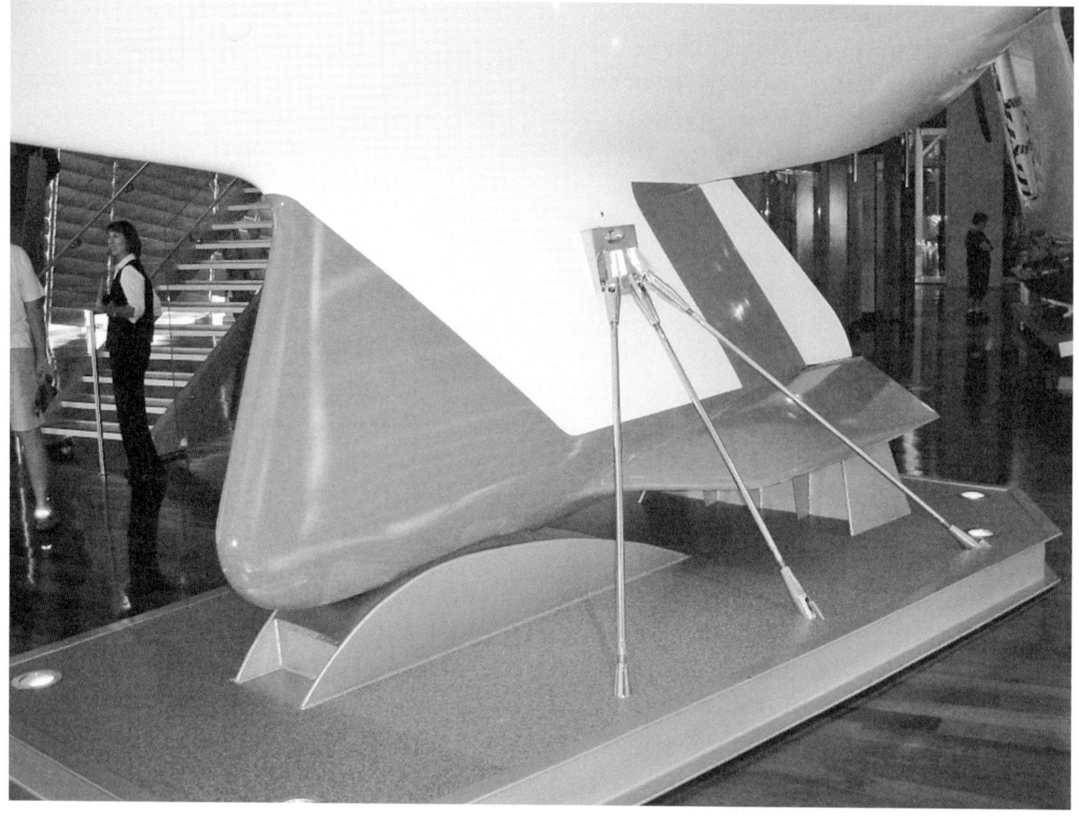

The famous winged keel of *Australia II* which, combined with radically new sail technology, helped Australia win the 1983 America's Cup. The 12-metre yacht is now on display at the Western Australian Maritime Museum.

Lake Macquarie Yacht Club. At this point the Railway, at his own request, transferred him to Sydney in order to be nearer the centre of sailing, and it was here that he became friendly with a kindly boating family, who gave him stability and self-respect.

Having made sails for a Flying Dutchman using terylene (then quite new) he decided to take up sailmaking full-time and moved to Brisbane. Despite money being tight, he built up a good client base through the simple art of listening to customers' concerns and acting on them. Following a serious fall from a mast, he was hospitalised and during this period of enforced idleness planned his first great breakthrough, the super-lightweight eighteen-footer *Taipan*, which under his helmsmanship altered this class for ever – indeed the hull is now exhibited at the Australian Maritime Museum. The sail business continued, but yacht design became more important and some notable hulls came from his drawing board including the ocean racer *Mercedes III* with an unusual lead fin keel and which sailed in the 1967 Admiral's Cup Races in Britain.

Through sundry good designs and successes, Ben was introduced to Alan Bond the Western Australian real estate developer, who in turn asked him to design the fine 58ft (17.6m) ocean racer *Apollo*. Ben and 'Bondy', as he liked to be called, developed a good relationship, one that would sustain them right through to the America's Cup victory, although the path would be long and stony. Bond's first attempt at challenging came with *Southern Cross* which proved unsatisfactory through 'over-manning and under-management', but the learning curve had commenced. Ben felt miserable about the result and decided to travel to the United Kingdom and if possible work in or alongside the boatyards of the Solent; this proved an unhappy experience with none of the excitement he had enjoyed 'Down-Under'. Alan Bond discovered the situation and arranged his return to Australia and in 1977 put him on the Bond Corporation payroll.

Work started on *Australia* with tank testing at Delft in The Netherlands and then construction in Steve Ward's yard near Perth. Despite copying the British *Lionheart*'s bendy mast design, the new boat did not win, but again experience had been gained for the next attempt which was not long in coming. For the successful *Australia II*, the hull testing was carried out again in The Netherlands, this time at Wageningen with meticulous planning and at great expense. Ben had tried winged keels before on small boats with mixed results, but was frightened that in the case of the contender, the wetted surface increase might overcome any residual benefits. The go ahead was given after comprehensive testing and one of the world's worst kept secrets was incorporated in the keel. Built again at Ward's the yacht was shipped to Newport, Rhode Island, and then prepared for work-up. Ben felt that the secrecy had been a mistake as the New York Yacht Club (NYYC) was concerned that the Australian yacht incorporated rule-breaking appendages, and indeed an official protest was raised just prior to the races with the NYYC claiming first that the challenger had increased draft through the flared wing tips, and secondly the design of the fins was Dutch. The Australian and American teams were at daggers drawn and Ben Lexcen, who had been publicly maligned, was taken to hospital with suspected heart trouble. The other contenders for the challenge were equally upset, but happily the races were able to begin when a letter from the NYYC with carefully thought through compromise wording was tabled. Throughout the long history of the America's Cup, it had been argued by the challengers that rule changes were for the benefit of the NYYC, while the American Club responded robustly that rule changes were solely for the benefit of the races. The rest is history: *Australia II* won handsomely on 26 September 1983 and the Cup was taken to Australia. Since then it has been to New Zealand and now is in Geneva, Switzerland.

Ben Lexcen died of a heart attack in May 1988. Despite humble beginnings and little academic training, he demolished the mystique surrounding yacht design and proved himself capable of designing successful yachts for the hardest competition in the world. Ben, a fast car enthusiast, would have been amused to learn that on his death the Australian-built Holden Commodore was rebadged as the Toyota Lexcen.

SOURCES:

Stannard, Bruce
Ben Lexcen, the Man, the Keel and the Cup
London, 1984

Further Reading

Chronological List of Books on Shipbuilding Technology

af Chapman, Fredrik Henrik, *Architectura Navalis Mercatoria* (Stockholm, 1768). Many facsimile editions now available.

Macquorn Rankine, W J *et al.*, *Shipbuilding, Theoretical and Practical* (London, 1866). A complete guide to mid-nineteenth century shipbuilding and design.

Walton, Thomas, *Steel Ships: Their Construction and Maintenance* (London, 1901). The key textbook in the days of riveted steel.

Middendorf, Friedrich Ludwig, *Bemastung und Takelung der Schiffe* (Berlin, 1903). A very fine descriptive volume of late nineteenth-century sailing ships, by a former official of Germanischer Lloyd, the German classification society.

Estep, H Cole, *How Wooden Ships are Built* (Cleveland, Ohio, 1918). An insight into the ways of the great American shipyards

Hardy, A C, *From Slip to Sea* (Glasgow, 1926). An overview of shipbuilding practice between the wars.

Winchester, Clarence (ed), *Shipping Wonders of the World* 2 vols (London, c1938). The bound version of a popular magazine of the late 1930s which is one of the best and most popular encyclopaedias of maritime matters ever published.

Underhill, Harold A, *Masting and Rigging: The Clipper Ship and Ocean Carrier* (Glasgow, 1946). One of several detailed descriptions of sailing ships by this author.

Abell, Sir Westcott, *The Shipwright's Trade* (Cambridge, 1948). A masterly oversight of ship design and construction through the ages.

Robb, A M, *Theory of Naval Architecture* (London, 1952). There are many excellent volumes on naval architecture and ship design; this one (in imperial units) is both exhaustive and clearly presented.

Sturmey, S G, *British Shipping and World Competition* (London, 1962). An analysis of the once-secretive British shipping industry during the first half of the twentieth century. This book gives a clear insight into the challenges and problems of international ship management.

Barnaby, K C, *Some Ship Disasters and Their Causes* (London, 1968). A book like this is required reading for all students of naval architecture. It is a gentle reminder to all naval architects, shipbuilders and engineers (both young and old) that they must study the conclusions of all Formal Enquiries and re-educate themselves as is a requirement for Continuing Education and Experience.

Rawson, K J, and Tupper, E C, *Basic Ship Theory* (London, 1968 and later editions). Another excellent text, this time with SI units.

Hocking, Charles, *Dictionary of Disasters at Sea during the Age of Steam 1824–1962* 2 vols (London, 1969). An introduction to an important subject. There are a few omissions, but this book is an excellent research tool.

Harland, John, *Seamanship in the Age of Sail* (London, 1984). This is a detailed exposition about the handling of big sailing ships.

Ferreiro, Larrie D, *Ships and Science: The Birth of Naval Architecture in the Scientific Revolution, 1600-1800* (Cambridge, Massachusetts, 2007). An overview of those who defined modern naval architecture.

Hattendorf, John B (editor-in-chief), *The Oxford Encyclopedia of Maritime History* Vols 1–4 (Oxford/New York, 2007). This is a useful and academic compilation on maritime history, albeit slightly lack-lustre.

Transactions of Engineering Institutions and Learned Societies

The Transactions (or Proceedings) of the following learned bodies are of especial importance as they have papers by almost every important English speaking naval architect and engineer over the past century and a half. Of additional historic interest, some of the transactions publish obituaries of the 'great and the good'.

The Royal Institution of Naval Architects
Published in London annually since 1860, these invaluable papers cover the widest range of matters concerning ship design, shipbuilding, hydrodynamics etc, over 150 years

The Society of Naval Architects and Marine Engineers
Since 1893 this organisation has published its transactions and papers from their offices in New Jersey.

The Institution of Engineers and Shipbuilders in Scotland
Published annually in Glasgow since 1857, these papers are probably the widest ranging in engineering topics, and are strong on nineteenth-century shipbuilding and engineering.

The North East Coast Institution of Engineers and Shipbuilders
These transactions were published in Newcastle from 1884 until 1993, and form an indispensable collection of papers centred on North East England.

The Institute of Marine Engineering, Science and Technology.
Marine engineering transactions published annually in London since 1889.

The Society for Nautical Research (SNR)
The SNR was founded in 1910, 'to encourage research into matters relating to seafaring and shipbuilding in all ages and among all nations, into the language and customs of the sea, and into other subjects of nautical interest'. From the beginning it has published *The Mariner's Mirror*, a quarterly journal which is academic with all work fully peer-reviewed and refereed. Its North American equivalent is *The American Neptune.*

Index

NB Page numbers in **bold** refer to main entries; page numbers in *italics* refer to illustrations.